INTRODUCTION
TO
APPLIED
STATISTICS

Under the Editorship
of
GARDNER MURPHY

INTRODUCTION

TO

APPLIED
STATISTICS

JOHN G. PEATMAN

Professor of Psychology
The City College of The City University of New York

HARPER & ROW, PUBLISHERS   New York, Evanston, and London

Introduction to Applied Statistics   Copyright © 1963
by   John G. Peatman

Harper & Row, Publishers, Incorporated
49 East 33rd Street, New York 16, N. Y.

B-N

Library of Congress Catalog Card Number: 63–7400

To Madeline and Mary

CONTENTS

LIST OF TABLES
IN APPENDIX

PREFACE

This introductory text in applied statistics is intended primarily for the use of students in psychology. It should be useful also to students in sociology and cultural anthropology, which with social psychology comprise the behavioral sciences. Within the field of psychology, recognition is accorded the statistical needs of the experimentalists working in the laboratory setting, as well as the needs of clinical and social psychologists working in a variety of settings. In general, the techniques of applied statistics presented are basic to and significant for students of psychology, irrespective of their particular specializations and goals.

The nature and scope of applied statistics are described at length in the introductory chapter. The kinds of data requiring statistical treatment are discussed in Chapter 2. The second chapter and the four succeeding chapters constitute a basic core presented in the following order: (1) methods for the organization of statistical data (Chapter 2); (2) methods for their summarization (Chapters 3 and 4); and (3) methods for measuring the possible association of two or more sets of related statistics (Chapters 5 and 6). The methods of these chapters are essentially the methods of DESCRIPTIVE STATISTICS. That is to say, they are methods for the organization and summarization of collections of statistical data. Just as yardsticks are needed to measure distance, scales to measure weight, and clocks to measure time, the statistical methods presented in Chapters 2 through 6 are needed to *measure* the character and results of *variation* and *covariation*, irrespective of whether the data are in centimeters, grams, seconds, amounts of *x*, ranks, or counts.

The last half of this book consists of a sequence of six chapters on the development of applied techniques of SAMPLING-INFERENTIAL STATISTICS. Chapter 7 lays the foundation in probability theory for statistical inference as applied to those *states of nature* characteristic of psychology and her

sister sciences. Chapter 8 develops techniques for the *estimation* of measures and characteristics of variables that have been only partially observed
through the data of samples. The remaining chapters present methods for
assessing a variety of statistical hypotheses that are significant to survey
research as well as to experimental research. These are known as methods
for *significance testing*. The attempt has been made in Chapters 9, 10, 11,
and 12 to introduce the student to the techniques of significance testing
most frequently needed and used in research.

   This text is designed for use in a one-semester introductory course at
either the undergraduate or graduate level of instruction. When such a
term course allows too few hours to permit the instruction to encompass
all of the text material, the sequence of chapter content is such that either
the last chapter or the last two chapters may be deferred.

   The student, undergraduate or graduate, should have little or no difficulty with what follows insofar as his preparation in mathematics is concerned, provided he or she (1) can correctly and efficiently put numbers
together and separate them, i.e., add and multiply, subtract and divide;
and (2) has some facility with elementary algebra. For those who may
wish to review: H. M. Walker's *Some Mathematical Essentials for Statistics*
(1952) is recommended.

   Attention is called to some useful details of this text. In addition to the
view of its subject matter provided by the preceding Table of Contents,
an overall view of the more detailed contents of each chapter is provided
at the beginning of each chapter. The headings on the left, even-numbered
pages of the text are the chapter titles. The headings on the right, odd-
numbered pages are the subsection titles within each chapter.   In
Chapter 1, beginning on p. 17, most of the Greek and Roman letter symbols used in statistics are listed with appropriate page references to their
introduction later in the text. The final chapter (12) includes a summary
of methods of significance testing for various research problems and types
of statistical data.   The student should also find that the more than
50 pages of statistical tables and charts of the Appendix will have continued
usefulness in his research and studies beyond his or her introductory course
in statistics.

   The author has also prepared about 80 problems and exercises and 650
study questions that parallel the text from subsection to subsection
throughout the book. A specific page reference to the text accompanies
each study question. These materials run to more than 200 pages and are
published separately as a paperback workbook with perforated pages and
an addendum of blank pages of graph paper, tabulation sheets, and correlation charts. Interested students should find they can accelerate their
learning and achievement by *programming* much of the text material on
3 by 5 cards and using these with themselves as their own *teaching machines*
between meetings of their classes.

Proper acknowledgment of all my sources of information would be a very lengthy and probably an impossible task inasmuch as I have been actively engaged in the teaching of undergraduates and graduates for many years, in the course of which I have naturally consulted the works of many authors. Specific acknowledgments are made at various points in the text, and all such references are brought together alphabetically in the section immediately following Chapter 12. These references are cited in the text by author and by the date of their publication.

For permission to reproduce various tables and charts, I am indebted to the authors and publishers of these materials. Due acknowledgment is given in the text and Appendix for each specific instance. I am especially indebted to the late Sir Ronald A. Fisher, F.R.S., and to Dr. Frank Yates, F.R.S., Rothamsted, also to Messrs. Oliver & Boyd, Ltd., Edinburgh, for permission to reprint Table III and Table IV from their book *Statistical Tables for Biological, Agricultural and Medical Research.* I am also indebted to E. S. Pearson and H. O. Hartley and to the Syndics of the Cambridge University Press of London for permission to reprint Tables C, H, and I from their book, *Biometrika Tables for Statisticians,* vol. 1, and for the adaptation of Table F from this same work.

I wish to express my sincere appreciation to various colleagues of the Department of Psychology at the City College of the City University of New York: especially to Professors Vivian Gourevitch and Alexander Mintz for their many helpful suggestions and criticisms; also to Professor Selby Robinson of the Department of Mathematics. To Dr. Robert Heath of the Educational Testing Service in Princeton, New Jersey, I am greatly indebted for a critical reading of both my original and final manuscripts. The responsibility for any errors or ambiguities that may remain in the text is of course mine. For assistance in the preparation of my manuscript, I am grateful to Mrs. Allan H. Glidden. And, finally, to my hundreds of students over the years, I am appreciative of their comments and inquiries. The classroom is an indispensable forum for the appraisal of all kinds of ideas and utterances, including those statistical. No educator should be without one.

JOHN G. PEATMAN

"Stonewood"
Silvermine, Connecticut
September 15, 1962

INTRODUCTION
TO
APPLIED
STATISTICS

INTRODUCTION

Variety's the very spice of life
That gives it all its flavour.

THESE familiar lines of the 18th-century poet William Cowper are especially germane to the life of a statistician, whose *raisons d'être* are the variations characteristic of all life phenomena. Variation is the key concept of statistics. It is its meat and its substance. It is its sometime chaotic appearance; it is its lawful nature. Out of the need to deal with variable phenomena emerges the aims of statistical method. In general, they are twofold:

1. The initial aim is the development of methods for the reduction of the multitude of variations (the countables, rankables, or measurables obtained in an investigation) to a form such that trained human intellects can comprehend their meaning or implications. This aspect of statistical method can be most succinctly characterized as *data processing*, or the reduction of data.

2. The study of populations or universes of variations from a knowledge of only a part (sample) of the whole; and as a corollary of this, the use of sample statistics for the estimation of universe values and for hypothesis testing.

The need to reduce statistical data to an intelligible form is illustrated in the laboratory as the scientist makes repeated observations and measurements. It is illustrated in the field, in life situations, by the accumulation of the data of observation and measurement. Variation is of the essence of all measurable or countable phenomena.

An important segment of statistics, the theory of errors, began to flourish in the 19th century when F. W. Bessel (1784–1846), the astronomer at Königsberg, began to measure and correct for the *personal equation*, the human variation (error) that enters into all measurements when sufficiently refined. The variations characteristic of the personal equation were found to be both *between observers* (individual differences) as well as *within* the observations of the same person. The variations were *reduced* to averages, average differences, as well as averages of the variations themselves. Thus one of the basic measures in statistics is an average.

This 19th-century interest of astronomers and mathematicians in error variations had been anticipated by several great mathematicians, especially Pierre Simon, the Marquis de Laplace (1749–1827). Laplace, as he is known, related probability theory to the variations characteristic of errors of measurement. In his treatise on probabilities he introduces his chapter on "The Application of the Calculus of Probabilities to Natural Philosophy," with the following:

The phenomena of nature are most often enveloped by so many strange circumstances, and so great a number of disturbing causes mix their influence, that it is very difficult to recognize them. We may arrive at them only by multiplying the

2

observations or the experiences, so that the strange effects finally destroy reciprocally each other, the mean results putting in evidence those phenomena and their divers elements. The more numerous the number of observations and the less they vary among themselves, the more their results approach the truth. We fulfil this last condition by the choice of the methods of observation, by the precision of the instruments, and by the care which we take to observe closely; then we determine by the theory of probabilities the most advantageous mean results or those which give the least value of the error. But that is not sufficient; it is further necessary to appreciate the probability that the errors of these results are comprised in the given limits; and without this we have only an imperfect knowledge of the degree of exactitude obtained. Formulae suitable to these matters are then true improvements of the method of sciences, and it is indeed important to add them to this method. (1951 edition, pp. 73–74.)*

This period in the development of science with the incidental aid of probability theory and statistical method is characterized by J. Neyman (1960) as one of *marginal indeterminism*, i.e., "research in science was all deterministic with just one domain, that of errors of measurement, treated indeterministically."

The 19th-century interests of the astronomers and mathematicians also illustrate the second aim of statistical method, viz., the study of populations or universes from a knowledge of but a part. The statistical population or universe consists of all instances of a given class of phenomena. "All" may be infinite or finite, depending on definitions and circumstances. The astronomers were interested in the determination of a particular person's average error in measuring the instant in time at which a star is observed to cross a wire in the field of the telescopic view. Obviously it is impractical or impossible to obtain more than a sample of all possible measurements that a person can make. So, from the average of the errors observed in his measurements, a generalization is attempted about his accuracy as an observer *at the time* (not also as an old man). The generalization is quantitative, such as, "his error on the average is four-tenths of a second."

This process of generalization from the part to the whole constitutes what today is called *inferential statistics*. The achievement of the first aim, viz., the reduction of data, is characteristically referred to as *descriptive statistics* even though the results of reduction are also required for inferential statistics.

The Census

The statistical problem of reducing masses of quantitative data to intelligible forms or results is perhaps most exhaustively illustrated by the decennial United States Census during the course of which every household is supposed to be visited by a census taker who in turn is supposed to obtain

---

*References, beginning on p. 387, are referred to in the text by date of publication.

accurate answers to many questions. Publications of the Bureau of the Census (1957) are full of statistical results that have been reduced to one or more of the following:

1. Tabulations.
2. Graphical presentations.
3. Calculations (such as percentages or averages).

These are the three forms that the reduction of statistical data may take; i.e., reduction from the unorganized mass of quantitative data to the organized, summarized results.

The Sample

But in recent decades the U.S. census taker has done an interesting thing. He has asked certain questions of only every twentieth household. He wound up, therefore, with two classes of statistical information:

1. Census information obtained from *all* households.
2. Sample information obtained from only 5% of all households.

Even more interesting is the fact that results based on sample information are practically as usable, as reliably useful, and as accurate as results based on all households. In other words, by means of the methods of modern statistics which are developed in this introductory text, it is possible to estimate with satisfactory degrees of accuracy statistical values for universes or populations from the information of only a small part (5%, or even much less) of the total.

DESCRIPTIVE, INFERENTIAL, AND SAMPLING STATISTICS

Historically, statistics first developed out of an interest in census taking. Just as geometry emerged from the demands of daily living, out of the need to measure and survey land along the Nile, so, too, statistics grew out of the need of rulers to "measure" their human resources, to know the number of males fit to bear arms, to know the number of family units that could be taxed. As in the beginnings of any science, statistics as a method was initially a procedure for the systematic collection, classification, and enumeration of information.

Today, statistical method has three essential and distinguishable aspects. In general, statistical method is a technique of science for obtaining and analyzing quantitative data. Its oldest use, as just indicated, is that of description in terms of the "hard facts" of census taking. This aspect is known as *descriptive statistics*.

A second aspect is *inferential statistics*. As already indicated, conditional inferences are made about populations from statistics of samples by means of logic and probability theory. A third aspect, closely related to the second, is that of using methods which will yield adequate samples for inferential statistics. This aspect is known as *sampling statistics*. Sampling and inferential statistics are twin aspects of a basic scientific methodology for the study of populations. Given a set of sample data, what inferences can reasonably be made?

Unlike the poet who may express wonderment at the hazy infinity of things around us, including the stars, the statistician is the Philistine who insists on an exact count. He seeks the facts. Descriptive statistics as a method and research tool is based on the canons and rules of scientific observation. There is no place in statistics for the shoddy count, the uneducated guess, or the "statistical lie." Honest errors do occur, of course, but part of the student's task is to learn to recognize them and to avoid them. A New York paper, for example, reported that the bank discount rate in England had been increased by 2%. Actually it had been increased from 5% to 7%, which is an increase of $\frac{2}{5}$, or 40%. Had the paper written an increase of "2 percentage points," it would have reported what it had intended to say.

Inferential Statistics

In modern times a form of conditional (as opposed to *necessary*) inference was added to the statistician's census taking, to his proclivities for descriptive statistics. The basis for this had its roots in some interesting correspondence in the 17th century between two mathematicians, Pascal and Fermat, concerning "the fortunes and misfortunes of the Chevalier de Méré, a great gambler, and by that token *trés bon esprit*, but alas (wrote Pascal) *il n'est pas géomètre*. Alas indeed. The Chevalier had made his pile by always betting small favourable odds on getting at least one six in 4 tosses of a die, and then had lost it by always betting small odds on getting at least one double six in 24 double tosses." (Hogben, 1957, pp. 36–37)

Pascal and Fermat eventually established some of the fundamental principles of probability. Christian Huygens in 1657 published a brief treatment on the chances of winning at certain card and dice games. Jacques Bernoulli, a Swiss mathematician, wrote the first *book* on probability, and it was published posthumously in 1713 by his nephew. Especially interesting to the applied statistician was Bernoulli's emphasis on the practical possibilities of probability theory for social phenomena.

In 1733, de Moivre gave the first mathematical formulation of the normal probability curve. Little attention was paid to it, however, until the time of Laplace and Gauss toward the end of the 18th century and the beginning of the 19th. Although the normal curve of error is often referred to as the "Gaussian curve," it might perhaps be more appropriate to call it the *curve of Laplace*, or the Laplace-Gaussian curve.

Beginning with Adolphe Quételet (1796–1874), the Belgian statistician and astronomer, statistical methods were employed descriptively in the study of man, and the attempt was made to apply the mathematical model of the normal curve of error, the normal probability curve, to individuals and to the social affairs of man (1846). Quételet made the inferential leap from samples of observations to mankind in general. His favorite paradigm was the normal curve of error. (See Fig. 4.1, Chapter 4.) He was convinced that the political and moral traits of man, when fully measured, would yield distributions conforming to the so-called normal law.

Sir Francis Galton (1822–1911), the English statistician and geneticist, cousin of Charles Darwin, attempted to use inferential statistics in his studies of genius (1869). Following Quételet's example and using the latter's probability tables, Galton classified the "natural intellectual gifts" of men. He inferred their distribution to be "an application of the very curious theoretical law of 'deviation from average',' this "law" being based on the variations characteristic of the normal curve of error. Thus this curve came practically to be idolized. Science seeks simplicity, and what was simpler than the model of the normal curve to describe the distribution of all human traits! In some quarters, especially among a few mathematicians and logicians, this kind of "statistical inference" was thought to generalize beyond the facts.

Inferential statistics today are still misused and abused in the sense that inferences are made beyond the facts, in spite of the facts, from too few facts, from inadequate facts, etc. Perhaps the chief task of an introductory course in applied statistics is to educate the beginner in the wise use of statistics. The student needs to learn some of the hazards and fallacies of statistical method in order to be able to recognize them and thereby reject or avoid them. He needs to know the limitations of his statistical tools as well as their serviceable functions. He needs to know which tools are best for particular problems.

Inferential statistics have certain logical limitations that the student would do well to be aware of from the start. He needs to be acutely aware of the *uncertainty of statistical inference*. He needs to be aware of a very common limitation of statistical inference, and that is its limited *generality*. A college class, for example, may have 5 women and 15 men students. Can it be logically inferred therefrom that in the total campus population there are 25% women and 75% men? The answer of course is NO. To be soundly made, any inference from sample result to a population has to be based on carefully drawn samples of a well-defined parent population, and even then any inference of value from such a small sample will be a range of possibilities rather than a particular percentage.

A fair degree of correlation (association) is found between students' entrance examination marks and their college grades obtained during the freshman year. Can it be therefore logically inferred from such statistics that a similar degree of correlation will obtain for next year's crop of entering freshman? Logically the answer is NO even though, speculatively, a *forecast* of this kind may work out fairly well. Next year's population of students cannot be sampled and statistically analyzed today. Today's population can be sampled and may be used as a statistical model of tomorrow's population, but guessing and forecasting the morrow are not examples of inferential statistics. They are examples of prophecy. Some prophetic guesses come close to the target; many don't.

Statistical inference is not a guessing game about the future; rather it consists in the estimation of numeric characteristics of populations made as reasonably as possible in the light of the statistical information obtained from properly designed samples of those populations.* Only the "future" behaviors of static, hypothetical, infinite populations of coin behavior, dice behavior, etc., lend themselves to statistical prediction. The dynamic world of people and events can be sampled today for today, but it cannot be sampled tomorrow until tomorrow is also today. Man can speculate, guess, or prophesy about the future, but he is not yet in a logical position to apply probability theory to the future.

Suppose X, a high school graduate, scores high on a college entrance examination. Are the odds therefore better than even that he will do well in his course work at college? The answer is again NO, this time because the question has not been properly formulated. As will be seen in Chapter 7, the odds of probability theory are not applicable to individual events such as the behavior of X on a college entrance examination. The mathematical models of probability theory are applicable, when applicable at all, only to a multitude of events under well-defined conditions. However, from the test information and experience with past relations of entrance examination scores and college performance, the psychologist may *hazard the decision* that X will *most likely* do satisfactory work in college. Making a decision, or advancing the best possible guess in the light of all information available, is logically quite different from attaching a probability value to a judgment or decision about the individual case.

Sampling Statistics

The *inferential* of *inferential statistics* is based on logic and probability theory. The *statistics* of *inferential statistics* need to be based, as just indicated, on the data of properly contrived samples of the population to be studied. This third aspect of modern statistics is nearly a discipline in its own right. (See Cochran, 1959; and Deming, 1960.) It is so closely related to inferential statistics, since the latter depends on the former, that they are distinguishable only as different operations in the use of statistical

---

*It is suggested in this connection that the interested student examine R. A. Fisher's 1959 publication, and Hogben (1957).

methods to study populations from sample data. Inferences are drawn or made from the latter.

The student needs to become familiar with some of the problems attendant on adequate sampling of a population. Perhaps one of the greatest fields of omission in psychology and the behavioral sciences lies in the failure of investigators and speculators to obtain adequate samples of populations for whom all kinds of generalizations are made.

Estimation of Parameters

The study of populations by sampling and inferential statistics has a twofold character. One statistical procedure is called *parameter estimation*, and this is the subject matter of Chapter 8. The other is called the *testing of statistical hypothesis*, and this is considered in the remaining chapters of the book following Chapter 8. Parameter estimation is a phrase to describe what the statistician does when he attempts to estimate a mean or a proportion, etc., of a population from the information of a sample of that population. The numeric measures of statistical populations are called *parameters;* the numeric measures of samples are called *statistics*. Parameter estimation is the result of a process of inductive inference whereby the statistics of samples and the paradigms of probability theory are used to estimate parameters of the populations sampled.

Significance Testing

It will be seen that the testing of hypotheses is also a way of studying populations from the statistics of samples by inferential statistics. It is a process of setting up certain statistical hypotheses about populations and then giving the facts, as gleaned from the sample data, the opportunity to nullify or refute the hypotheses being tested. Thus one may claim that there is a sex difference in the mechanical ability of boys and girls. For the argument, it may be granted that the claimant has adequate test procedures to measure mechanical ability. His first problem then is to define the population(s) to be sampled and studied. His second problem is to draw an adequate sample of boys and girls whose mechanical abilities will then be measured. He then gives the facts obtained from these measurements the opportunity to "nullify" the statistical hypotheses that in the populations sampled there is really no difference between the averages and between the measures of variation of mechanical ability of the girls and of the boys. In other words, he tests the hypotheses that they are equal on the average and in their distributions of variations in performance. Some differences between any two groups are naturally to be expected, as a matter of chance, but the statistical question is whether it is reasonable to conclude that all the differences are just a matter of chance. If the sample information is such as to indicate rather strongly that the differences are too great to be likely by chance, then the hypotheses of equality are rejected and a decision is made to support the generality of a sex difference in the population studied.

Descriptive vs. Sampling-Inferential Statistics

The three distinguishable aspects of statistical method in effect reduce to two, descriptive statistics and sampling-inferential statistics. In descriptive statistics no attempt is made to generalize beyond the data as organized and summarized. The aim of descriptive statistics is the reduction of the quantitative data to a form that can be readily comprehended. Census taking has already been pointed to as perhaps the greatest example of descriptive statistics. The grade data a teacher collects over a term from a class may be treated statistically in a purely *reductive-descriptive* fashion, with no attempt made to generalize, with no interest in generalizing beyond the single group's results. On the other hand, as has been emphasized, the aim of sampling-inferential statistics is that of generalizing beyond the data at hand.

Such generalizations often are mainly descriptive of the population as a whole. Thus a public opinion pollster attempts to *describe* the opinions of a population from a study of the statistical data of only a sample of that population. If during an election campaign 55% of a nation-wide sample of eligible voters are found to favor candidate X, what inference can be made about X's standing in the total population of eligible voters? This is a problem of parameter estimation (see Chapter 8) and the goal is essentially descriptive. However, the description is attempted by the method of sampling-inferential statistics rather than by a census. The problem may also be tackled by testing the hypothesis that no more than 50% of the *population* favor X. If the facts, as assembled, warrant the decision to reject this hypothesis, then the conclusion may be made that a majority (more than 50%) favor X. The conclusion may thus be reached by significance testing that at least a simple majority of the population favors X.

ROLE OF STATISTICAL METHOD IN RESEARCH

It is suggested as an exercise that the student examine in some detail one of the current research publications of his field of interest. Each article should be examined for the role played by statistical method. In general it will be found that the value of statistical method in research lies in one or the other of the three areas discussed in the following paragraphs.

Statistical Method and Experimental Design

Statistical method serves an indispensable and closely integrated role in the design of experiments.* It enters into the operations at several stages of an experimental investigation.

---

*See R. A. Fisher, 1949; Cochran and Cox, 1960; Edwards, 1960.

First, it appears in the decision about the population to be studied and the sample of observations or measurements to be made. The importance of this role is often inadequately recognized. The eventual outcome of the experiment, the validity of any inferences drawn, depends on the adequacy of the sample of observations or measurements.

Second, statistical method enters into the design of the experimental procedure to be followed in obtaining the observations or measurements. A statistical requirement is that errors be randomized insofar as possible. To this end, the order of two or more experimental procedures is randomized. When a sample is to be divided up into several subgroups, for control groups and experimentally treated groups, the assignment of persons to each is often randomized.*

Third, statistical method is needed for the analysis of the quantitative results of an experiment. Statistical hypotheses relevant to the investigation are set up at the beginning of the experiment and then the obtained information is given the opportunity statistically to nullify them. Parameter estimates will also be relevant oftentimes after certain hypotheses are rejected.

Statistical Method and Surveys

The role of statistical method in survey research is somewhat similar to its role in experimentation. The problems of sampling may loom larger, especially if one is trying to survey the attitudes or opinions of an entire adult population such as that in the United States. The distribution of errors is randomized as far as possible by carefully designed field procedures (rather than laboratory procedures, as in experimentation). For example, if the survey is being conducted with households as the sampling units, operating procedures are laid out in advance, or randomized along the way, by means of tables of random numbers,** so that the investigator's likes or dislikes, whims or prejudices, etc., will not enter into the selection of the household or of the respondent in the household. And, finally, in the analysis of the assembled data of a survey, some hypotheses may be tested, but more often the researcher will attempt to describe aspects of the population surveyed from the statistics of the samples by means of techniques for the estimation of parameters.

Statistical Method and Psychometrics

In the third general category of the services rendered by statistical method to research is the general field of psychometrics. The relationship

---

*Cochran and Cox (1960, p. 7) point out that RANDOMIZATION is one of the few aspects of modern experimental design that appears to be really modern. Experiments of 100 years ago can be found that embody all the sound requirements of modern design, with the conspicuous exception of randomization.

**See Appendix, Table L; Kendall and Smith, 1938.

is so close here that, historically, statistical methods and psychometric methods have sometimes been identified as one and the same. But they are clearly distinguishable, as a perusal of books like the following will show: *Measurement and Evaluation in Psychology and Education,* by R. L. Thorndike and E. Hagen, and *Psychometric Methods* by J. P. Guilford. Statistical methods are indispensable to the development of techniques of measurement in psychology and related fields: in the development of aptitude tests, achievement tests, proficiency tests, etc.; in the development of rating scales, attitude scales, etc. In this area the statistical techniques of correlation are indispensable. They are essential to the appraisal of the reliability and validity of most instruments of psychological measurement because a psychological instrument is basically a relationship—a transaction—with persons.

And, finally, in this third category should be placed the role of statistical method in the attempt by methods of factor analysis (they are essentially statistical) to develop and test various theories of mental organization or mind functioning. Here, as in test construction, the statistical technique mainly relied upon is again that of correlation.*

SOME BASIC ASSUMPTIONS ON THE PROPER USE OF STATISTICS

The proper application of statistical methods to the research data of psychology and the behavioral sciences is contingent on the satisfaction of certain conditions. Assumptions play a determining role in sampling-inferential statistics. Even in descriptive statistics, assumptions play an important role; as for example, in the use of the midvalue of an interval as a satisfactory average of all the measures tallied in the interval. (See p. 35.)

An exhaustive summary of the role of assumptions in applied statistics is not contemplated here. However, two of the more important and frequently occurring ones will be mentioned at this time. Others will be referred to as they arise in the ensuing chapters. It is hoped thereby that the student thus alerted will be sensitive to this general problem in his use of the various statistical techniques.

Probability Sampling

The basic assumption underlying sampling-inferential statistics applied to the real world of people and events is that of probability sampling. The method is described and defined on p. 176. It is a *sine qua non* to the utilization of the implications of probability theory, in the estimation of parameters and in the significance testing of statistical hypotheses.

---

*The student interested in exploring this area could hardly do better than begin with an article, now a classic, by E. E. Cureton (1939): "The Principal Compulsions of Factor-Analysts."

The way to satisfy this assumption can be briefly stated. The researcher needs to draw his samples of observations or measurements by means of carefully planned procedures that will include the technique of RANDOM-IZATION. In other words, he needs to use methods that will satisfy the requirements of probability sampling.

Normally Distributed Populations

Some of the most widely used methods of inferential statistics are based on the assumption that the particular measurements of a study are drawn randomly from variables whose population distributions have the form of the Gaussian normal curve of error. (See Fig. 4.1, p. 66.) This is usually referred to as *the normal distribution assumption*. Statistical methods not dependent for their proper use on this assumption are often referred to as *distribution-free methods*.

The use of statistical techniques with the *measurables* of small-sample, experimental research is generally based on the assumption that the variables of the parent populations are normally distributed. Most of the methods conditional on this assumption are those used in the significance testing of hypotheses about means and mean differences, either by *t* tests or by analysis of variance. (Chapters 10, 11.)

The satisfaction of the normal distribution assumption is difficult to assess inasmuch as the populations in question are usually unknowns. The distributions of large random samples can be tested for their possible divergence from the normal (by chi-square, Chapter 9). However, such appraisals cannot be effectively made with small samples.

Box (1953) has shown that departures of small sample distributions from normality can be considerable without seriously affecting the applicability of the analysis of variance method. Since such departures are more likely to underestimate rather than to overestimate the variations characteristic of sample results, the criteria used in significance testing can be selected in a way to compensate for this. (See *alpha levels of significance*, p. 312, ff.)

When marked divergencies from normality of the distributions of either small or large samples occur, then the researcher may resort to statistical methods *free* of the normal distribution assumption. These methods are sometimes described as *nonparametric* methods. Some are nonparametric in that they cannot be used to estimate parameters as can the methods described for this purpose in Chapter 8. However, their main feature lies in their substitution for statistical methods *not free* of the normal distribution assumption; hence this writer's preference for the label, "*distribution-free methods*," which is an elision of "methods free of the assumption of normally distributed populations."

Population variables whose numerics are *countables* or *rankables* are not normally distributed. Thus the use of distribution-free methods with *measurables* is achieved by reducing the original measures of a sample result to *counts* or to *ranks*. (See Chapters 9, 12.)

Over the past few years there has been somewhat of a faddish use of distribution-free methods. The attitude apparently prevailing in some quarters is that these methods can satisfactorily do the required statistical job, without regard to the source of data (parent population) and the way in which the data are obtained (method of sampling). The distribution-free methods for significance testing are *not* free of the assumption of probability sampling; nor are they free of scientific standards of observation and measurement. They are free only of the assumption of normally distributed parent populations. They are no substitute for nonprobability sampling or for shoddy workmanship.

SOME STATISTICAL DEFINITIONS AND CONVENTIONS

Statistics

The term *statistics* has several somewhat different meanings, each of which is ordinarily recognized by the context of its usage. Statistics may be:

1. The branch of science that deals with the data of variables.
2. The method of statistics.
3. Quantitative data (note: *data*, plural; *datum*, singular).
4. Values of samples of observations or measurements, such as means and proportions.

The word is often used in the singular, e.g., "A mean statistic is a mean of a sample of measurements." ("Sample" is defined on p. 15.)

Variable*

Inasmuch as variation is the essence of phenomena that are statistical, it may be well at this point to define a variable as a statistical concept. Formerly a variable was defined as a trait or characteristic that manifests differences (or variations) *in magnitude*. In contradistinction, an *attribute* was defined as a trait or characteristic that manifests differences in kind, or in quality, rather than in magnitude (see Yule, 1912). Today, however, the concept *variable* is used to refer to any trait or characteristic that manifests differences, irrespective of whether the differences are quantitative or qualitative. Thus attributes or characteristics such as sex, eye color, nationality, and race are variables that manifest qualitative differences. Characteristics such as height, weight, brightness, perceptual acuity, and speed of reaction are variables that manifest quantitative differences.

T. L. Kelley (1947), in discussing the difference between quantitative and qualitative data, pointed out that one of the most fruitful lines for analysis is to attempt to discover a sense in which data are *not* qualitative. If no such discovery can be made, then the variable is qualitative, at least in the

---

*In mathematics a variable is defined as a quantity that can take on any numbers of some set.

sense that it cannot be quantified. Color is a case in point. Eye color, for example, is usually treated psychologically as a qualitative variable. But if eye color is measured and indexed according to the physics of light, then the variable is the quantitative one of wave-length composition. Insofar as *skin color* can be arranged in a scale or in a series from light to dark, it is a quantitative rather than a qualitative variable. A color blind person would have little or no difficulty in ranking skin color from light to dark, but a person with normal vision would be faced with perceptible qualitative differences as well as quantitative ones.

The statistical data of variables may be classified as:

1. Countables.
2. Rankables.
3. Measurables.

They are described in some detail in Chapter 2.

Variate

A variate was formerly used to designate a single instance or measure of a variable. Today, however, the word is often used as a synonym of "variable." It is more or less exclusively used with the prefixes "uni," "bi," and "multi," to designate a distribution of a single variable (a univariate), of two associated variables (a bivariate), and of more than two related variables (a multivariate).

Population, Universe, or Collective

These three terms are used synonymously. They refer to the total *set* of items (actual or hypothetical) defined by some characteristic of the items. The total set may be infinitely large, in which case the statistical population or universe is an infinite one; or the total set may be finite.

Parent Population and Frame

That population from which samples are drawn is designated as the parent population or as the frame. The latter concept is used especially in survey research, where a frame consists of all the sampling units of a population that can be identified with serial numbers and sampled either at a given time or over a specified period of time. The *target population* of a study will be larger than the population frame when the list of sampling units is not 100% complete. Thus a population to be sampled might consist of all members of the American Psychological Association, but the frame of sampling units (the list of members) would be less than 100% if the most recent directory did not include the last batch of new members.

The phrase *parent population* is used in the preceding sense for the term *frame*. It is also used to designate an indefinitely large, theoretical population that is sampled, as in the sampling of the behavior of a person (or persons) or of coins or of dice, etc., under specified conditions of experimental control, observation, and measurement.

Sample

A sample is a finite portion of a statistical population or universe. It is a part of the whole. A probability sample is obtained by a technique known as randomization. (See Chapter 7.) Such a sample can provide reliable information about a finite statistical population, at a small fraction of what the cost in time, energy, and dollars would be otherwise. Infinite populations can be empirically studied only through the data of samples.

Parameter

In statistics a parameter is used to signify a measure derived deductively from a hypothetical population or statistical universe (usually infinitely large) or estimated inductively from observed values of a finite population. In applied statistics, many unknown parameters are hypothesized.

A parameter value may be hypothesized as a constant, or it may be estimated. One area of *inferential statistics*, viz., *significance testing*, proceeds by hypothesizing parameter values and then "testing" them. Another area, viz., *parameter estimation*, is, as already indicated, literally concerned with the estimation of parameter values of statistical populations.

Coefficient

A coefficient is a constant quantity in an expression or equation as distinguished from a variable quantity. In the linear equation $y = bx$, b is a constant known in statistics as the *regression coefficient*. In the expression $b_{yx} = r_{yx}(s_y/s_x)$, r_{yx} is the *correlation coefficient*.

Function

A quantity that varies with the variation of another quantity is a *function*. In the expression $y = f(x)$, y is a function of x. The value of y is dependent on the value of x; hence y is the dependent variable and x is the independent variable in this relationship.

Index

An index is a pure number formed by a ratio of one dimension of an object or person to another dimension. The I.Q. (intelligence quotient), as the ratio of a person's mental age to his chronological age, is an *index of brightness*. The ratio of maximum breadth of the head to its maximum length is the *cephalic index*. Both indices are usually multiplied by 100.

STATISTICAL SYMBOLS AND CONVENTIONS

Variables

A single variable is usually symbolized by x (lower case).

Two variables are often symbolized by x and y (lower case).

Three variables are sometimes symbolized by x, y, and z; also by numerical subscripts with x, as x_1, x_2, and x_3.

More than three variables are symbolized by numerical subscripts with x. Zero is also sometimes used as a subscript symbol of a variable in correlation. Thus r_{01} symbolizes the correlation between variable 0 and variable 1.

Note that x is also generally used to symbolize the deviate value of a measure from the arithmetic mean: $x = X - \overline{X}$, where X symbolizes any measure and $\overline{X}$ (bar X) symbolizes the mean.

Measures

A single measure of a variable is usually symbolized by the capital letter of its letter symbol; thus X for variable x, Y for variable y. Different individual instances are denoted by numerical subscripts beginning with X_1 for the first case and ending with X_n.

Frequencies

The number of cases, i.e., the frequency of instances in a sample or population is denoted by f or $\mathbf{F}$, and (or) n or N. Usually the frequencies per class, or category, are symbolized by f. The total number of f's for a sample or group of data is symbolized by n or N:

$$\Sigma f = n \quad \text{or } N$$

where Σ, Greek capital letter sigma, symbolizes the operation of algebraic summation.

In descriptive statistics either n or N is used for Σf. In sampling-inferential statistics, n is used for Σf of a sample and N is used for $\Sigma \mathbf{F}$ of the population; hence N will have a numeric value only when the statistical population is finite; otherwise $N = \infty$.

The symbol m is often used to designate the number (or frequency) of subgroups or subsamples into which a variable is divided or classified. The symbol for a subclass or subsample is k, which is also used interchangeably with m.

Statistics and Parameters

In sampling-inferential statistics, lower case Roman letters are generally used to symbolize statistics of samples, and lower case Greek letters are used to symbolize parameter measures of populations. But there are definite exceptions to this because of historically prior usages. Thus the Greek letter pi (π) is always used to symbolize the ratio of a circle to its diameter, 3.14159+. Where a Greek letter is thus already preempted, the capital Roman letter is often used for the parameter, the lower case one for the statistic. Thus f and F indicate sample frequency and population frequency; n and N, for sample and for population; p and P, sample proportion and parameter proportion, respectively.

Variations in Symbols

The student will soon discover that there is no uniformity in the use of symbols by the textbook writers on statistics. Such variations as exist perhaps are illustrative of the essential character of statistical phenomena, but it is nevertheless unfortunate that a standard code of practice has not been worked out. The field needs a Napoleon to codify: a Napoleonic committee with representatives from the various fields whose symbols tend to differ—mathematics, agriculture, economics, engineering, as well as psychology and the behavioral sciences.

Greek Letters in Statistical Usage

Since students in U.S. colleges do not usually study the Greek language, the Greek alphabet is reproduced here.

Upper Case	Lower Case	Name	Upper Case	Lower Case	Name
A	α	Alpha	N	ν	Nu
B	β	Beta	Ξ	ξ	Xi
Γ	γ	Gamma	O	o	Omicron
Δ	δ	Delta	Π	π	Pi
E	ϵ	Epsilon	P	ρ	Rho
Z	ζ	Zeta	Σ	σ	Sigma
H	η	Eta	T	τ	Tau
Θ	θ	Theta	Υ	υ	Upsilon
I	ι	Iota	Φ	ϕ	Phi
K	κ	Kappa	X	χ	Chi
Λ	λ	Lambda	Ψ	ψ	Psi
M	μ	Mu	Ω	ω	Omega

The more commonly used lower case Greek symbols are:

α *alpha*, level of significance (p. 195).
β *beta*, coefficient of certain regression equations (p. 119).
δ *delta*, a difference between two parameters (p. 262).
ζ *zeta*, parameter value of Fisher's Z transformation function (p. 215).
η *eta*, correlation ratio; a measure of nonlinear correlation (p. 132).
θ *theta*, a common designation of an angle.
μ *mu*, arithmetic mean of a population; a parameter mean (p. 176).
ξ *xi*, a deviate from a population mean.
π *pi*, the value of the ratio of the circumference of a circle to its diameter, viz., 3.1416
ρ *rho*, parameter Pearsonian correlation coefficient (p. 214).
σ *sigma*, the standard deviation of a population distribution (p. 52); sigma squared being the variance of a population.
ϕ *phi*, a coefficient of correlation (p. 135).

χ *chi*, usually used as chi-square (p. 245), which represents a relation of differences between statistics and population values.

Roman Letters in Statistical Usage

Most Roman letters used in statistics are italicized and have the following denotations:

a = angle.
b = regression coefficient (p. 108).
C = centile (p. 38); also, contingency coefficient (p. 136).
d = difference.
D = decile (p. 43); D range (p. 47); $\overline{D}$ = a mean difference (p. 290).
E = expectation; $E(x)$ is read as "the expectation of x" (p. 176).
$\mathbf{E}$ = index of efficiency of prediction in correlation (p. 114).
e = error.
f = frequency.
F = variance ratio (p. 291); $\mathbf{F}$ = parameter or *expected* frequency (p. 191).
H = hypothesis, usually with a subscript; also the H statistic of the Kruskal-Wallis test (p. 376).
i = size or width of a class interval; also any case in a row of values, usually as a subscript.
j = any case in a column of values, usually as a subscript.
ij = any case in an intersecting row and column of values, usually as subscripts.
k = coefficient of alienation (p. 106); also the designation for classes or subclasses, samples or subsamples. (*klasse* = German for *class*.)
l = lower (subscript).
m = the sum of or number of k subclasses, or elements; also, a *moment* (p. 76).
M = the arithmetic mean of a group of data in descriptive statistics.
n = $\sum f$ of a sample.
N = $\sum \mathbf{F}$ of a population.
p = a proportion.
P = a parameter proportion; also a permutation (p. 156).
$\mathbf{P}$ = probability; $\mathbf{P}(x)$ is read as "the probability of x" (p. 150).
q = $1 - p$.
Q = $1 - P$; also a quartile (p. 43).
r = Pearson's correlation coefficient (p. 91).
R = multiple correlation coefficient (p. 117); also, a rank (p. 44).
s = standard deviation (p. 52).
S = subset (p. 154); also, standard measure (p. 69).
t = *Student's t* (p. 209).
T = a total or sum of a group of measures; the lesser of two sums of ranks (p. 374).
U = the statistic of the Mann-Whitney test (p. 368).
V = variance in descriptive statistics (p. 52)
W = concordance coefficient (p. 382).
x = a deviation, $X - \overline{X}$; also, a variable.
$\bar{x}$ or $\overline{X}$ = arithmetic mean (p. 51).
X = any measure of variable x.
$\overline{X}_G$ = geometric mean (p. 109).
y = an ordinate variable; also a deviation, $Y - \overline{Y}$.
$\overline{Y}$ = any measure of variable y.
z = a deviation from a mean in units of standard deviation (p. 67).
Z = Fisher's transformation statistic for r (p. 215).

Word Abbreviations

Abbreviations are frequently used for terms to avoid repetition and to economize on space. The following abbreviations are used in this text:

A.D.   average deviation (p. 53)
c.c.   confidence criterion (p. 195); also, critical criterion (p. 289)
c.f.   cumulated frequencies (p. 33)
C.I.   centile interval (p. 44)
c.p.   cumulated proportions (p. 33)
C.R.   critical ratio (p. 290)
d.f.   degrees of freedom (p. 210)
D.K.'s   don't knows (p. 253)
I.Q.   intelligence quotient
Ku   kurtosis (p. 74)
mdn   median (p. 46)
MDN   a parameter median (p. 222)
Q.D.   quartile deviation (p. 48)
S.D.   standard deviation of a group of data in descriptive statistics (p. 52)
Sk   skewness (p. 73)
S.U.   sampling unit (p. 204)
T.M.   tentative mean (p. 61)

Diacritical Marks

Two diacritical marks are often employed in statistics. They are the *tilde* and the *circumflex*.

A tilde over a symbol is used to indicate an estimate computed from a regression equation, as $\tilde{X}$ or $\tilde{Y}$ (pp. 107 ff.). Some authors use the tilde to designate population figures.

A circumflex over a symbol signifies that it is *an estimate of*, rather than an exact measure of, as illustrated by $\hat{\sigma}_{\bar{x}}$ (Eq. 8.4, p. 194), rather than $\sigma_{\bar{x}}$ (Eq. 8.3, p. 193).

Symbols for Operations

$=$ is equal to.
$\neq$ is not equal to.
$\cong$ is approximately equal to.
$a > b$ a is greater than b, or b is less than a.
$a < b$ a is less than b, or b is greater than a.
$a \geq b$ a is equal to or greater than b; a is not less than b.
$a \leq b$ a is equal to or less than b; a is not greater than b.
$\sum$ the sum of.
$|a|$ the numerical value of a with the sign taken as positive.

CHAPTER 2

KINDS OF STATISTICAL DATA
AND THEIR ORGANIZATION

Nature has given us the seeds of knowledge,
not knowledge itself.

Seneca

Once statistical data are obtained, the initial task is their organization and summarization, irrespective of whether they are to be used only descriptively or also inferentially. *How* they are organized and summarized depends on the nature or kind of statistical information one has to work with.

NATURE OF STATISTICAL DATA

It was emphasized in the preceding chapter that *variation* is perhaps the chief concept that underlies all statistics. *Variation* is the fact of change or of differences characteristic of the biological and behavioral sciences. A *variable* is that which manifests variation. It is the entity, object, attribute, trait, or quality that varies or reveals differences. It is the recording of the manifestations of change or of differences for a given variable that gives rise to numerical data which are the data of statistics. Such data need to be organized in the sense of being arranged into meaningful groupings or classes. They need to be summarized in the sense that two or three measures may effectively describe essential overall aspects of the results.

Statistical data may take one or the other of three forms:

1. *Countables.*
2. *Rankables.*
3. *Measurables.*

The mode of their organization depends on whether they are

1. Univariates (data of single variables).
2. Bivariates (data of two logically related variables).
3. Multivariates (data of more than two logically related variables).

Finally, the methods used for the summarization and analysis of statistical data will depend on whether they are:

1. A probability sample of a defined population.
2. Not such a sample.

If they are the former, the methods of sampling-inferential statistics are needed; if the latter, only the methods of descriptive statistics are required.

COUNTABLES

Values obtained simply by counting are perhaps the oldest historically; mathematically they are the most elementary of the three classes of statistical data. They are countables and are obtained by the *method of simple enumeration*. Most of the descriptive information of a census is assembled from the individual schedules used with each household or dwelling unit. They become the numerical data of a count.

*Population tables** prepared by the U.S. Bureau of the Census are illustrative:

1. U.S. population by States at the time of the official decennial Census, 1790 to 1960.
2. Marital Status of Persons (in the U.S.) 14 Years Old and Over.
3. U.S. Population by Age, Color, and Sex.
4. Illiteracy in the United States, Persons 14 Years Old and Over (classified by skin color, and urban vs. rural nonfarm and rural farm).
5. Farm and Not-Farm Population of the United States.
6. American Indian Population by States.

Vital statistics include data defined as measurables, such as height and weight, as well as countables such as:

1. Number of births and deaths per unit of time over a series of units (such as years) for the U.S. as a whole, or for the various States.
2. The number of single and plural live births in the U.S. over a sequence of years.
3. The number of marriages and divorces, by States, from year to year.
4. A classification of the causes of death and an enumeration of the number of cases per category over a given period of time such as a year.
5. A classification of types of accidental deaths and an enumeration of each type for a month or longer period.
6. The number of patients in public mental hospitals per State at a stated time, etc.

ORDERABLE AND NONORDERABLE COUNTABLES

How the data of countables are organized depends on whether or not they are orderable. The data of a variable are orderable if they can be meaningfully arranged in relation to a progression of quantities from least to most (or most to least). Any set of numerical data can be arranged in order of size, but this in itself does not necessarily signify they are orderable. It is the changing or differentiable *property* of an object or entity, known as the variable, that is quantitatively ordered from least to most. None of the preceding examples of countables is orderable. Statistics by categories such as states of the Union, marital status, skin color, sex, urban vs. rural residence, and farm or nonfarm are not orderable into

*See *Statistical Abstract of the United States,* or *The World Almanac.*

series from least to most. Rather they are classifiable into subgroups or categories that should be (for good statistics):

1. *Exhaustive* of all instances for the given variable; i.e., there needs to be a category for each differentiable case. Oftentimes the category "Other" is used as a catchall for the odds and ends that are infrequent.
2. *Mutually exclusive* of each other and so defined that there will be no ambiguity in the assignment of the collection of instances or observations to the categories.

Nonorderable variables whose data are countables are sometimes called *nominal variables.* Each class or category of a nominal variable differs qualitatively rather than quantitatively. That is to say, the differences are differences in *kind,* as e.g., the male and female categories of the sex variable.

Countables that are orderable but difficult to scale into equal intervals are fairly common in social statistics and psychological measurement. Hair shades, regardless of hue, may be identified (with the aid of sample swatches) as *very light, light, medium, dark,* and *very dark.* Personality variables such as sociability and aggressiveness may consist of countable data ordered into a few broad classes such as *not-at-all, somewhat, definitely, very,* and *very-very.* Classes such as these have to be carefully described for each personality variable if the process of identification of persons and their classification is to be satisfactorily reliable and valid.

Scalable Countables

A countable that is scalable as well as orderable is illustrated by a variable such as the size of household units or the number of siblings per family. The former variable might range from one person per household to any number found to exist in a census or a sample of a population of household units. A *tally* (or tabulation) is made of such information and the total number of *frequencies* in each class 1, 2, 3, 4 · · · k is obtained. Similarly a *scaled distribution* of the number of siblings per family unit can be set up with a range of from zero to k. Such distributions of countables are called *discrete* because there are no fractionate values; the value for each successive interval is an exact count of the frequencies (f's) per interval.

Bivariates and Multivariates

Countable data may be obtained not only from a single variable or univariate but also from a bivariate and from multivariate distributions. The Census data giving marital status by sex of persons 14 years old and over is an example of a bivariate whose data are countables. One variable is marital status; the other is sex. The Census data as of March, 1959, show the bivariate relations of Table 2.1. Note that although the data are based on a count, the count is not given as an exact figure but as an approximation to the nearest thousand. For such large numbers as 60 million, an exact count is very difficult if not impossible, and it is not needed anyway.

A multivariate relationship would be had if in addition to the two variables of marital status and sex, a third (such as skin color) and a fourth variable (such as native-born persons vs. nonnative-born), etc., were added to the classificatory design.

Finally it should be apparent that countable data may be obtained either from populations as a whole or from samples of defined populations. Many governmental agencies, including the Bureau of the Census, today *estimate* population counts from information obtained from samples of those populations. Such estimations are based on inferential statistics, and methods for making them will be described in Chapter 8.

Table 2.1. A Bivariate Distribution of Countables
(Marital Status and Sex in the U.S.)
(Numbers Are in Thousands)

Marital Status	Sex		Total
	Males	Females	
Single	14,768	11,884	26,652
Married	41,236	42,127[a]	83,363
Widowed	2,161	8,002	10,163
Divorced	1,093	1,548	2,641
Total	59,258	63,561	122,819

SOURCE: *World Almanac*, 1961, p. 462.

[a] The nearly one million more married women than married men is explained by several factors: certainly not by bigamy, although this may be one factor. There are doubtless many instances of separations with the wife counted because she was at home and available for interviewing but the husband was away and therefore not counted.

Table 2.2. The Countables of Table 2.1 Summarized and Compared by Proportions

Marital Status	Sex		Total
	Males	Females	
Single	.249	.187	.217
Married	.696	.663	.679
Widowed	.037	.126	.083
Divorced	.018	.024	.021
	1.000	1.000	1.000

Statistical Organization and Summarization of Countables

The discrete quantitative distributions of scalable countables, such as the number of siblings per family unit, are usually organized and summarized by the same methods that are employed with measurables. Hence they will be considered with them later in this chapter.

The qualitative divisions into two or more categories of nonorderable variables are in themselves the mode or manner of their organization. As already indicated, the categories have to be mutually exclusive as well as exhaustive in order that all the variations or differences characteristic of a variable may be classified. Once the categories have been established, the statistical procedure for handling the data is relatively simple:

1. A *tally* is made as each observation is identified and related to the particular category of the design.
2. A *count* is made of the occurrences or frequencies per category.
3. The frequencies (symbolized as f) per category are summed to give the total number of observations; this total is symbolized by n.
4. Frequencies per category are usually converted to proportions or percentages where a proportion, p, of any category, k, is equal to

$$p_k = \frac{f_k}{n} \qquad (2.1)$$

where f_k is the number of frequencies or count for any category k.

Proportions are more meaningful than frequencies for summary and comparative purposes because the former are taken to a base of 1.00 irrespective of the size of n. A percentage is, of course, a proportion taken to a base of 100:

$$\%_{ok} = 100p_k \qquad (2.2)$$

Three techniques are available for the organization and summarization of a set of statistical data, whether the data are countables or measurables:

1. Tables (as Table 2.1, 2.2, etc.)
2. Graphs (as Figure 2.1, 2.2, etc.)
3. Statistical calculations (as proportions; and, later, as means, etc.)

The data of Table 2.1 might be more meaningfully summarized if the proportions of each sex as well as of the whole group were calculated. This is the case because the sex groups are unequal in size, and consequently more women might be expected in a marital status category just because there are more women than men in the population at the time of the census, or survey. When there are less women than men in a given category, the comparison of their *relative frequencies*, i.e., their respective proportions will give even greater weight or impact to the differences. Thus

Table 2.2 shows less than 19% of women to be single as against nearly 25% of men. The *proportionately greatest* difference is in the "widowed" category: 3.7% men as against 12.6% women.

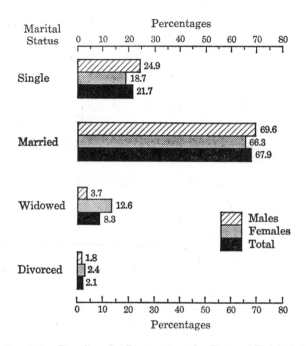

Fig. 2.1. Bar Graphs Portraying the Data of Table 2.2
(With Proportions Converted to Percentages)

Graphic comparisons of the marital status of the sexes would not look the same for the countable data of Table 2.1 and for the derived proportions of Table 2.2. The latter are much simpler to use and would ordinarily be chosen in graphic presentation because the conversion of the frequencies per category to proportions puts the data of each sex on the same scale of values, viz., a base of 1.0 and hence in comparable terms. For example,

$$\text{Single males:} \quad 14{,}768 : 59{,}258 :: p : 1.0; \quad p = \frac{14{,}768}{59{,}258} = .249$$

$$\text{Single females:} \quad 11{,}884 : 63{,}561 :: p : 1.0; \quad p = \frac{11{,}884}{63{,}561} = .187$$

The bar chart in Fig. 2.1 portrays in a summary fashion the marital status of the sexes. Horizontal bars are used, with the scale of proportion values indicated at the top and bottom of the graph. Vertical bars instead of horizontal bars can be employed, but the horizontal forms are often to be preferred for the nonscalable data of countables so that the vertical design will not be confused with scaled distributions as portrayed, for example, by the histogram of Fig. 2.2.

Statistical values that measure the correlation or extent of the relationship between nonorderable countables, as between sex and marital status, are developed in Chapter 6.

RANKABLES

Rankables are orderable and are often scaled. They may be univariates or bivariates or multivariates. They may be data for a sample or for a population. There are two general classes of rankables:

1. A single series of ranks, first $\cdots$ nth, or $1 \cdots n$.
2. A series of ranked intervals each of which may have more than one frequency.

The first type of rankable consists of *ordinal* values. That is to say, *rank positions* beginning with "first," then "second," etc., and ending with the nth rank are assigned to a group or sample of objects or persons with respect to some quality, attribute, or characteristic. Thus the "melodic quality" of a number of different musical compositions may be ranked; or the "outgoingness" of several individuals' personalities may be ranked; or the "hardness" of stones may be ranked. Whereas melodic quality and outgoingness might be ranked entirely on the basis of subjective judgments, the hardness scale of rank position is based on the "scratch test." That stone is hardest which will scratch all others; that stone is least hard which can be scratched by all others. Ordinal positions of stones in between the hardest and softest can be determined accordingly.

The distinctions in an ordinal series of ranks are thus *positional rather than quantitative*. Each object or instance of a rankable variable can be assigned a position such that it is "less than" or "more than" other instances and possibly in some cases "equal to." If five persons are ranked according to the *evenness of their temperament* by someone who knows them well, the result might be recorded as follows:

Evenness of Temperament	Rank Position
Mr. A	first
Mr. B	second
Mr. C	third
Mr. D	fourth
Mr. E	fifth

Very often in psychological measurement the data of rankables are quantified by assigning cardinal numbers to the ordinal ranks. When this is done, they are scaled with equal integer intervals. Thus:

Evenness of Temperament	Rank Position
Mr. A	5
Mr. B	4
Mr. C	3
Mr. D	2
Mr. E	1

Note that Mr. A, judged to have the *most* even temperament, is accorded the nth, or highest, cardinal value, and Mr. E, judged to have the *least* even temperament, is accorded the lowest, or cardinal value of 1. This assignment of numbers to the rank positions necessarily assumes a scale of equal intervals when the numbers are summed and averaged. For comparative purposes and for summary purposes, this assumption is often made not only for a univariate series of ranks but also for the analysis of the relationship between two sets of rankables associated in a bivariate distribution. (See Spearman's rank-difference method of correlation, Chapter 8.) Oftentimes the assumption made is difficult or impossible to justify.

Sum and Mean of n Ranks

The statistical treatment of a series of n ranks, scaled by assignment of cardinal values, may be facilitated by the following short-cut method for their summation:

The Sum of Ranks: $$\sum(1 \cdots n) = \frac{n(n+1)}{2} \qquad (2.3)$$

When there are five ranks, the sum $= 15$, since $5(6)/2 = 15$. The arithmetic mean rank is therefore:

Mean of Ranks: $$\overline{X}_{\text{rank}} = \frac{\dfrac{n(n+1)}{2}}{n} = \frac{n(n+1)}{2n} = \frac{n+1}{2} \qquad (2.4)$$

since the mean of a collection of n numbers is their sum divided by n. The mean of the 5 ranks is thus the integer value of the midrank.

$$\overline{X}_{\text{rank}} = \frac{5+1}{2} = 3$$

When n is even, the mean rank will be the average of the *two* middle ranks.

Ranked Intervals or Classes

It is difficult if not impossible satisfactorily to assign different rank positions on some trait or quality of a large group of objects or persons. In order to obtain a result that is harmonious with the differentiations and rankings that can more reasonably be made, several ranked *intervals* may be used rather than a single series of n ranks. Thus a foreman in an industrial setting might be asked to classify the workers under his supervision into one or the other of four ranked classes with respect to their amenability to suggestion:

> First interval: very amenable
> Second interval: more amenable than not
> Third interval: not very amenable
> Fourth interval: definitely not amenable

The four ranked classes are in effect an ordinal rating scale. In order to obtain a mean rating, cardinal numbers have to be assigned each class. However, a *median* rating can be obtained directly from the ordinal positions. As used for a series of ranks, the median is defined as the *midrank*. When n is even, then the median is taken as the average of the two middle ranks. If the foreman classifies 50 men as follows, then the median rank is in the second interval:

Interval Rank	f
First	10
Second	20
Third	15
Fourth	5
	$n = 50$

If cardinal values are assigned each class or interval and the *assumption* therefore made of *equal intervals*, the mean rank is obtained as follows:

Interval Rank	Rank Value R	f	$f \times R$
First	4	10	40
Second	3	20	60
Third	2	15	30
Fourth	1	5	5
		$n = 50$	$\sum = 135$

where $\sum$ symbolizes the operation of summing the fR products. The mean is therefore

$$\overline{X}_{rank} = \frac{\sum (fR)}{n} = \frac{135}{50} = 2.7$$

MEASURABLES

The third general class of data which require statistical organization and treatment consists of magnitudes whose variables may be described as measurables. A variable is a measurable when its members or instances can be quantitatively differentiated on a continuous scale of values. Such scales of quantitative magnitude are treated statistically *as if* their intervals were numerically equal. Although such equality of intervals is difficult if not impossible to demonstrate for psychological variables, such as I.Q.'s, the quantitative data of this kind of measurable are nevertheless added, subtracted, multiplied, and divided in the computation of statistical values such as mean, variances, etc.

There are two classes of measurables:

1. Those whose scales have a true zero.
2. Those that don't have a true zero.

The first class is described by Cohen and Nagel (1934) as fundamental measurement that yields extensive magnitudes with the property of additivity. Examples relevant to measurement in psychology and the behavioral sciences are:

1. The weight of persons in grams or pounds.
2. The height of persons in centimeters or inches.
3. The age of persons in months or years.

Thus the operations of the CGS (centimeter, gram, second) system are used to obtain magnitudes which on their defined scales are equal. A person weighing 150 pounds is equal *in weight* to any other person of 150 pounds; a three-footer is half as tall as a six-footer; and a newly arrived nonagenarian is three times as old as a person of 30 years.

Characteristically, all these measures are approximations rather than exact inasmuch as theoretically they may be fractionated even more finely than the finest measuring instrument permits. Although their values or magnitudes are approximations, they are taken as point values on a continuous scale ranging from zero to an X value that will include the largest.

The second class of measurable, whose scale has no true zero point, is illustrated by a wide variety of psychological and educational tests: I.Q. tests, tests of various aptitudes and capacities. The magnitudes of these measurables are I.Q. ratios (mental age/chronological age during the growth period) or test scores. The latter are often obtained as countables insofar as their value is simply a count of the number of items correctly answered by the persons taking the test. As countables they form discrete distributions of measurables with true zeroes whose intervals are equal with respect to the count but rarely if ever equal with respect to the behavioral trait(s) designated by the count. Thus a person who scores 40 correct items on a spatial relations test achieves twice as many correct items as the person who scores only 20. But it does not follow from this that the first person is twice as bright in the qualities tested as is the second person.

Test data are interpreted as measurables. They are *inexact approximations* of variables that are considered as if continuously distributed. Abilities, achievements, and aptitudes such as verbal fluency, number facility, word knowledge, and mechanical aptitude are held to be continuously distributed without, however, a true zero point on their respective scale of values. All such magnitudes as test scores are a mixture of "true" values and error—errors of sampling both of persons and of the trait as well as of measurement; hence the emphasis on the fact that not only are they approximations but also that they are *inexact* approximations.

Since each magnitude of a measurable is an approximation on a continuous scale, each needs to be identified with an interval on the scale. Thus a test score of 64, although inexact, is interpreted as occupying a unit interval of one integer, the exact lower limit of which is 63.5 and the upper limit of which approaches 64.5 as a limit:

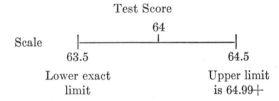

If the psychological measure is reaction time in milliseconds, the same convention is employed. That is, each measure is the midvalue of an interval. The interval is now fractions of a second and the scale is obviously a continuous one:

Irrespective of whether one or more measurables have a true zero, the statistical methods for their organization and summarization are basically the same. It's the interpretation that differs. The organization of a univariate measurable is accomplished by means of the frequency distribution. The organization of bivariate or multivariate measurables is effected by means of crosstabulations and scattergrams or correlation charts. (See Chapter 5.)

Frequency Distribution

The way in which a frequency distribution organizes the data of a measurable variable can best be described by working through an example. The data of Table 2.3 consist of 50 test scores obtained from a multiple-choice vocabulary test of 80 items. These are the original measures and are known as *the raw data*. They are "raw" in the sense that nothing has been done to them. Each score is a *count* of the number of correct items achieved by a student on the test.

Table 2.3. Raw Data of a Measurable Variable
(Vocabulary Test Scores)

$n = 50$

65	68	37	56	56	64	62	63	42	49
30	63	51	54	55	53	52	60	45	36
52	42	59	42	59	68	54	45	45	61
71	36	36	44	65	67	51	47	50	31
42	50	46	57	39	52	53	44	48	48

Table 2.4. Tallies and Frequency Distributions of the Data of Table 2.3

FOUR-UNIT INTERVAL Scale of Measures	Tally	*f*	FIVE-UNIT INTERVAL Scale of Measures	Tally	*f*
68–71		3			
64–67		4			
60–63		5	70–74		1
56–59		6	65–69		5
52–55		8	60–64		6
48–51		7	55–59		7
44–47		6	50–54		11
40–43		5	45–49		7
36–39		4	40–44		7
32–35		0	35–39		4
28–31		2	30–34		2
		$n = 50$			$n = 50$

Table 2.5. Distribution of a Measurable Cumulated by Frequencies and by Proportions

Scale of Measures	Frequencies *f*	Proportions *p*	Cumulated *f*'s, *c.f.*	Cumulated *p*'s *c.p.*
70–74	1	.02	50	1.00
65–69	5	.10	49	.98
60–64	6	.12	44	.88
55–59	7	.14	38	.76
50–54	11	.22	31	.62
45–49	7	.14	20	.40
40–44	7	.14	13	.26
35–39	4	.08	6	.12
30–34	2	.04	2	.04
	$n = 50$	$\Sigma = 1.00$		

Although the data of Table 2.3 are "organized" into ten columns of five cases each, it should be apparent that this is not a statistically meaningful organization. They are meaningfully organized into frequency distributions in Table 2.4. The results there are arrived at by the following steps:

1. *The range of the scores* is determined by

$$\text{Range} = (X_l - X_s) + 1 \tag{2.5}$$

where X_l is the largest score or measure in the distribution of n cases and X_s is the smallest, and a unit is added in order to extend the range to its exact limits, 0.5 at each end. The range is thus determined by scanning the raw data for these two values. They are found to be:

$$\text{Range} = (71 - 30) + 1 = 42$$

Stated in terms of exact limits, the result is the same:

$$\text{Range} = 71.5 - 29.5 = 42$$

2. *The size of successive class intervals* on the scale of measures is determined. These are often taken so as to give an overall view of a distribution *as if* it consisted of many measures instead of only 50 or fewer. If unit intervals were used as the size of each interval, there would be as many intervals as the range. For the data of Table 2.3 there would thus be 42 intervals. With an n of only 50, a distribution with 42 intervals would not only be pretty flat but it would also be like a row of saw teeth with some of the teeth missing.

As the size of the class interval is increased from unit intervals to two units ($42/2 = 21$ intervals), to three units ($42/3 = 14$ intervals), to four units ($42/4 = 10.5 = 11$ intervals), to five units ($42/5 = 8.4 = 9$ intervals), etc., the distribution takes on an increasingly smoother form, and hence the overall view may be improved. But from the point of view of the measures eventually to be calculated, such as an arithmetic mean, this consolidation of data into larger and larger class intervals is not desirable because of arithmetical inaccuracies. In computation the midvalue of each class interval is taken as the average of the measures in the interval. When the size of intervals is small, the amount of error will be small. When intervals are large, errors may be large.

With only 50 measures, about ten intervals should give a result that is satisfactory both for the overall view and for the calculations to be made. Hence the data of Table 2.3 may be tabulated into class intervals either of four units or of five units. The former gives 11 class intervals; the latter gives 9. Both are presented in Table 2.4. It will be noticed that the lower score limit of each interval is taken as a multiple of the size of the interval. This is simply a convention made for ease of interval-size identification.

Generally calculations made from a frequency distribution should not be based on only a few broad intervals if more than just a few are feasible. This is the case, as already indicated, because of the greater arithmetical inaccuracies that are likely to arise from only a few intervals.

3. *The tally of the original measures* (as in Table 2.3) is made with the class intervals of Table 2.4.

4. *The frequencies, f, for each interval* are written according to the sum of the tally of each. This gives the distribution of frequencies and hence the frequency distribution. Their sum is n (number of cases):

$$\Sigma f = n \tag{2.6}$$

The scale of possible values of the vocabulary test variable of Table 2.4 ranges continuously from 27.5 to 71.5 (as a limit) when i, the size of the interval, is four units. When five-unit intervals are used, the scale of possible values is from 29.5 to 74.5. Even though the *written* limits are integers like the test scores, the exact limits, unexpressed, are half a scale unit above and half a scale unit below each integer value. All the measures of each interval are taken as equal, on the average, to the midvalue of their respective intervals. (See Fig. 2.2.) This is the *midvalue assumption* and is made for computational purposes. Thus

$$\text{Midvalue} = \frac{68 + 71}{2} = 69.5$$

$$\text{or} \qquad \frac{70 + 74}{2} = 72$$

and so on. When the size of the interval is an odd number of units, the midvalue is a scale unit (in this case an integer) instead of a fractionated value on the scale, and hence it is somewhat easier to work with than when the size of the interval is an even number of scale units.

Relative Frequencies: Proportions

As in the case of nonorderable countables, the frequencies of a scaled variable are often converted to proportions or percentages. For one thing, it is essential to make a *linear transformation* from frequencies to proportions (or percentages) when two distributions with considerably different n's are to be compared on a graph. Such transformations are most simply done by computing the p value of a single case and then using this as a multiplier with the frequencies of each interval. This has been done in Table 2.5. The proportionate value of a single case, when $n = 50$, is .02, since $1/n - 1/50 = .02$. *The reciprocal* of n is thus the desired multiplier. (See Table M of Appendix, which includes reciprocals of number 1 to 1000.)*

---

*It is suggested that the student also have access to *Barlow's Tables of Squares, Cubes, Square Roots, Cube Roots and Reciprocals of all Integer Numbers up to 10,000.* Originally published in 1814 at the Royal Military Academy, Woolwich, England, by Peter Barlow.

Cumulated *f*'s and *p*'s

Methods for the summarization of the data of univariate measurables are developed in the subsequent two chapters. The method of Chapter 3 is the *centile method*. It works with the *position* of measures on the scale of a variable. The method of Chapter 4 is the method of the arithmetic mean and deviations from the mean. It works with the actual magnitudes of the measures. The computation of the median and other centiles is thus presented in Chapter 3. For such computations, as well as for the graph of Fig. 2.4, the cumulated frequencies and proportions of the last two columns of Table 2.5 are employed.

The number or the proportion of the total frequencies cumulated from the lower end of a distribution through any interval tells at a glance the number or the proportion of the frequencies beyond the particular interval. Hence it will be seen in Chapter 3 that this considerably facilitates the location of centile values. Thus an examination of the last two columns of Table 2.5 shows that approximately three-quarters (.76, or 38) of the frequencies of the vocabulary test scores are below a value of 60. Three-fifths $(1 - .40 = .60)$ are test scores of 50 or more, etc.

GRAPHIC PORTRAYAL OF FREQUENCY DISTRIBUTIONS

The data of nonscalable countables are conveniently portrayed by means of bar charts, pie charts, and pictograph charts. Figure 2.1 presented a HORIZONTAL BAR CHART for the data of Table 2.1. The chart keeps the original order of the categories for marital status as reported in *The World Almanac*. Oftentimes, however, the order is rearranged according to the number of frequencies per category, or the size of the proportions per category.

The construction of charts and graphs is facilitated by the use of cross-sectioned graphing paper. For a PIE CHART, a protractor as well as a ruler is needed. A pie chart is what the name implies: It is a circular chart divided into sections, each section being a sector. These are usually used to portray the frequencies or proportionate sizes of the several classes or categories of a nonorderable countable. The whole pie is taken as equal to 1.00 (or 100%), but in laying off the sectors, each proportion is converted to the proper fraction of 360 degrees and a protractor is used to cut the pie into appropriate pieces. A category with 50% of the frequencies gets half a pie.

Despite the continuity of a pie chart, it is ordinarily employed only with the countable data of nominal variables, i.e., nonorderable countables. It is *not* used with measurables, since scales are more meaningfully laid off as straight lines whose magnitudes range from low to high values; hence they depart from each other in opposite directions rather than circle back on each other.

For measurables whose frequency distributions have been set up, either one of two kinds of charts is ordinarily employed:

1. THE HISTOGRAM, consisting of a series of rectangles set up proportionate to the scale width and f height of an interval, as in Fig. 2.2.
2. THE FREQUENCY POLYGON, consisting of a line graph as in Fig. 2.3.

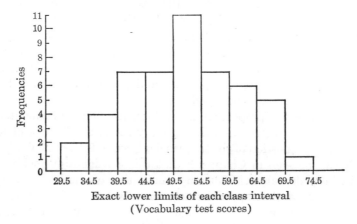

Fig. 2.2.   Histogram of Five-Unit Interval Distribution of Table 2.4
($n = 50$)

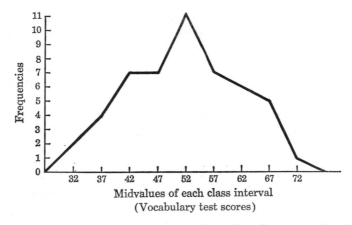

Fig. 2.3.   Frequency Polygon of the Same Distribution as Fig. 2.2
($n = 50$)

The Histogram and the Frequency Polygon

At first glance, the histogram of Fig. 2.2 may appear similar to a bar chart, with the bars drawn vertically instead of horizontally. However, there are *no gaps* between successive intervals as in a bar chart. The continuity of the scalable measurable, viz., *vocabulary knowledge*, is thus emphasized. Frequencies for histograms as well as for frequency polygons, as in Fig. 2.3, are always scaled on the *ordinate*, or vertical, axis. The measures themselves are scaled on the *abscissa*, or horizontal, axis. In the histogram, the vertical lines of each rectangle are drawn from the exact limits of each class interval. The midvalues of each interval are therefore at the vertical center of each.

A histogram tends to emphasize differences in the frequencies from interval to interval. The line graph, or frequency polygon, on the other hand, tends to emphasize the continuity and overall sweep of the distribution. Differences can, of course, be seen in Fig. 2.3, just as continuity and form can be seen in the histogram of Fig. 2.2. When the distribution of only a single set of data or sample result is to be portrayed, the choice of graph is mainly a matter of personal preference. But when two or more distributions are to be compared on the same set of coordinate axes, then the frequency polygon or line graph is to be preferred because the several distributions can be more readily differentiated with lines than with rectangles.

In the construction of the frequency polygon, points are plotted on graph paper perpendicularly from the midvalues of each class interval at the intersection with an imaginary line drawn horizontally from the specified frequency of the vertical scale. The points of successive class intervals, beginning with either end of the scale, are then connected by *straight* lines. The graph is ordinarily closed at both ends of the scale, at frequency values of zero for the midvalues of the intervals just beyond the upper and lower intervals of the distribution. This closure of the graph completes the polygon: total frequencies are equal to total area within the polygon. When the frequencies are converted to proportions or percentages, the total area of the polygon will be 1.00, or 100%.

Cumulative Frequency Distribution and Centile Graph

The cumulated data of Table 2.5 are often used as the basis for a *centile graph* (or *ogive*) from which any centile value (see Chapter 3) for a given measure can be "read off" the graph or from which any measure for a given centile value can be obtained. The cumulated proportions are scaled on the left vertical axis of Fig. 2.4; corresponding values in percentages (centiles) for these proportions are scaled on the right vertical axis. The exact limits of each interval of the measurable are scaled both at the top and the bottom of the chart. Unlike the plotting of the frequency polygon, the points plotted are located vertically from the upper exact limit of each class interval. This is the case because the f's and the p's are cumulated *through* each interval rather than to their midvalues.

Once the points are plotted, they are connected by straight lines, beginning with zero at the interval below (to the left of) the lowest interval that has frequencies and ending with 1.00, or 100%, at the upper exact limit of the interval of the upper end of the scale of measurables.

By projecting a vertical line from any point on the scale of measures to the graph line and then projecting horizontally to the cumulative proportion scale, the *rank location* of any particular measure can be readily determined. Since the ranks are on a scale of 100 units (either to a base of 1.00, or 100), they are equivalent to statistical measures known as *centiles* (or percentiles). A *centile interval* includes 1/100, or 1%, of the total frequencies of a distribution. Each such interval is bounded by *centile point values*, which are thus the proportions of the left vertical scale of Fig. 2.4.

There are 101 centile point values to a distribution, beginning with that of zero and ending with 1.00 (or 100). These point values are usually symbolized as C_0 and C_{100}, respectively. The 50th centile point value has been located on the graph of Fig. 2.4 at a p value of .50. The value on the scale of measures for a centile point value of .50 is the *median*, defined as a value that divides the distribution of frequencies into two equal parts. Since the area of frequency polygon is based on the distribution of frequencies, the median therefore divides the *total area* of a distribution into two equal parts.

A centile graph, such as Fig. 2.4, can be used either to locate the values of measures, scaled on the horizontal axis, that correspond with any chosen centile measure of the vertical axis, or to locate the values of centiles that

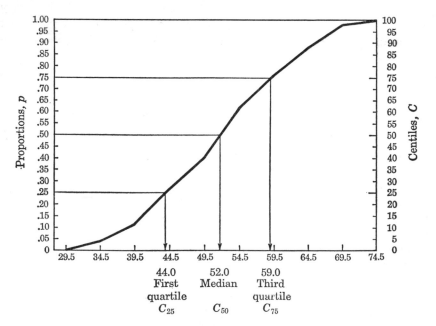

Fig. 2.4.   The Centile Graph
(A Cumulated Distribution of Proportionate Frequencies)
(Data from Table 2.5)

correspond with the measures. The latter procedure is a considerable time-saver when many different centile values are to be used, since their computation by methods described in Chapter 3 takes more time than their estimation from the centile graph. If a large sheet of graph paper is employed, the accuracy of the projected results should be as satisfactory as the calculated results.

Two additional centile values are located on the centile graph of Fig. 2.4, viz., C_{25} and C_{75}. As will be seen in the next chapter, these are the first and third quartile points of a continuous distribution, and the scale range between these points, known as the *interquartile range*, is the range of the middle 50% of the measures of a distribution.

THE MEDIAN AND
THE CENTILE RANK METHOD

*The application of continuity to cases where
it does not really exist illustrates the great
utility which fictions sometimes have in science.*

Charles S. Peirce

THE statistical organization of the data of a variable is achieved by methods pertinent to the nature of the data. In the preceding chapter it was shown that the various modes of *organization* consist of:

1. Categories or mutually exclusive classes for unordered countables.
2. Ordered series or ranked-interval, discrete frequency distributions for rankables.
3. Scaled frequency distributions for ordered countables as well as for measurables.

It was also noted that there are three general ways of *summarizing* the data of variables:

1. By tabulations into statistical tables.
2. By calculation of statistical measures.
3. By graphical portrayal of the data of tables and statistical measures.

Countables were seen to be summarized by the f's or the p's (proportions) or the percents per category, and graphically portrayed by bar charts. Rankables were summarized by rank-interval positions for data organized into rank intervals; otherwise, a series of ordered ranks from 1 to n is its own summary.

An ordered series of ranks has, however, no generality. That is to say, each series is specific for a given n. Two series of n ranks are not comparable when the n's differ or, if rank intervals are used, when the number of rank intervals differ. In Table 2.5 a method was developed to relate all such rank series to a standard series of rank positions that will be general for any set of rankables, or of measurables, regardless of the size of n. This was the method of cumulated proportions from which the centile graph of Fig. 2.4 was set up. Such a graph permits the estimation of the centile value of any measure on a scaled distribution.

In this chapter the method of centile ranks will be further developed and explored as a way of summarizing the data of both rankables and measurables. This approach to the problem of summarizing statistical data by various kinds of measures, such as a median, relates original measures to a scale of rank positions, ranging from zero to 100. Each case or datum has equal weight with other cases in the determination of values. Thus the median is a point value on a centile rank scale such that 50% of the cases are less in value and 50% are higher in value. The latter 50% may be anywhere in the distribution as long as they are higher in value than the median value. They may all have the same value or they may all have different values, as in a series of ordinal ranks. When a distribution is bilaterally symmetrical, the values of the arithmetic mean, the median and mode (point or interval of most frequencies), are the same. When a distribution is skewed, as in Fig. 4.5, the value of the mean is most radically affected, being pulled in the direction of the tailing out of the measures, whereas the value of the median and mode may remain about the same.

Around the turn of the 20th century, some writers felt the median to be a more "democratic" measure than the arithmetic mean because all cases of a distribution have equal weight insofar as the value of the median is concerned. By contrast, the method to be developed in Chapter 4 yields measures, such as the arithmetic mean and the standard deviation, that are based on the *weights* (or magnitudes) of each case.

CENTILE INTERVALS VS. CENTILE POINT VALUES

Confusion sometimes arises in the use of a centile value, such as a median, because of the failure to distinguish between a centile point value and a centile interval. A scale of centile ranks takes the following form at its limits:

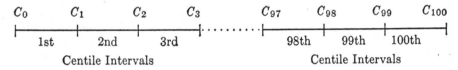

The centile point values are indicated at the limits of each centile interval. Any interval is designated by the limiting value of its upper limit. Thus the first centile interval marks off the range on the scale from the lowest score to a point value C_1, which will separate 1% of all the frequencies (or 1% of the total area) of the distribution from the remaining 99% of the frequencies (or area). The 100th centile interval also includes 1% of the total frequencies, and they are located in the scale interval above a centile point value C_{99}, which divides the frequencies into two parts, 99% of which are below the point and 1% above the point.

Only if a distribution is rectangular in form will the scale intervals of centile ranks be equal. This is illustrated in the middle graph of Fig. 3.1.

On the other hand, if a distribution is similar in form to a bell-shaped, bilaterally symmetrical distribution, the centile intervals at the extreme ends of the scale will be broader than at the center. This is illustrated in the top graph of Fig. 3.1. The bottom graph of Fig. 3.1 illustrates how centiles can be used to summarize any form of distribution, including the so-called J-type.

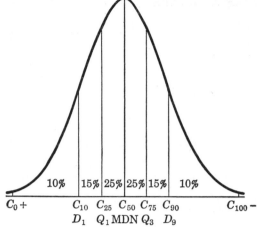

Centile intervals of a normal, bellshaped type of distribution are narrow in range at the center of the distribution because of the great concentration of frequencies around the median, or modal point.

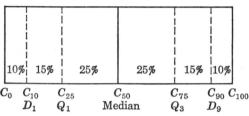

In a rectangular type of distribution, all centile intervals are equal in size because the frequencies are uniformly distributed throughout the scale.

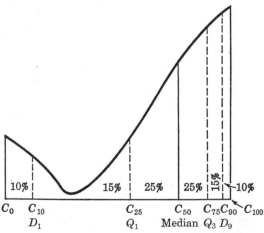

In a J-type distribution, centile intervals are unequal in size; furthermore, centile points above and below the median are not symmetrically distributed as in the bellshaped and rectangular types of distributions.

Fig. 3.1. Location of Centiles on Various Types of Distributions

Quartile intervals are marked off on all three graphs, with C_{25} symbolized as Q_1; C_{50} as the median (it is also Q_2); and C_{75} as Q_3. The points marking off the *D range* are also indicated, viz., D_1 as the first *decile*, being at C_{10}; and D_9 as the ninth *decile*, being at C_{90}. Thus the *D range* is the scale range of the middle 80% of a distribution.

CENTILES AS RANKS

When the number of rankables is less than or more than 100, it is nevertheless a relatively simple task to convert them into a series of 100 centile ranks. Thus, if 20 professors of one department and 10 professors of another department are ranked by their academic dean for their manifest dedication to their jobs, rank positions within departments may need no transformation. But rank positions *between* departments can be directly compared only by the conversion of one series to the other (10 ranks to a 20-rank series, or 20 ranks to a 10-rank series) or by the conversion of both series to the centile series of ranks. The latter represents the standard procedure because a series of centile ranks is readily understood and widely used for comparative purposes.

To locate the centile intervals of any series of n ranks:

Centile Interval: $$C.I. = \frac{R - .5}{n} \, (100) \tag{3.1}$$

where $C.I.$ is the midvalue of the appropriate centile rank interval and R designates the rank position of a measure in the original series of n ranks. Thus, for the first group of 20 professors,

Rank 1: $C.I. = \dfrac{1 - .5}{20} \, (100) = 2.5;$ therefore $R_1 = C.I._{2.5}$

Rank 2: $C.I. = \dfrac{2 - .5}{20} \, (100) = 7.5;$ therefore $R_2 = C.I._{7.5}$

etc., in successive steps of five centile units to $C_{97.5}$ for R_{20}.

For the second group of 10 professors:

Rank 1: $C.I. = \dfrac{1 - .5}{10} \, (100) = 5.0;$ therefore $R_1 = C.I._{5}$

Rank 2: $C.I. = \dfrac{2 - .5}{10} \, (100) = 15.0;$ therefore $R_2 = C.I._{15}$

etc., in successive steps of ten centile units to $C.I._{95}$ for R_{10}.

It will be observed that in both series of ranks the transformation consists in relating the original ordinal positions to the midpositions of successive intervals.

CENTILES AS MEASURES ON A SCALE

Centiles are more often used with quantitative data that are scaled on a continuum of measures ranging from the least value to the greatest value. Thus William H. Sheldon in *The Varieties of Human Physique* (1940) uses a seven-point scale for the classification of somatic types. On this scale, the value 7 represents an extreme manifestation of the somatotype, as for example, the endomorphic, which is described as a soft, round physique; the value 4 represents a halfway point between extremes; and the value 1 represents extreme antithesis to the somatotype, i.e., no trace of it whatsoever (zero, so to speak).

Thirty-six male students were "measured" for endomorphy with Sheldon's scale by a fellow student who obtained the distribution of results given in Table 3.1.

Table 3.1. Distribution of Endomorphy "Measurements"

Endomorphy Scale Values	f	c.f.*
7	0	36
6	1	36
5	4	35
4	9	31
3	9	22
2	12	13
1	1	1
	$n = 36$	

*c.f. = cumulated f's

Although Sheldon's seven scale values are essentially discrete in that each person's "degree of endomorphy" is "measured" by identification with a particular integer value, the contention can be advanced that the scale is ultimately a continuous one. The current lack of an instrument to measure endomorphy in the way that height and weight are measured on a ratio scale of extensive magnitudes with a true zero point does not preclude the treatment of these seven scale values *as if* they were approximations of a continuous series of endomorphic measures ranging from 0.5 through 7.5. These are the exact limits, since on a continuous scale of values, each integer value is interpreted as the midpoint of a unit interval: the value 1 being the midpoint of the interval 0.5 to 1.5⁻ as a limit, and the value 7 being the midpoint of the interval 6.5 to 7.5⁻ as a limit.

THE MEDIAN: A SUMMARY MEASURE OF THE TYPICAL VALUE OF A GROUP

The distribution of the 36 measures is *skewed*, in that the frequencies pile up toward the lower values. The *modal* value is at 2.0, i.e., the interval with the most frequencies has a midvalue of 2.0. The group is obviously not overloaded with endomorphs. How might they be described as a group? What are they like "on the average"? The "average" that can be developed by the centile method is the median, which was described in the preceding chapter as the midvalue, or C_{50}, in a series of 100 centile ranks.

Where $n = 36$, $\frac{1}{2}n$ is 18 and therefore the median is a *point value* on the continuous scale of measures such that exactly half (18) of the measures are greater in value and the remaining half (18) are less in value. By inspection of the cumulated frequencies, the median is seen to be in the interval whose scale value is 3.0. This interval ranges in value on the scale from 2.5 to 3.5^- as a limit. Hence the median is estimated by *linear interpolation* as follows:

The Median: $\qquad mdn = X_L + \dfrac{\left(\dfrac{n}{2} - f_b\right)}{f_i} \cdot i$ $\qquad\qquad$ (3.2)

$$= 2.5 + \frac{\left(\dfrac{36}{2} - 13\right)}{9} \cdot 1.0$$

$$= 2.5 + \frac{5}{9} = 3.06$$

where X_L is the exact lower limit of the interval with which the value of the median is identified; n is the total number of frequencies in the distribution; f_b is the number of frequencies *below* the lower limit of the scale interval in which the value of the median is to be interpolated; f_i is the number of f's in the interval of the median; and i is the scale size of the class interval; in this case i is 1.0. Linear interpolation is based on the assumption of an even distribution of measures over the class interval.

The median position of the group of 36 endomorphic measures has a scale value of 3.06. This signifies that typically endomorphy is "present but below the midvalue of 4.0 on Sheldon's scale."

In order properly and usefully to summarize the measures of a distribution, an "average" such as the median, or arithmetic mean, is not sufficient. This is the case because the variation or spread of scores of two or more distributions may be quite different, but their averages may be approximately the same. Averages do not measure the variation of a distribution. For this evaluation, additional statistical measures are needed: measures of range or dispersion as well as measures of variation from a point in a distribution, such as the point value of the arithmetic mean.

The Interquartile Range and the D Range

The variability characteristic of the group of 36 observations can be described in terms of a range whose limits are marked off by the scale values of certain centiles. Either the *interquartile range* or the *D range* is usually used for this. Sometimes both are employed. The interquartile range marks off the range of the middle 50% of the measures. Hence:

$$Interquartile\ range = C_{25}\ to\ C_{75} \tag{3.3}$$

The D *range* marks off the range of the middle 80% of the measures. Hence:

$$D\ range = C_{10}\ to\ C_{90}\quad or\quad D_1\ to\ D_9 \tag{3.4}$$

The interquartile range eliminates sizable tails of the distribution: 25% of the measures at each end. The D *range* is less drastic: Only 10% of the measures are eliminated at each tail. The interquartile range is thus used to mark off the center of the variation of a distribution of measures, usually the area of greatest concentration in unimodal (one peak) distributions, even if they are skewed. The D *range*, on the other hand, is used to mark off the substantial range of total variation, with the relatively unstable (in small samples) upper 10% and lower 10% eliminated.

The computations of the four centiles needed for these two measures of variation are made by the same method as was used for the median.

The Value of Any Centile:

$$C_c = X_L + \frac{(pn - f_b)}{f_i} \cdot i \tag{3.5}$$

where X_L is equal to the exact *lower* limit of the interval in which the desired centile value is located; p is the proportion of the distribution needed for any particular centile value, as for example, $p = 10/100$ when C_{10} is to be calculated; n is the total number of frequencies in the distribution; f_b is the number of frequencies *below* the lower limit X_L; f_i is the number of frequencies in the interval in which the desired centile value is located; and i is the size of the class interval.

For the data of the 36 endomorphic values the centile values needed for the interquartile range and the D *range* are as follows:

$$C_{10} = 1.5 + \frac{(10/100 \cdot 36) - 1}{12}\ (1.0) = 1.5 + 0.22 = 1.7$$

$$C_{25} = 1.5 + \frac{(25/100 \cdot 36) - 1}{12}\ (1.0) = 1.5 + 0.67 = 2.2$$

$$C_{75} = 3.5 + \frac{(75/100 \cdot 36) - 22}{9}\ (1.0) = 3.5 + 0.56 = 4.1$$

$$C_{90} = 4.5 + \frac{(90/100 \cdot 36) - 31}{4}\ (1.0) = 4.5 + 0.35 = 4.8^*$$

*Note: In rounding off 4.85 to 4.8, the following rule of thumb is employed so that roughly half the time the value of the number will be left as it is and half the time it will be raised one unit: If, in division, the remainder is equal to exactly one-half the number value of the divisor, (1) leave the value of the last obtained digit of the quotient unchanged if the digit is even; (2) increase the value of the last digit of the quotient by 1 if the digit is odd. This may be elided to: "If even, leave even; if odd, make even." Thus, 4.85 is left even at 4.8; 4.15 would be made even by raising to 4.2.

The interquartile range is 2.2 to 4.0, and thus exactly half of the group of 36 persons range in endomorphy from only slight traces thereof to the halfway value of 4.0. Furthermore, since 25% of the group will necessarily be in that tail of the distribution with measures of less than 2.2, it can be inferred that 75% of this group are *below* the halfway point of Sheldon's scale for endomorphy.

The D range is 1.7 to 4.8. This range indicates that this group is substantially *not* endomorphic. Only 10% are beyond a scale value of 4.8. The value 5.0 signifies "endomorphy strong but not outstanding." It may be apparent that for a small distribution of only 36 cases, the *D range* does not give much information additional to that obtained by inspecting the range of the distribution of measures.

The Quartile Deviation

A measure of variation based on centiles is the quartile deviation. However, it is somewhat of a misnomer because it is not a measure taken as a deviation from any point on a scale of measures. Only if the median C_{50} is approximately midway between C_{25} and C_{75} will this measure work out satisfactorily as a measure of "deviation." It is equal to half of the interquartile range:

Quartile Deviation: $$\text{Q.D.} = \frac{C_{75} - C_{25}}{2} = \frac{Q_3 - Q_1}{2} \tag{3.6}$$

The Q.D. therefore marks off a range on the scale that will include either the upper half of the interquartile range or the lower half. If the median is midway between C_{25} and C_{75}, then

$$\text{Median} \pm \text{Q.D.} = \text{the interquartile range}$$

This measure is not very often computed, since the centile point values of C_{25}, C_{50}, and C_{75} are the significant figures and in themselves give the desired summary information about a distribution.

GENERAL USEFULNESS OF CENTILES

Even though centiles cannot be averaged as are measurables, they literally measure what they signify, regardless of the shape or form of a distribution. They are unambiguous in their implications. C_{10}, for example, is a value on a scale of measures exceeded by 90% of the cases in a group or sample of measures; C_{95} is a value exceeded by only 5% of the group. *Subscript notations for centiles, written as proportions,* are often employed to designate scale locations in both descriptive and sampling-inferential statistics. In later chapters, for example, various probability distributions will be used in the development of estimates of parameters and of significance tests. Usually reference will be made to such distributions by means of "critical values" whose location will be signified by subscripts corresponding to particular proportionate values. Such designations are *general*, regardless of the form of the particular probability distribution. Thus the following symbols are for statistics of probability distributions:

$$z_{.95}, \quad t_{.95}, \quad \chi^2_{.95}, \quad F_{.95}$$

All refer to a point on each probability distribution such that 95% of the hypothesized occurrences are below the scale value of the statistic (whatever it may be) and only 5% are beyond the value.

The centile rank method is thus useful not only for descriptive statistics but also for inferential statistics. In the preceding chapter, as in this one, the method represents a general way of summarizing and describing the data of rankables and of measurables. It is useful for measurables whose distributions are discrete as well as for those that are continuous. If the discrete character of a distribution is to be maintained in its summarization, then centiles can be used as values on the discrete scale rather than as point values on a continuous one. On the other hand, for inferential statistics, the usefulness of the centile rank method is adjunctive. It provides auxiliary services that are nonetheless valuable, as will be seen in later chapters.

CHAPTER 4

THE MEAN, STANDARD DEVIATION AND NORMAL DISTRIBUTION

*The range of mental power between the greatest and
least of English intellects is enormous. There is
a continuity of natural ability reaching from one
knows not what height, and descending to one can hardly
say what depth . . .* all according to *the very curious
theoretical law of 'deviation from an average'.* . . .

Sir Francis Galton

THE MEAN AND STANDARD DEVIATION

THE arithmetic mean is one of the most useful measures to be found in
the statistical tool kit. It is a measure doubtless familiar to most students since grade school days. It is useful for descriptive statistics in that
it provides a weighted average as the typical value of a distribution. It is
indispensable to sampling and inferential statistics. This is the case because the means of randomized samples of measures ordinarily provide
the best single value estimates of the mean of the parent populations. (See
Chapter 8.)

The Arithmetic Mean:* $\quad \overline{X} = \dfrac{\sum\limits_{j=1}^{n} (X_j)}{n}$ $\hfill (4.1)$

The mean is based on the concepts of statistical deviation and the
weights or magnitudes of the measures of a distribution. Statistical deviation is symbolized by lower case x and is equal to the difference between
any measure of a distribution and the mean of that distribution.

The Deviation: $\qquad\qquad x = (X - \overline{X})$ $\hfill (4.2)$

The algebraic sum of all the deviations of a distribution checks the correctness of the mean. This is true because the mean is to a distribution of
measures as a knife-edge is to a balance scale in equilibrium. The sum of
the weights or magnitudes of those measures whose values are greater than
the mean exactly balance the sum of those less than the mean so that the
algebraic sum of the deviations equals zero. The mean is thus A MEASURE
OF LOCATION.

$$\sum_{j=1}^{n} (X - \overline{X}) = \sum_{j=1}^{n} (x) = 0 \hfill (4.2a)$$

---

*The notation with the summation sign, $\sum$, serves to indicate the measures to be
summed. For the arithmetic mean, the summation is for all values of X, starting with
the first case of j and ending with the nth case. When the nature of a summation is clear,
these notations will be omitted. In some instances, however, a superscript will be used
without a subscript in order to make clear, for example, that $\overset{k}{\sum}$ is a summation of
measures of k subsamples or classes rather than of j measures.

The x deviations provide the standard basis for measuring the variation characteristic of a distribution of measurables. In both descriptive and sampling-inferential statistics, the standard measure of variation is based on the mean of the squared deviations, oftentimes referred to as *the mean square*.

The Variance: $\qquad\qquad \sigma^2 \text{ or } V = \dfrac{\sum(x^2)}{n}$ $\qquad\qquad$ (4.3)

The Estimate of Variance: $\quad s^2 = \dfrac{\sum(x^2)}{n-1}$ $\qquad\qquad$ (4.4)

These two formulas for the calculation of the variance of distributions differ only in the role of one frequency in the ratio of the sum of the squared deviations to the number of observations, or size of sample, n. For descriptive statistics and for statistical populations, the divisor is simply n. For sampling-inferential statistics, where the measures are derived from a sample, the best single value estimate of the variance of the parent population is provided by Eq. 4.4. The mean square is based on $n-1$ rather than on n only. The symbols s^2 or $\hat\sigma^2$ are used to indicate that the measure of variance is an estimate based on the data of a sample rather on the data of the entire population. Generally the symbol s^2 will be employed for the variances of the distributions of samples. The other symbol, $\hat\sigma^2$, with the circumflex over the *sigma* will be used for *estimates* of the standard deviations of sampling distributions. (See Eq. 8.4, for example.)*

The square root of the variance of a distribution yields the standard deviation. It is symbolized by s for the distributions of samples and by σ for distributions of populations. For descriptive statistics, the letters S.D., for standard deviation, are preferred.

The Standard Deviation for Populations:

$$\sigma = \sqrt{\dfrac{\sum x^2}{N}} \qquad\qquad (4.5)$$

For Samples: $\qquad\qquad s = \sqrt{\dfrac{\sum x^2}{n-1}}$ $\qquad\qquad$ (4.6)

For Descriptive Statistics: $\quad$ S.D. $= \sqrt{\dfrac{\sum x^2}{n}}$ $\qquad\qquad$ (4.7)

Although σ and S.D. are calculated in the same way, they differ in their implications. As indicated, the symbol of *sigma* is used when the frame of

---

*The student will find as he refers to other statistical texts or to references to statistics in the professional literature that a completely standardized, single set of symbols among authors is still a *desideratum* rather than a reality.

reference is that of statistical populations and samples. The symbol S.D. is used when the frame of reference is simply that of summarizing the variation of a distribution considered without reference to samples and statistical populations.

The standard deviation of a distribution is thus the square root of the variance. Although the variance is the more useful measure of variation in certain analyses of sampling-inferential statistics (as, for example, in the analysis of variance of Chapter 11), the standard deviation has the more immediate serviceable advantage in that it is a measure of variation in the original scale units of the variate whose variation has been measured. Thus the variance of a distribution of I.Q. scores would measure the variation of the square of I.Q. scores, whereas the standard deviation measures the variation of the I.Q. scores themselves.

Students sometimes ask why the standard deviation is preferred over the average deviation in statistics. The latter measure is obtained by summing the deviations of a distribution without regard to sign, and then averaging them.

The Average Deviation: $\text{A.D.} = \dfrac{\Sigma |x|}{n}$ (4.8)

There are several reasons for preferring the standard deviation over the average deviation. The essential reason lies in the fact that the standard deviation is the more useful and efficient measure of variation for sampling-inferential statistics. Although it might not make much difference in descriptive statistics whether S.D. or A.D. is used, it is well for the student to become familiar with the standard deviation and learn to use it because of its superiority over the A.D. in most research problems, whether they be experimental, the survey type, or the analysis of psychological test results. The best technique of correlation for bivariate distributions of measurables is based on the standard deviations of each variate. (See Chapter 5.) The estimation of parameters (Chapter 8) and the testing of statistical hypotheses (Chapters 9, 10, and 11) are based on estimates of sampling variation most efficiently made by means of the standard deviation and the variance.

COMPUTATION OF THE MEAN AND STANDARD DEVIATION

Several methods for the computation of the mean and standard deviation will be presented in this section. The vocabulary test data cited in the preceding chapter will be used as the data. Each method developed has certain advantages over the others, depending on circumstances, as discussed below.

For Ungrouped Data

The mean and standard deviation can be computed for a collection of measures that have not been organized into either an array or a frequency distribution. There is the "long" approach and the "short-cut" approach to such ungrouped data.

The long version is useful only for very small distributions. Otherwise the method is too tedious, especially since exactly the same result can be obtained by the short method. The long method entails the computation of the mean and then the calculation of each x deviate value. These in turn are squared, and the mean of their sum is the variance. The routine of the method is illustrated in Table 4.1, using the first five measures of Table 4.2.

Table 4.1. Computation of Mean and Standard Deviation by Long Method
(Original Data Ungrouped)
($n = 5$)

X	x $(X - \overline{X})$	x^2
65	13	169
30	−22	484
52	0	0
71	19	361
42	−10	100
$\Sigma = 260$	$\Sigma = 0$	$\Sigma = 1114$

$$\overline{X} = \frac{260}{5} = 52.0$$

$$V = \frac{1114}{5} = 222.8$$

$$\text{S.D.} = \sqrt{222.8} = 14.9$$

$$s^2 = \frac{1114}{4} = 278.5$$

$$s = \sqrt{278.5} = 16.7$$

The short-cut method, illustrated in Table 4.2, works best with machine computation in which each original measure is successively fed into a machine and squared, and the sums of the X and X^2 values are separately cumulated to give for the entire set of data the following sums:

$$\Sigma(X) \quad \text{and} \quad \Sigma(X^2)$$

Regardless of the availability of a machine that will do the job, this method is particularly useful for the development of those computations needed in analysis of variance (Chapter 11).

Table 4.2. Computation of Mean and Standard Deviation by Short Method

(Original Measures, Listed as Obtained from Students' Vocabulary Test Results)

Case No. (1)	X (2)	X^2 (3)	Case No. (1)	X (2)	X^2 (3)
1	65	4225	26	64	4096
2	30	900	27	53	2809
3	52	2704	28	68	4624
4	71	5041	29	67	4489
5	42	1764	30	52	2704
6	68	4624	31	62	3844
7	63	3969	32	52	2704
8	42	1764	33	54	2916
9	36	1296	34	51	2601
10	50	2500	35	53	2809
11	37	1369	36	63	3969
12	51	2601	37	60	3600
13	59	3481	38	45	2025
14	36	1296	39	47	2209
15	46	2116	40	44	1936
16	56	3136	41	42	1764
17	54	2916	42	45	2025
18	42	1764	43	45	2025
19	44	1936	44	50	2500
20	57	3249	45	48	2304
21	56	3136	46	49	2401
22	55	3025	47	36	1296
23	59	3481	48	61	3721
24	65	4225	49	31	961
25	39	1521	50	48	2304

$$\overset{50}{\sum} = 2565 \qquad 136{,}675$$

$$\overline{X} = \frac{2565}{50} = 51.3 \qquad \sum x^2 = 136{,}675 - \frac{(2565)^2}{50} = 5090.5$$

$$V = \frac{5090.5}{50} = 101.81 \qquad \text{S.D.} = \sqrt{101.81} = 10.1$$

$$s^2 = \frac{5090.5}{49} = 103.89 \qquad s = \sqrt{103.89} = 10.2$$

If all original measures are not positive, for machine computation they may be made so by adding a constant amount of sufficient size to each measure, to eliminate the negatives. On the other hand, if all the original measures are positive and their magnitudes are large, the computations of Table 4.2 required for the mean and standard deviation may be somewhat simplified by subtracting a constant equal in value to the smallest measure or by taking a rounded value near to but less than the smallest one. Thus, if a distribution of measures ranges from 118 to 198, the 1 of the 100's column can be ignored, since in effect 100 would be subtracted from each value. The squares of Table 4.2 could have been reduced by the subtraction of 30 (the value of the smallest measure) from each measure. Had this been done, then the mean, $\overline{X}$, would have been equal to the mean of the residual values plus 30.

The addition of a constant or the subtraction of a constant from each measure of a distribution will not affect the values of the variance and standard deviation. The value of the mean will, of course, be affected. The mean of the remainder values or of the greater values, depending on whether a constant has been subtracted or has been added, is corrected accordingly.

Summary of Computations for Ungrouped Data

The computations of Tables 4.1 and 4.2, by the long and the short methods for ungrouped data, should yield exactly the same results when the data are the same. An adding machine and the table of squares (Table M of the Appendix) will considerably facilitate the arithmetic that has to be done. Since there is not inherent in either method an independent check on the accuracy of the two sums (of measures and the squares of the measures), it is best to double check as follows:

1. Check each entry as it is made from the original protocols or records to the table.
2. Check the sum of the X's, the square of each X, and the sum of the squares.

The mean of the 50 vocabulary test scores is found to be equal to 51.3 in Table 4.2. Two values for the standard deviation are given, viz., S.D. = 10.1 and s = 10.2. Thus the difference between the standard deviation as a purely descriptive measure and the standard deviation as an estimate of σ is slight for these data. Were S.D. mistakenly used for s, then σ would be underestimated and biased by the amount of the difference between S.D. and s.

Some researchers are inclined always to calculate s for distributions of data regardless of whether they consist of a randomized sample from which the estimate of a parameter is to be made or a statistical hypothesis is to be tested. Such a practice will make little difference when n is large, but in small samples, the effect of n vs. $n - 1$ as a divisor will be noticeable and may be appreciable. Therefore it is best to calculate S.D. when S.D. is the correct computation and s when s is called for by the nature of the data.

Since the operations of Table 4.2 are extensively used in research for the computation of the mean and standard deviation, they will be summarized as follows:

1. The sum of the measures in column 2, $\sum(X)$, divided by n, the number of measures, gives the mean.

2. The squares of each measure are entered in column 3. These are summed to obtain $\sum(X^2)$.

3. The sum of the squared deviations from the actual mean is next calculated and is equal to:

Sum of the Squared Deviations:

$$\sum(x^2) = \sum(X^2) - \frac{(\sum X)^2}{n} \qquad (4.9)$$

This measure, often referred to as the *sum of squares*, is basic to the computations needed in analysis of variance (Chapter 11).

4. The variance of the distribution of measures is obtained by dividing the sum of squares either by n or by $n - 1$, depending on whether the measurements are considered only descriptively, or as a population, or as a sample of a population. When a population, σ^2 is preferred as the symbol for the variance (V is the symbol for descriptive statistics):

Variance for Population Statistics:

$$\sigma^2 = \frac{\sum(x^2)}{N} \qquad (4.10)$$

Formulas for the variance and standard deviation of populations and of samples have already been presented (Formulas 4.3, 4.4, 4.5, and 4.6). The operation to remember to perform in working with the method of Table 4.2 is that of the computation of the sum of the squared deviations from the actual mean (Formula 4.9) before the desired variance and standard deviation have been computed.

A *useful characteristic of the standard deviation* as a measure of variation is that, regardless of the form or size of a distribution, the scale range of the mean ± 1.0 S.D. ordinarily includes at least 50% of all the measures in the distribution. When distributions are of the normal, bell-shaped type, this range of $\overline{X} \pm 1$ S.D. includes about two-thirds of the measures. An inspection of the data of Table 4.2 shows that 34 of the 50 cases are within the range of

$$\overline{X} \pm 1 \text{ S.D.} = 51.3 \pm 10.1 = 41.2 \text{ to } 61.4$$

Since $34/50 = .68$, 68% of the measures are within this range.

Computations for Grouped Data

The organization of a distribution of measures into the class intervals of a frequency distribution is usually done for the purpose of either simplifying computations or of permitting an inspection of the form of the variation characteristic of the distribution. Unfortunately these considerations are sometimes at crosspurposes. When samples are small, for example, the form of the distribution can be ascertained, if at all, only by the use of a few class intervals. But when intervals are too few, the midvalue assumption for the class intervals may be so poorly satisfied that the calculated measures will be subjected to appreciable error. The assumption is that the midvalue of each class interval is at least approximately the average of the measures within the interval.

On the other hand, if many intervals are used for small samples of data, there will be little or no opportunity to see what the "generalized form" is like; that is to say, what the form would be like if the sample or group consisted of many more measurements.

The effect of the number of class intervals on the visible form of a frequency distribution was illustrated in the second chapter for the data of Table 2.3 with the two distributions in Table 2.4. In sampling-inferential statistics, *accuracy* in small samples should not be sacrificed to *form* by the use of too few class intervals. If the samples are very small, it may be better for computational purposes not to group them at all and to use the method of Table 4.2 to obtain the mean and standard deviation.

Computations are usually simplified by the organization of a set of data into a frequency distribution. Once they are thus grouped, there is a choice again between a long method and a short-cut method. Actually it is not much of a choice inasmuch as the long method has no possible advantage over the short method. Except for dropped decimals, the results of both methods should be exactly the same when the same class intervals of the frequency distribution are employed.

The long method is perhaps useful only to illustrate the unnecessary time consumed in its use compared with the time required by the short method. It, the long method, is illustrated in Table 4.3.

The short method, as already suggested, is the recommended method whenever data are organized into the groupings of class intervals. It is a method of simplified coding and is the least time consuming of any method when a machine is not available. It is also useful in the computation of the linear correlation of bivariate distributions of measurables. (See Table 5.6, p. 97.)

Long Method

The computations of Table 4.3 are indeed *long* compared with those of Table 4.4. Aside from the first two columns of data, which make up the frequency distribution, an additional six columns of calculations are required in Table 4.3 as against only three additional columns in Table 4.4. The differences in the sizes of the numbers entered in the columns offer further contrasts, all pointing toward the great simplicity of the short method of Table 4.4.

Table 4.3. Computation of Mean and Standard Deviation by Long Method*
(With Original Data Grouped Into Class Intervals)
(Measures of Table 4.2)

X Interval	f	X Mid-values	fX	x $(X - \overline{X})$	fx	x^2	fx^2
(1)	(2)	(3)	(4)	(5)	(6)	(7)	(8)
70–74	1	72	72	20.3	20.3	412.09	412.09
65–69	5	67	335	15.3	76.5	234.09	1170.45
60–64	6	62	372	10.3	61.8	106.09	636.54
55–59	7	57	399	5.3	37.1	28.09	196.63
50–54	11	52	572	0.3	3.3	0.09	0.99
45–49	7	47	329	−4.7	−32.9	22.09	154.63
40–44	7	42	294	−9.7	−67.9	94.09	658.63
35–39	4	37	148	−14.7	−58.8	216.09	864.36
30–34	2	32	64	−19.7	−39.4	388.09	776.18

$n = 50$
Range $= 29.5–74.5$ $\Sigma = 2585$ $\Sigma = 0$ (Check) $\Sigma = 4870.50$

$$\overline{X} = \frac{2585}{50} = 51.7 \qquad V = \frac{4870.50}{50} = 97.41 \qquad \text{S.D.} = \sqrt{97.41} = 9.87$$

$$s^2 = \frac{4870.50}{49} = 99.40 \qquad s = \sqrt{99.40} = 9.97$$

*The differences between these results and those of Table 4.2 indicate the extent to which the midvalue assumption is not satisfied.

The several steps required for the long method of Table 4.3 are as follows:

1. The midvalues of each class interval are entered in column 3.
2. Each midvalue is multiplied by the number of frequencies of its interval in order that all the magnitudes of each interval will be accounted for (at least on the average with respect to the midvalues). The products are entered in column 4.
3. The products of column 4 are summed and divided by n to give the mean.
4. The x deviations, $X - \overline{X}$, for each midvalue of each class interval are entered in column 5.

5. The products of the x deviations of column 5 and their respective frequencies per class interval are entered in column 6. As a check on the accuracy of the mean, the sum of this column should be zero (except for dropped decimals).
6. The x deviate values of column 5 are squared and entered in column 7.
7. The products of the squared deviations and their frequencies per class interval are entered in column 8. Their sum is the sum of the squared deviations, $\sum(x^2)$.
8. The variance and standard deviation are then computed as indicated in Table 4.3.

Short Method

The computations of Table 4.4 are simplified by the reduction of the original measures to the smallest possible integers. The process of doing

Table 4.4. Computation of Mean and Standard Deviation by Short Coded Method
(With Grouped Data of Table 4.3)

X Interval (1)	f (2)	x' (3)	fx' (4)	$x'(fx') = fx'^2$ (5)
70–74	1	4	4	16
65–69	5	3	15	45
60–64	6	2	12	24
55–59	7	1	7	7
50–54	11	0	0	0
45–49	7	−1	−7	7
40–44	7	−2	−14	28
35–39	4	−3	−12	36
30–34	2	−4	−8	32
	$n = 50$		$+38$	$\sum = 195$
			-41	
		$\sum = -3$	

$$\overline{X} = \text{T.M.} + ic, \text{ where T.M.} = \text{tentative mean} = 52.0$$
$$i = \text{scale size of interval} = 5$$

$$c = \frac{\sum(fx')}{n} = \frac{-3}{50} = -0.06$$

$$\overline{X} = 52.0 + 5(-0.06) = 52.0 - 0.30 = 51.7$$

$$V = (i^2)\left[\frac{\sum(fx'^2)}{n} - c^2\right] = (25)\left(\frac{195}{50} - 0.0036\right) = 97.41$$

$$\text{S.D.} = \sqrt{V} = \sqrt{97.41} = 9.87$$

this is called *coding*. It establishes *unit intervals* with which to work out the required arithmetic. The coding consists of

1. The *subtraction* of a constant amount from the midvalue of each class interval, and
2. The *division* of the remainder by a constant amount equal to i, the scale size of the class interval.

The steps in the computation of the mean and standard deviation by the short method of Table 4.4 can be summarized as follows:

1. The operations of coding are automatically accomplished, or nearly so, by writing zero in column 3 at or near the midinterval of the frequency distribution. Usually the interval with the greatest number of frequencies is selected because the product of f and zero will be zero and hence this will be the simplest computation of any. However, the "zero interval" can be selected anywhere within, or outside, the distribution without affecting the accuracy of the results.

The third column consists, then, of *unit interval deviates*. They are the smallest possible integer values, ranging upward from zero one unit at a time and downward minus one unit at a time. Deviate intervals taken from a point on a scale other than the mean are symbolized by x' (deviate x prime). All such deviates are taken from the midvalue of the interval, or point on the scale, whose value is set at zero. The scale value of this zero starting point may be characterized as the value of the *tentative mean* (T.M.). In Table 4.4, T.M. = 52.0.

Since each interval is also reduced in size by the division of the size of the interval i, the values of the unit interval x' deviates are in effect equal to the following:

x' Unit Interval Deviate:

$$x' = \frac{(X - \text{T.M.})}{i} \tag{4.11}$$

where X is the mid-value of a class interval. Since the mid-value of the lowest interval of Table 4.4 is 32, its x' value is -4:

$$x' = \frac{32 - 52}{5} = -4$$

2. The unit interval deviates of column 3 are multiplied by the f's of their respective intervals to give the $f(x')$ products of column 4.

3. The mean of the algebraic sum of this column is the mean of the residual (or remainder) values of the distribution. When this mean is multiplied by i, the size of the class intervals, the resulting product measures the amount of the difference between the tentative mean and the actual

mean. This product is usually symbolized as c and called the *correction.* Hence:

The Mean: $\qquad \overline{X} = \text{T.M.} + i\dfrac{\Sigma(fx')}{n} = \text{T.M.} + ic$ $\qquad\qquad$ (4.12)

4. The squares of the unit interval deviations multiplied by their respective frequencies are entered in column 5. Since $x'(fx') = f(x'^2)$, these products can be most simply obtained by multiplying the x' values of the third column and the fx' values of the fourth column.

5. The variance in unit interval values is calculated as follows:

Variance of the Unit Interval Distribution:

$$V_i \text{ or } \sigma_i{}^2 = \frac{\Sigma(fx'^2)}{n} - \left[\frac{\Sigma(fx')}{n}\right]^2 = \frac{\Sigma(fx'^2)}{n} - c^2 \qquad (4.13)$$

The value of the variance for the original distribution of measures is obtained by multiplying V_i or $\sigma_i{}^2$ by i^2. Therefore,

The Variance: $\qquad V = i^2\, V_i, \text{ or } \sigma^2 = i^2\sigma_i{}^2$ $\qquad\qquad$ (4.14)

6. As already indicated several times, the standard deviation is the square root of the variance. For the data of Table 4.4, S.D. (or σ for a population), $= 9.87$, which also is the value obtained by the long method in Table 4.3. They, or course, should be exactly the same except for dropped decimals.

Variance and Standard Deviation by the Short Method for a Sample of Measurements.

When the variance and standard deviation for a sample is needed, and therefore the sum of the squared deviations should be divided by $n - 1$ to avoid the bias of dividing by n alone, the procedure to use with the short method is as follows:
The sum of the squared deviations, Σx^2, is obtained from the variance σ^2.

The Sum of Squares:

Since $\sigma^2 = \dfrac{\Sigma x^2}{n}$,

$$\Sigma x^2 = n\sigma^2 \qquad (4.15)$$

The Variance of a Sample Therefore:

$$s^2 = \frac{\Sigma x^2}{n - 1} = \frac{n\sigma^2}{n - 1} \qquad (4.16)$$

For the vocabulary test measures of Table 4.4,

$$s^2 = \frac{50\,(97.41)}{49} = 99.40$$

The standard deviation of the sample result is, of course, the square root of the variance. Hence, for the vocabulary data, it is $\sqrt{99.40} = 9.97$. This is the same value to two decimal places obtained by the long method of Table 4.3.

The Mean of Means

The arithmetic mean of several sample means is sometimes needed. This is especially the case in sampling-inferential statistics when several sub-samples instead of a single sample are employed. (See p. 203.)

The mean of the measurements of two or more samples is easy to compute, since it is equal to the sum of *all* the measures divided by the total n:

Mean of Means:

$$\overline{X}_t = \frac{\Sigma(X_t)}{n_t} = \frac{\Sigma(X_1) + \Sigma(X_2) + \cdots + \Sigma(X_k)}{n_1 + n_2 + \cdots + n_k} \qquad (4.17)$$

where the subscript t signifies the total for all groups combined, the numerical subscripts refer to the different sample or subgroup results, and k is the number of samples whose measurements are being combined.

When only the sample means and their respective n's are available, then the overall mean may be obtained by the use of the product $(n\overline{X})$, since $\Sigma(X) = n\overline{X}$. Each such product for each subsample result would give the needed sums for the numerator of Formula 4.17. However, it is to be noted that if the size of two or more samples is the same, then Formula 4.17 simplifies to

When n_j's Are Equal:

$$\overline{X}_t = \frac{\overline{X}_1 + \overline{X}_2 + \cdots \overline{X}_k}{k} = \frac{\sum\limits^{k} \overline{X}}{k} \qquad (4.18)$$

Variance and Standard Deviation of Two or More Sets of Measurements

The variance and standard deviation for two or more samples or groups are easy to obtain when *the sums of the squares of the original measurements* are available. The total sum of squares of all the measures is first obtained and then the sum of squared deviations (Formula 4.19) and the variance (Formula 4.20) and standard deviation are computed.

Total Sum of Squared Deviations:

$$\Sigma(x_t{}^2) = \Sigma(X_1{}^2) + \Sigma(X_2{}^2) + \cdots$$
$$+ \Sigma(X_k{}^2) - \frac{(\Sigma X_1 + \Sigma X_2 + \cdots + \Sigma X_k)^2}{n_1 + n_2 + \cdots + n_k} \qquad (4.19)$$

The Variance: $\qquad s_t{}^2 = \dfrac{\Sigma(x_t{}^2)}{n_1 + n_2 + \cdots + n_k - 1} \qquad (4.20)$

The standard deviation of all groups or subsamples combined is thus the square root of the variance obtained by Formulas 4.19 and 4.20. When S.D. is to be calculated, the denominator of Formula 4.20 is simply the sum of the n's of the several groups.

When the sums of the squared measures of each sample or group are not available, then the variance and standard deviation for the combined data of two or more samples or groups are more complicated to compute. This is the case because the squared deviations of each sample need to be corrected to what their value should be when all deviations (x's) are taken from the overall mean $\overline{X}_t$. The sums of the squared deviations of each sample cannot be directly averaged (unless all sample means are equal, a rare condition for measurables but not for rankables).

The sum of the squared deviations for any set of sample data will be in error by the square of the difference between the sample mean and the total mean, with the difference weighted by the number of measures or observations in the sample.

Correction Factor: $c_k = n_j(\overline{X}_k - \overline{X}_t)^2$ (4.21)

Note that k is used to signify any sample or group as well as the number of samples or groups, and j signifies the number of measures or observations *within* a sample or group.

The sum of the squared deviations of any sample result can be obtained as follows:

Since
$$s_k{}^2 = \frac{\sum(x_j{}^2)}{n_j - 1}$$

therefore
$$\sum(x_k{}^2) = (n_j - 1)s_k{}^2 \qquad (4.22)$$

The variance of the measures of two or more samples may now be obtained with the aid of Formulas 4.21 and 4.22, as follows:

Variance of Combined Samples:

$$s_t{}^2 = \frac{(n_1 - 1)s_1{}^2 + (n_2 - 1)s_2{}^2 + \cdots + (n_k - 1)s_k{}^2 + c_1 + c_2 + \cdots + c_k}{n_1 + n_2 + \cdots + n_k - 1}$$

(4.23)

The standard deviation for the measurements of all samples combined will, of course, be the square root of the variance obtained by Formula 4.23.

Variance and Standard Deviation of Rankables

The sum of a set of n ranks, being the first n integers, is as follows:

Sum of n Ranks: $\sum R = \dfrac{n(n + 1)}{2}$ (4.24)

The mean of n ranks is therefore the sum of the ranks divided by the number of ranks. (This was presented earlier as Eq. 2.4.)

Mean of n Ranks: $\quad \overline{X}_R = \dfrac{n(n+1)}{2n} = \dfrac{n+1}{2}$ $\qquad$ (4.25)

A distribution of 10 rankables, 1 to 10, therefore has a mean rank of $(10 + 1)/2 = 5.5$.

The variance of a series of n ranks can be computed by Formulas 4.9 and 4.10 for ungrouped data. Thus,

Variance of n Ranks:

$$V = \frac{1}{n}\left[\sum_{}^{n}(R^2) - \frac{(\sum R)^2}{n}\right] \qquad (4.26)$$

where $\sum^n (R^2)$ is the sum of the squares of each rank and $(\sum R)^2$ is the square of the sum of the ranks. This latter sum is obtainable by use of Formula 4.24. The former sum is obtainable by direct computation, by squaring each rank and then summing. However, the entire set of operations can be simplified to the following:

Variance of n Ranks: $\qquad V = \dfrac{n^2 - 1}{12}$ $\qquad$ (4.27)

Hence the variance of 10 ranks is $(100 - 1)/12 = 8.25$, and the standard deviation is the square root of 8.25, which is 2.87.

MEAN AND VARIABILITY OF THE NORMAL PROBABILITY DISTRIBUTION

The distribution that is perhaps most frequently employed in sampling-inferential statistics is the Laplace-Gaussian normal probability distribution of Fig. 4.1. This distribution may be generated by the randomized behavior of an indefinitely large number of events (determiners, so to speak), each of which has equal probability of occurring or of not-occurring. The variations empirically found for many organismic and psychological traits or characteristics tend to pattern themselves in a manner similar to that of Fig. 4.1. It is *as if* the variations of a complex trait such as height or "intelligence" were the consequence of an enormous number of determiners (or the absence of them). Some philosopher-psychologists have contended the analogy supports the thesis of CHANCE, as opposed to DESIGN, in the ontogenesis of the many characteristics of *homo sapiens*.

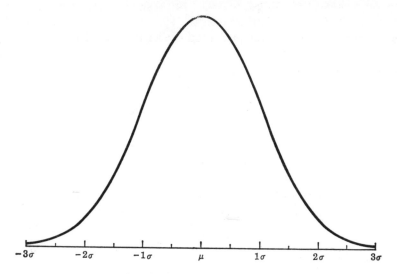

Fig. 4.1.   Laplace-Gaussian Normal Probability Distribution

Some Properties of the Normal Distribution

Some of the notable properties of the normal probability distribution are as follows:

1. It is a unimodal distribution.

2. It is bilaterally symmetrical with respect to the modal peak of the curve.

3. The arithmetic mean is the value on the scale at the exact center of the distribution. This follows from the fact of symmetry and is true also of any bilaterally symmetrical distribution.

4. The values of the mean, median, and mode coincide.

5. The curve is asymptotic with respect to the abscissa; i.e., it extends from the mean in both directions toward infinity.

6. The standard deviation, σ, is the standard measure of variation.

7. The range of the mean plus and minus 1.0σ marks off approximately the middle 68% of the area of the distribution. (See Table A of the Appendix.) Since any part of the normal distribution is a proportionate part of the entire distribution, the proportion characteristic of any particular area is the probability value of results occurring within that area. Hence the range of the mean $\pm 1.0\sigma$ includes 68% of the probabilities of the normal probability distribution (read $\pm$ as *plus and minus*).

Some additional, frequently used areas employed in sampling-inferential statistics are the following, with the lower case Greek letter mu, μ, symbolizing the mean of a population:

$\mu \pm 2\sigma$ includes approximately 95% of the area (probabilities).

$\mu \pm 2.5\sigma$ includes approximately 99% of the area (probabilities).

$\mu \pm 3.0\sigma$ includes approximately 99.7% of the area (probabilities).

8. The range of randomized sample results obtained from normally distributed parent populations usually does not exceed $\pm 2.5\sigma$ unless samples are very large.

9. The scale values are generalized as z *deviate* values, viz.,

$$z = \frac{X - \mu}{\sigma} = \frac{x}{\sigma} \qquad (4.28)$$

The mean value of the z deviates of a normal distribution is equal to zero. Since all z values are deviates in units of standard deviation, the range of $\mu \pm 1.0z$ is the same as that of $\mu \pm 1.0\sigma$, etc.

10. The total area signifies all occurrences and hence a total probability of unity, or 1.0. The probability of the occurrence of results within the range of any z deviate values, or beyond any z deviate value in either direction on the scale, can be determined from the tabulations of fractionate parts in Table A of the Appendix.

The formula for the normal probability distribution is as follows:

$$y = \frac{1}{\sqrt{2\pi}} e^{-x^2/2\sigma^2} \qquad (4.29)$$

where x is the deviation from the mean of a normal distribution with variance equal to σ^2, and y is the ordinate value for the given value of x. (See p. 174.)

Centile Implications of Normal z Deviates

The normal probability distribution is frequently employed as a frame of reference, or *probability model*, in the analysis of empirical distributions of sample results. Results are located on a distribution by a transformation of their original scale values into z deviate values. Then, in turn, added meaning is given the z deviate values by relating them to their centile implications on the normal distribution.

Thus any measure at the mean of a normal distribution has a z deviate value of zero. Since .50, or half, of the area of the distribution is below the z deviate value of zero, the mean is at the 50th centile point value. Hence $z_{.50}$ is a z deviate at the 50th centile.

The centile interval of any z deviate measure can readily be determined by use of Table A of the Appendix. The given z deviate value is located. The second column of the table gives the proportion of the area of the distribution from the mean. Column 3 gives the proportion of the area in the larger portion; column 4, the proportion of the area in the smaller portion. The appropriate proportion for a z deviate value is thus readily obtained and then related to the centile interval.

For example: If a measure has a z deviate value of -1.4, Table A indicates the area between the mean and $-1.4 = .4192$. Hence $.50 - .4192 = .0808$. This value is the entry in column 4 for a z deviate of 1.40 and can be obtained directly. Since $.08+$ of the area of the distribution is subtended beyond a z deviate of -1.4, the original measure is in the 9th centile interval. This is the case because the 9th centile interval is bounded by C_8 and C_9 point values, as indicated in the preceding chapter.

A measure whose z deviate value is $+1.4$ is in the 92nd centile interval. This is the case because, by column 3 of Table A, .9192 of the area is below a z deviate of 1.4.

Again it is to be emphasized that the foregoing interpretation of z deviates in terms of their centile locations is based on the assumption that the distribution is normal, or at least approximately so. The centiles mark off area (or probability) values. Thus $z_{.025}$ and $z_{.975}$ are scale values at points that mark off the middle 95% of the area of the normal distribution.

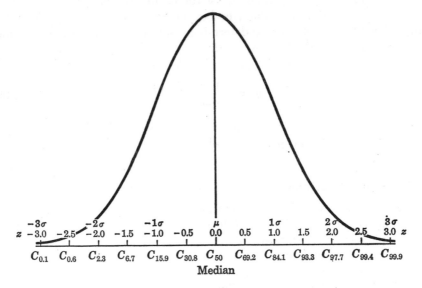

Fig. 4.2.   Normal Curve of Error as a Model for Relating Standard Scores and Centile Ranks by Means of z Deviates of Table A (Appendix)

The scale values of $z_{.005}$ and $z_{.995}$ mark off the middle 99% of the area (probabilities), since $\frac{1}{2}$ of 1% is subtended at each tail of the normal distribution.

Comparative Usefulness of z Deviates

A little reflection should serve to make clear the uselessness of attempting to compare two measures from different distributions when the units of measurement also are different. Thus a score of 14 on a number completion test and a score of 114 on a vocabulary test cannot meaningfully be compared unless more information is available. If the test results are available for *the same population of persons,* or for randomized samples of the same population, the measures can be compared by any one of the three methods developed in this and the preceding chapters, as follows:

1. By *rankables:* determining their respective ranks in each distribution; useful only when the n's of each distribution are the same.
2. By *centiles:* calculating their centile rank values in their respective distributions.
3. By z *deviates:* calculating their z deviate values in their respective distributions.

The ranking procedure or the use of centiles without z deviates is resorted to for distributions that are definitely not of the normal curve type, such as a J-curve, or an extremely skewed, or a rectangular type of distribution. In psychological measurement, the z deviate procedure is usually employed when it appears permissible to assume that the population distribution of measurements is normal in form.

Standard Measures

Since about half of the z deviate values for an empirical distribution will be negative, it is often either desirable or necessary to transform them to positive values. This can be done in several ways. One of the most practical and simplest modes is that of the standard measure, S:

$$S = z + 5.0 \qquad (4.30)$$

Standard measures thus have the same variance and standard deviation as z deviates, viz., 1.0 in both cases. The essential differences are that all the measures of the S distribution are positive, and the mean is 5.0 instead of zero.

Stanines

Original measures of different distributions are also sometimes converted to *stanines* so that they may be compared with each other. The word "stanine" is an elision of "standard nine-interval scale." Each interval of a stanine distribution spreads over half of a standard deviation, with the interval of the mean bounded by z deviate values of $-.25$ and $+.25$. As in the case of S measures, the mean value of a stanine distribution is taken as 5.0. However, the standard deviation of the stanine scale units is 2.0 because the mid-values of each stanine interval is an integer, beginning with 1.0 at the lowest interval and ending with 9.0 at the highest interval.

Original measures of a distribution are easily converted into stanine values by a percentage allocation to each of the nine intervals of the original measures. They are arranged in order of size. Beginning with the mid-measure, 10% of all the measures are counted off in both directions so as to locate the middle 20% of the measures in the mean interval with a stanine value of 5. It is often impossible, however, to have exactly the desired percentages of cases in each of the nine intervals because all measures of a given value need to be assigned to the same stanine interval in order that they will have the same stanine value. Whenever the percentages do not balance out symmetrically with respect to the mean interval, then the actual value of the mean of the stanine measures will be only approximately 5.0.

The Stanine Scale

STANINES	1	2	3	4	5	6	7	8	9
Percent of Measures Allocated to Each	4%	7%	12%	17%	20%	17%	12%	7%	4%
Cumulated Percents	4%	11%	23%	40%	60%	77%	89%	96%	100%

The percentages are rounded values, to the nearest integers, for the limits of each interval originally set in terms of z deviate values. As already indicated, each interval is half a z deviate in width, except for the two intervals at each end of the distribution. The z deviate limiting values are therefore as follows:

z Limits of Intervals:		-1.75	-1.25	$-.75$	$-.25$	.25	.75	1.25	1.75	
Stanines:	1		2		3		4	5	6	7	8	9

∧____∧____∧____∧____∧____∧____∧____∧

Some Relative Comparisons

When a person has the same z deviate scores or the same stanines on two or more test variables, or when two or more persons have the same z scores or stanines on a single test variable, the performances or levels of achievement are *relatively* the same. Their sameness is *relative* to the parameters of these measures in their parent populations, viz., the population mean and the population standard deviation. In other words, all such comparisons need be made with the *same* normative population providing the yardstick or frame of reference.

The data of Table 4.5 illustrate the relativity of achievement. Various grade averages of a graduating senior who majored in psychology are given in the first column, as follows:

$$G = \text{general average at time of graduation} = .79 \text{ (B}-)$$
$$P = \text{average grade in all psychology courses} = 1.06 \text{ (B)}$$
$$S\text{-}E = \text{average grade in statistics and}$$
$$\text{experimental psychology} = .43 \text{ (C}+)$$

The student population whose grades are used as the frame of reference for the comparisons of Table 4.5 consisted of 154 graduating seniors, all of whom had majored in psychology at the City College of the City University of New York. Their means and standard deviations are given in columns 2 and 3. The original grades of student coded No. 020 (Table 5.9) have been transformed to z, S, and stanine values in columns 4, 5, and 6.

Overall, this particular psychology major had a graduating average somewhat above the mean G of his fellow majors. His average was B— (.79); theirs was also B—, but at .64. Although this student's average of B in his psychology courses was higher than his general average of B—, it was nevertheless just *below* the average P grade of his fellow majors. His C+ average in S-E (statistics and experimental) was considerably below the average S-E of the psychology majors, as indicated by a z of —.94, or an S of 4.06, or a stanine of 3.

Table 4.5. **Relativity of Psychological Statistics Illustrated with Grade Measures of Achievement**

Grade Indices	Original Measures of No. 20*	$\overline{X}$	s	Normal z Deviates	Standard Scores S	Stanine Interval
G, General Average	.79	.64	.42	.36[a]	5.36	6
P, Psychology Average	1.06	1.15	.44	—.21[b]	4.79	5
S-E, Average in Statistics and Experimental Psychology	.43	1.03	.64	—.94[c]	4.06	3

$$\text{(a) } z_G = \frac{.79 - .64}{.42} = .36; \quad \text{(b) } z_P = \frac{1.06 - 1.15}{.44} = -.21;$$

$$\text{(c) } z_{S\text{-}E} = \frac{.43 - 1.03}{.64} = -.94$$

Frame of Reference: The grades of 154 graduating seniors who majored in psychology: $F = -2.0$; $D = -1.0$; $C = 0$; $B = 1.0$; $A = 2.0$.

*From Table 5.9, p. 120.

On the assumption of normal variability in these small populations of grades, the centile implications of the z deviates can be obtained from Table A of the Appendix. Thus, a z deviate value of .36 for G is in the 65th centile interval; a z of —.21 for P is in the 42nd centile interval; and a z of —.94 for S-E is in the 18th centile interval. *Presumably* this psychology major was exceeded in G by only 35% of the psychology majors but was exceeded in *S-E* by 82% of them. Whether these percentages are approximately correct for these particular distributions can be readily determined by calculating the centiles directly from the original data.

Correlation by *z* Deviates

If the student's *z* deviate scores were the same on a pair of variables (say, *G* and *P*) and if each student in turn in the population of 154 psychology majors had paired *z* deviates that were the same (*within* each pair; not *between* pairs), then the overall analysis would show what is called *perfect correlation*. *Relatively*, each student would have had the same level of achievement on both variables.

As will be shown in the next chapter, the correlation is 1.00 (perfect) when there is no difference *within* each pair of *z* deviates of a bivariate distribution of measurables. The correlation coefficient is symbolized by *r*:

z Deviate Correlation:

$$r_{xy} = 1.00 - \frac{\sum\limits^{n'} (z_x - z_y)}{2n'} \tag{4.31}$$

where *x* denotes one variable and *y* the other variable of a bivariate distribution, and *n'* denotes the number of *pairs* of measures.

SKEWNESS AND KURTOSIS

Skewness

Some of the important distributions of statistics are not symmetrical. When they are not symmetrical with respect to their mean, they are said to be *skewed*. It will be seen, for example, beginning with Chapter 7, that the sampling distributions of various statistics are skewed. Thus the distributions of proportion statistics and of correlation coefficients become increasingly asymmetrical as the parameter values of these measures approach limits of zero and 1.00 (in the case of proportions) or +1.00 and −1.00 (in the case of correlation coefficients). The statistics of chi-square are extremely skewed when there are only a few classes or categories of frequencies. The sampling distributions of *F* statistics consist of the largest family of sampling distributions of all that are skewed.

The distributions of Fig. 4.3 are illustrative. When measures are scaled with low values at the left end of the abscissa, a distribution is said to be *positively skewed* if the measures pile up toward the lower values and the upper tail is extended. The reverse, with the lower tail extended, is described as *negative* skewness. When a distribution is extremely skewed, the median may be a better *descriptive* statistic of central tendency than the mean. The value of the latter is pulled away from the locus of greatest

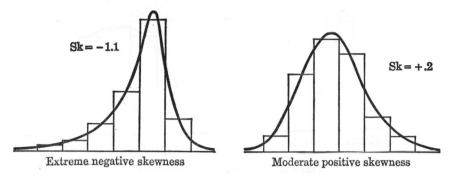

Fig. 4.3. **Skewness of Distributions**

Redrawn from Victor Goedicke, *Introduction to the Theory of Statistics*, 1953, Harper, New York. By permission of the publisher.

score concentration by the magnitude of the measures in the extended tail of a skewed distribution.

The skewness of a distribution can be measured by the mean of the cubes of the deviations taken in ratio to the cube of the standard deviation.

$$\textit{Skewness:} \qquad \text{Sk} = \frac{\overline{\sum (X - \overline{X})^3}}{(\text{S.D.})^3} = \frac{\dfrac{\sum (x)^3}{n}}{\left[\sqrt{\dfrac{\sum (x^2)}{n}}\,\right]^3} \tag{4.32}$$

A distribution is bilaterally symmetrical with respect to its mean when this measure of skewness is equal to zero.

Kurtosis

The way in which the measures of a symmetrical distribution concentrate around the mean and spread out toward the tails of a distribution is known as the *kurtosis* of the distribution. If a variable has the form of the Laplace-Gaussian probability curve of Fig. 4.1, it is described as *mesokurtic*. The detailed area differentiations of such distributions are given for fractionate values of z deviates in Table A of the Appendix.

Some sampling distributions, especially those of means when n_j is less than 15 or 20 are noticeably *leptokurtic*, as illustrated in Fig. 4.4. Compared with the normal distributions, leptokurtic ones have a narrower middle and a greater concentration of measures in the tails of the distribution. A *platykurtic* distribution, on the other hand, has a broader concentration of measures around the mean in the modal part of the distribution. It has a flattened top and thinner tails. Whereas leptokurtic sampling distributions are very important to statistical inferences about means of small samples (see Table B of the Appendix), there are few truly platykurtic distributions significant to statistical theory.

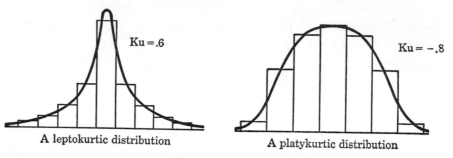

Ku = .6

Ku = −.8

A leptokurtic distribution   A platykurtic distribution

Fig. 4.4.   Kurtosis of Distributions

Redrawn from Victor Goedicke, *Introduction to the Theory of Statistics*, 1953, Harper, New York. By permission of the publisher.

The kurtosis of a distribution can be measured by the mean of the fourth power deviations taken in ratio to the standard deviation to the fourth power.

$$\textbf{\textit{Kurtosis:}} \quad \text{Ku} = \frac{\overline{\sum(X - \overline{X})^4}}{\text{S.D.}^4} - 3.0 = \frac{\dfrac{\sum(x^4)}{n}}{\left[\dfrac{\sum(x^2)}{n}\right]^2} - 3.0 \qquad (4.33)$$

(Note that the square of the variance, V^2, is the same as S.D. to the *4th* power.) When a distribution is mesokurtic, the value of Ku is zero. When Ku is less than zero, a distribution diverges from mesokurtosis

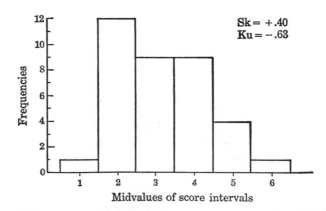

Sk = +.40
Ku = −.63

Fig. 4.5.   Skewness and Kurtosis of a Distribution
(Data and Computations in Table 4.6)

toward platykurtosis. When Ku is more than zero, then the divergence is toward leptokurtosis.

Computation of Sk and Ku

The computation of these measures of skewness and kurtosis is described in Table 4.6. By inspection, the distribution is seen to be skewed. It is illustrated in Fig. 4.5. Its positive skewness measures .40. Its kurtosis measures $-.63$, indicative of a fairly marked degree of platykurtosis.

The method used in Table 4.6 is the "long method" of computation with class intervals. That is, the mean is first computed from the products of column 3 and the x deviate values of column 4 are obtained. These x deviates are squared (column 6), cubed (column 8), and taken to the fourth power (column 10). Each is then multiplied by the appropriate frequency of column 2. The means of the sums of the resulting sets of products give the measures needed for the computation of Sk and Ku.

Table 4.6. Computation of Sk and Ku (Skewness and Kurtosis)
(Data of Table 3.1)

X (1)	f (2)	fX (3)	x (4)	fx (5)	x^2 (6)	fx^2 (7)	x^3 (8)	fx^3 (9)	x^4 (10)	fx^4 (11)
6	1	6	2.83	2.83	8.01	8.01	22.67	22.67	64.14	64.14
5	4	20	1.83	7.44	3.35	13.40	6.13	24.52	11.22	44.88
4	9	36	0.83	7.47	0.69	6.21	0.57	5.13	0.47	4.23
3	9	27	-0.17	-1.53	0.03	0.27	-0.005	-0.05	0.001	0.01
2	12	24	-1.17	-14.04	1.37	16.44	-1.60	-19.20	1.87	22.44
1	1	1	-0.217	-2.17	4.71	4.71	-10.22	-10.22	22.17	22.17
$\sum$'s	36	114		$+17.74$		49.04		$+52.32$		157.87
				-17.74				-29.47		
				0				22.85		
				(Check)						

$$\overline{X} = \frac{114}{36} = 3.17$$

$$Sk = \frac{\dfrac{\sum(fx^3)}{n}}{\left[\sqrt{\dfrac{\sum(fx^2)}{n}}\right]^3} = \frac{\dfrac{22.85}{36}}{\left(\sqrt{\dfrac{49.04}{36}}\right)^3} = \frac{.6347}{(1.166)^3} = .40$$

$$Ku = \frac{\dfrac{\sum(fx^4)}{n}}{\left[\dfrac{\sum(fx^2)}{n}\right]^2} - 3.0 = \frac{\dfrac{157.87}{36}}{\left(\dfrac{49.04}{36}\right)^2} - 3.0 = \frac{4.385}{(1.362)^2} - 3.0 = -.63$$

METHOD OF MOMENTS

The statistical measures developed in this chapter have been based not only on the magnitudes of continuous distributions (in fact, or by assumption, in the case of distributions whose values are discrete but whose variables are postulated to be continuous); they have also been based on deviations, x, from the arithmetic mean. The sum of these x deviations for any distribution is equal to zero. The method of this chapter is thus based on deviates and is usually known as the *method of moments*.

The method of moments is a much more important method for applied statistics than is the centile method of the preceding chapter. The latter is mainly useful as a *descriptive* technique. The method of moments is essential to the development of sampling-inferential statistics. An important distinction or difference between the two methods lies in the fact that centile measures are based on the *positions* of cases in a distribution; measures obtained by the method of moments are based on the *magnitudes* of the cases.

The nth moment of a continuous distribution is the mean of the nth power of the x deviations from the mean. The four moments useful to statistics have been employed in previous sections and are given below.

The First Moment: $\qquad m_1 = \dfrac{\sum(x)}{n} = 0$ $\qquad\qquad$ (4.34)

The first moment thus defines the *arithmetic mean as a measure of location*. The mean tells where the knife-edge balance of a distribution is located on a scale of measurements. The subtraction of the mean from each measure, as is done to obtain the x deviate values, locates a distribution at the origin, with a mean of zero, and hence permits the comparison of different distributions, regardless of their original location.

The Second Moment: $\qquad m_2 = \dfrac{\sum(x^2)}{n}$ $\qquad\qquad$ (4.35)

The second moment about the mean is the variance of a distribution (of a population). The square root of this moment yields the standard deviation as the *standard* measure of the variability of a distribution in original scale units.

The Third Moment: $\qquad m_3 = \dfrac{\sum(x^3)}{n}$ $\qquad\qquad$ (4.36)

The third moment about the mean provides a measure of skewness inasmuch as the cubing of the deviations gives considerably greater weight to larger deviations than to small ones; hence m_3 will be negative or positive when the magnitudes of a distribution are not asymmetrically located around the mean.

Since the value of the third moment, m_3, is affected by the size of the measures of a distribution, it does not provide a *standard* measure of skewness. However, when the result is expressed in units analogous to x/σ, or z deviates, a satisfactory measure of "pure skewness" is obtained:

$$\text{Sk} = \frac{m_3}{\sigma^3} \tag{4.37}$$

In the case of the distribution of Table 4.6, Sk was found to be positive and equal to .40 (with σ of a population taken as equal to S.D. of the group of 36 cases). A value of .40 represents a fair degree of skewness, as is borne out by an inspection of the distribution of Fig. 4.5.

It is to be noted that the numerical value of Sk of Formula 4.37 will be about $+1$ or -1 for very extreme examples of skewness. Furthermore, in psychological measurement, skewed distributions are often the consequence of the transactional character of a test and the testees: (1) a test too difficult for a group is likely to yield a positively skewed distribution; (2) one that is too easy is likely to have a negatively skewed distribution, with most testees obtaining the maximum or near-maximum possible score. A test of the desired standard of difficulty in test construction is, by definition, one that yields test scores (from the population for which it is designed) whose distributions are not skewed. It is thus a test neither too difficult nor too easy.

The Fourth Moment: $$m_4 = \frac{\sum(x^4)}{n} \tag{4.38}$$

The fourth moment about the mean provides a measure of kurtosis. It is not affected by skewness, since all fourth powers are positive. The peakedness and the spreading out of measures into the tails of a distribution were seen to describe its kurtosis. The higher the even power to which x deviates are raised, the greater the weight of large deviations on the results. When the deviations of a normal distribution are raised to the fourth power and expressed as a ratio to the standard deviation taken to the fourth power, the measure of "pure" mesokurtosis will be 3.0:

Mesokurtosis: $$\frac{m_4}{\sigma^4} = 3.0 \tag{4.39}$$

Or this may be written as in Formula 4.33, with 3.0 subtracted from the ratio, in which case mesokurtosis = zero. Formula 4.33 for kurtosis will yield values of around $+1.0$ for marked leptokurtic distributions with narrow middles and fattened tails. The value of Ku will be around -1.0 for marked platykurtic distributions with fat middles and thin tails.

CHAPTER 5

PEARSON'S *r* CORRELATION AND REGRESSION ESTIMATION

Statistical Correlation as an Aid to Discovery and Confirmation · Correlation as a Measure of Association or Covariation · Logical Basis for a Bivariate Distribution

Not chaos-like together crush'd and bruis'd,
But, as the world, harmoniously confused:
Where order in variety we see,
And where tho' all things differ, all agree.

Alexander Pope

Most distributions so far considered have been for data of single variables. Many of the most important distributions of psychology and the behavioral sciences are based, however, on the *relatedness* of two variables. They are called *bivariate distributions*, and if the data are in fact related in some systematic manner, they are said to be *correlated* (*co-related*).

Statistical Correlation as an Aid to Discovery and Confirmation

Many of the known relations of the biological and behavioral sciences have been discovered or confirmed through the use of the statistical technique of correlation. That is to say, innumerable relations have been found to exist where none was known or only somewhat vaguely surmised before. The relations of traits of parents with those of their offspring are perhaps the classical example. It was Sir Francis Galton (1886) who invented the technique of correlation in order to ascertain (discover) the extent to which adult sons' heights are associated with their fathers' heights. In fact the developments of applied statistics in the 19th century followed "naturally" from the work of Darwin. Statistical methods became necessary because of the great concentration of scientific observation and measurement of *individual differences*, of the variable characteristics of plants, and the behavior of organisms, including man, of course. *Darwinism* opened up innumerable problems of research that could be handled only by techniques of applied statistics. Of these, the technique of correlation invented by Charles Darwin's cousin, Sir Francis Galton, proved to be one of the most useful.

The technique of correlation is also used as an instrument to investigate superstitions and "old wives' tales" as well as to test the plausibility of socially approved beliefs and conceptions. What relationship, if any, is there between measures of the shape or magnitude of human skulls and I.Q.? Do persons with high I.Q.'s have relatively large skulls with bulging frontal contours? Do person's with low I.Q.'s have relatively small skulls with receding foreheads? These are questions of correlation. The character of the answers will depend on the nature of the sample of persons and the precision and accuracy of the skull and I.Q. measurements.

Is there a correlation between characteristics of people's behavior and the changing phases of the moon? The history of the word "lunacy" is a history of belief in such a correlation. Is there a correlation between any aspects of behavior and character of handwriting? Between students' classroom achievements and their achievements outside the classroom, such as in athletics, or on the job? Between intellect and social adjustment? Between friendliness and perspicacity?

It is apparent that there is a great multitude of questions in psychology and the behavioral sciences whose answers require correlative information as well as scientific sampling and measurement. The statistical information needs to be as precise (*reliable*) and as accurate (*valid*) as possible. The samples of information need to be broadly based if the results are going to serve broad inferences about man and society.

Correlation as a Measure of Association or Covariation

Statistical correlation signifies some degree of association or concomitant variation, or covariation, between two variables. This means that changes or differences in the values of the measures of one variable are associated more or less with particular changes or differences in the values of the measures of the other variable. Unlike the strict, invariant relation between the size of the radius of a circle and its area, the correlations of the biological and behavioral sciences are not perfect or invariant. Thus common sense observations indicate that tall people weigh more than short people, and short people weigh less than tall people, but there are many exceptions. The relationship is not a perfect one in the sense that all people over 6 feet tall weigh more than all people under 6 feet, or that all people 5 feet short weigh less than those over 5 feet, etc.

The following kinds of statistical questions are asked about bivariate distributions:

1. Is there any correlation between the measures of two variables meaningfully associated together in a bivariate distribution?
2. If there is, how are the variables associated, and to what degree?
3. To what extent can one generalize or make inferences about the measures of one variable from information about the measures of another variable when it has been found they are correlated to some degree?
4. Is the observed correlation in a bivariate distribution of a sample result significantly greater in value than that expected simply on the basis of random variation from a population in which the correlation is zero?
5. To what extent can one generalize or make inferences about the magnitude of correlation in bivariate populations from the information of correlation observed in *samples* of such populations?

The answers to the first three questions will be dealt with in this and the next chapter. The other two questions will be considered in Chapters 8, 9, and 10.

Logical Basis for a Bivariate Distribution

When two variables have something in common so that observations or measurements obtained for each can be meaningfully paired, such pairings over a series of measurements create or constitute a bivariate. Rather bizarre and apparently meaningless bivariates can be set up by the use of *chronology* as a basis for pairing observations of two variables. Thus, when daily, weekly, monthly, or annual data are available simultaneously on any two variables, there is a basis for the pairing of measurements and the calculation of a measure of correlation. Stock market averages can be correlated with suicide rates or with marriage rates, etc., to give bivariate distributions over a period of time. Sunspot activity similarly can be correlated with mundane activities, such as birth rates and accident rates.

Chronology, however, is not usually in itself a sufficient basis for the establishment of meaningful bivariates. The two variables should be associated in some context other than just the clock. In the zoological and behavioral sciences the basis for association is usually one of the following:

1. The identity of the individual organism (the animal or person).
2. Blood relations (parent-offspring, twins, siblings, cousins, etc.).
3. Social relations (husbands-wives, sweethearts, etc.).

The first class constitutes the most generalized basis for bivariate relations. In psychology and the behavioral sciences the person is the entity common to two or more variables whose measurements are assembled into a bivariate distribution. If one wishes to determine the correlation, if any, between height and intelligence, he draws his information from a sample of *persons*. For each person a *pair* of measurements is made, a height measure and an intelligence measure.

It has already been noted that Galton's early studies (1886) in correlation were of bivariate distributions of blood relations: parents' and their offsprings' heights. He was particularly interested in this kind of pairing of measurements because of his search for evidence to support his views on the inheritance of organismic and psychological traits. E. L. Thorndike's (1905) use of twins and nontwin siblings in the study of the possible differential effects of close blood relations as against less close blood relations, as against *chance* ones, set a pattern for much research on the relative roles of nature and nurture in intellectual functioning and development.

CLASSIFICATION OF BIVARIATES

Bivariate distributions take different forms, depending on the nature of the variables associated. There are consequently a variety of statistical techniques for measuring their correlation. There are also techniques for the correlation of multivariates, i.e., for the multiple correlation, say, of the combined measures of a battery of psychological tests with a criterion of success.

The various forms of bivariate correlation can be meaningfully outlined in terms of the nature of the variables correlated. Techniques for the measurement of their degree of correlation will be developed in this and the following chapter.

There are five general classes of bivariate distributions, as follows:

1. Both variables consisting of unordered countables (note that *ordered* countables are usually treated as "measurables").
2. Both variables consisting of rankables.
3. Both variables consisting of measurables.
4. An unordered countable associated with a measurable.
5. A rankable associated with a measurable.

1. *A bivariate distribution of unordered countables* may consist of
   a. A simple 2 by 2 relationship, as in the crosstabulation of two dichotomized countables. The correlation of such a bivariate distribution is usually measured by the *phi* coefficient, ϕ (p. 135).
   b. The *contingency coefficient, C,* (p. 136) is used to measure the correlation of all other combinations of unordered countables, such as a 2 by 3 crosstabulation, or 3 by 3, etc.
2. The degree to which *one rankable variate is associated with another rankable* is usually measured by Spearman's rank-difference method of correlation (p. 140).
3. *A measurable with a measurable* represents perhaps the most common correlative association. There are various forms:
   a. When both measurables are continuously distributed and the relationship is linear, Pearson's *r* correlation is obtained either from the relative differences of the associated pairs or from their products. The latter procedure is known as the *product-moment method*. It is the most widely used measure of correlation in the biological and behavioral sciences and is developed in this chapter.
   b. The correlation of a dichotomized measurable associated with a distributed measurable is determined by means of a method for biserial *r*, r_{bi} (p. 126).
   c. The correlation of a trichotomized measurable associated with a distributed measurable is determined by a method for triserial *r* (p. 128).
   d. The correlation of one dichotomized measurable associated with another dichotomized measurable is determined by tetrachoric *r*, r_t (p. 130).
   e. The correlation of two measurables not linearly associated is determined by a method for measuring nonlinear or curvilinear correlation and results in a correlation coefficient known as *eta*, η (p. 132).

4. *Unordered countables associated with measurables* also form various types of bivariate distributions:

    a. The correlation of a dichotomized countable (such as sex) with a distributed measurable is determined by means of point biscrial r, r_{pb} (p. 143).

    b. The correlation of an unordered countable of more than two classes with a distributed measurable is determined by *eta*, η.

    c. The correlation of a countable of two or more categories with a measurable of only two or a few classes may be determined by *phi*, ϕ (when 2 by 2), or otherwise by C, the contingency coefficient.

5. *Rankables associated with measurables* are usually correlated by the conversion of the measurable to a series of ranks, i.e., a rankable, and then the use of Spearman's rank-difference method as the measure of correlation.

CROSSTABULATIONS

A bivariate distribution may consist simply of four cells. This kind of distribution occurs when each variable is a dichotomy or has been dichotomized (meaning, literally, to be cut into two parts). Whether such bivariates are correlated can readily be determined by means of a crosstabulation of their joint frequencies and the consequent location among the cells of the *correlational frequencies*. Each such frequency represents the associated relationship of a *pair* of observations. If a bivariate distribution consists of 100 pairs of observations, then there will be 100 correlational frequencies, as illustrated in Table 5.1. Such a four-celled tabulation is often referred to as a 2 by 2 correlation chart.

Table 5.1. Correlation of Sex with Attitude Toward Baseball

		SEX		
		Male	Female	f_r
ATTITUDE	Like:	40	10	50
TOWARD BASEBALL	Dislike:	10	40	50
	f_c	50	50	$n' = 100$

NOTE: f_r refers to the frequencies of the rows; f_c, to the frequencies of the columns; and n' to the total number of correlational frequencies or *pairs* of observations ($n' = n/2$, where n is the total number of observations).

Table 5.1 shows a high correlation between sex and attitude toward baseball. The group of 100 is evenly divided between males and females and evenly divided in their attitudes. (The data are purely fictional.) Although there is correlation, the relationship between sex and attitude is not invariant; i.e., not all women dislike baseball and not all men like it. Some don't and some do. On p. 270 a method will be developed to help one decide whether such a correlation is high enough to permit the conclusion that the relationship is not just a matter of chance.

Table 5.2 (again fictional) exhibits *no correlation* between the attitudes of 100 persons toward statistics and hockey. One may well ask what do statistics and hockey have in common. Rationally they may not have anything in common, but 100 persons may manifest attitudes toward each which are either similar or different. They may like both, dislike both, or like one but not the other. In Table 5.2, the ratios of attitudes are the same: Vertically they are 1:1 (20:20, and 30:30); horizontally they are 2:3 (20:30). And the sum of the frequencies in the diagonal cells *a* and *d* is equal to their sum in the diagonal cells *b* and *c*.

This kind of result signifies zero correlation in the sense that persons who like statistics have no greater liking or disliking for hockey than those who dislike statistics. Contrast this zero relationship with the bivariate distribution of Table 5.3.

Table 5.2. Correlation of Attitudes Toward Statistics and Hockey

| | | ATTITUDE TOWARD HOCKEY | | |
		Like	Dislike	f_r
ATTITUDE TOWARD STATISTICS	Like:	*a* 20	*b* 30	50
	Dislike:	*c* 20	*d* 30	50
	f_c	40	60	$n' = 100$

Should you meet one of the fictional persons whose attitudes are cross-tabulated in Table 5.3 and learn that he likes spinach, you can conclude he is also a gum chewer. Of if you learn he is an eschewer of gum, you can conclude he dislikes spinach. But not all who dislike spinach eschew gum: 20 of the 70 happen to be gum chewers. An analysis of all the relational elements of Table 5.3 will show the correlation to be at the maximum possible in the light of the *marginal frequencies*, but the correlation is not perfect:

Cell *a*: 1. None who like spinach eschew gum.
          2. None who eschew gum like spinach.
Cell *b*: 3. All who like spinach also chew gum.
          4. A majority (30 of 50) who chew gum also like spinach.

Cell c: 5. Most (50 of 70) who dislike spinach eschew gum.
            6. All who eschew gum also dislike spinach.
Cell d: 7. Some (20 of 70) who dislike spinach chew gum.
            8. Some (20 of 50) who chew gum dislike spinach.

A 2 by 2 crosstabulation of a bivariate thus yields eight correlative propositions. If they were all like (1), (2), (3), and (6), the correlation for Table 5.3 would be perfect in that each subrelation would admit of no exception. In the next chapter, methods will be developed to measure the *degree of correlation* of such 2 by 2 bivariates.

Table 5.3.   Correlation of Attitudes Toward Spinach and Chewing Gum Behavior

		GUM BEHAVIOR		
		Eschewer	Chewer	f_r
ATTITUDE	Like:	*a* 0	*b* 30	30
TOWARD SPINACH	Dislike:	*c* 50	*d* 20	70
	f_c	50	50	$n' = 100$

Crosstabulation of Measurables

When the measures of bivariate distributions are distributed over several or many classes, they cannot be so readily categorized into a series of logical propositions about each cell, as can be done for a simple 2 by 2 distribution. Hence statistical techniques for assessing the overall correlationship becomes essential. Several are available. Which to use depends first on the linearity of the relationship. If the relationship is found to be linear, then the choice of method for the measurement of the correlation is pretty much a matter of computational facilities (for example, availability of adding and (or) calculating machines).

The possible linearity or nonlinearity of a bivariate distribution can often be satisfactorily inferred from an inspection of either a

1. Scattergram map of the distribution, or a
2. Correlation chart.

The former device is illustrated in Figs. 5.1, 5.2, and 5.4. The latter is illustrated in Tables 5.5 and 5.6. Both devices are cross tabulations of bivariate data. The scattergram is usually made with respect to the original "point" scale values of each variable. The correlation chart is made with respect to interval values set up for each variable (as in Table 5.6).

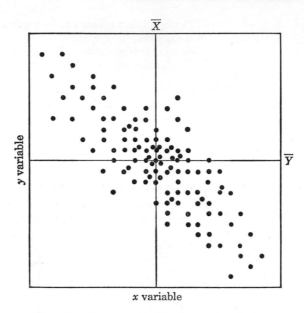

Fig. 5.1. Scatter of a Negative Correlation

The two scattergrams of Figs. 5.1 and 5.2 illustrate the difference between a linear relationship (Fig. 5.1) and a nonlinear or curvilinear rela-

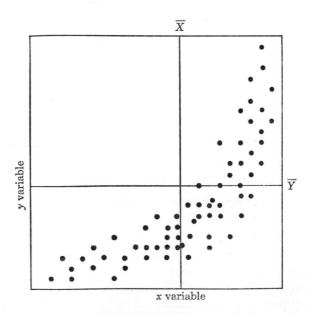

Fig. 5.2. Scatter of a Nonlinear Correlation

tionship (Fig. 5.2). It is not, however, always so easy to tell *by inspection of the scatter of frequencies* whether a bivariate distribution tends to be linear or nonlinear. In some cases, statistical tests for linearity and nonlinearity may need to be employed (see p. 342).

When a bivariate relationship between measurables can be assumed to be satisfactorily described by a *linear function (straight line equation)*, then the statistical method used to assess or measure the overall correlation is one that yields Pearson's *r* coefficient. This measure of correlation may also be used to measure how much of the total covariation is linear in an overall curvilinear relation.

The *E* and *V* data of Table 5.4 have been crosstabulated into the bivariate distribution of Table 5.5. This latter table shows the relationship between endomorphy *E* and viscerotonia *V* for the 36 males whose endomorphic data were presented earlier in Table 3.1. The viscerotonia temperament is described by Sheldon with such terms as "relaxation in posture and movement," "love of physical comfort," "love of polite ceremony," "evenness of emotional flow," and "complacency." A scale value of 7 represents the maximum *V*; a value of 4, an average *V*; and a value of 1, practically zero.

An inspection of the 36 correlational frequencies in the bivariate distribution of Table 5.5 leads to the inference that variations in somatotype are correlated with variations in temperament. Only 12 of the 49 cells have correlational frequencies. Since the scale value of 7 is not represented with a frequency in either variate, the number of cells that would have frequencies if the correlation were perfect is *six*. In one-third, or 12, of the 36 correlational frequencies, there is a paralleling of scale values of the two variates. Thus, six cases are in the cell whose scale values are 2 and 2, three are in the cell whose values are 3 and 3, and three are in the cell whose values are 4 and 4. And of the remaining 24 correlational frequencies, all are within one scale interval of the preceding cell correspondencies.*

Concomitant Variation

The following propositions are descriptive of the bivariate distribution of Table 5.5:

1. Males judged to have little or no *E* manifest little or no *V*, and vice versa.
2. Males judged to have an average amount of *E* are about average in *V*, and vice versa.
3. The five males with *E* of more than 4.0 (the scale average) manifest more than average *V*.

---

*It is to be noted that such correspondence of *original* scale values of two correlated variables is exceptional rather than the rule.

Table 5.4. Correlation of E Somatotype with V Temperament: Pearson's r

Subject	X (E)	Y (V)	X^2 (E^2)	Y^2 (V^2)	XY (EV)
1	3	4	9	16	12
2	3	4	9	16	12
3	5	6	25	36	30
4	1	2	1	4	2
5	4	5	16	25	20
6	2	2	4	4	4
7	2	1	4	1	2
8	2	2	4	4	4
9	4	4	16	16	16
10	3	3	9	9	9
11	6	5	36	25	30
12	4	3	16	9	12
13	4	5	16	25	20
14	2	3	4	9	6
15	5	6	25	36	30
16	2	3	4	9	6
17	2	2	4	4	4
18	4	4	16	16	16
19	3	3	9	9	9
20	5	6	25	36	30
21	4	3	16	9	12
22	2	3	4	9	6
23	2	2	4	4	4
24	3	4	9	16	12
25	3	2	9	4	6
26	2	2	4	4	4
27	4	3	16	9	12
28	2	2	4	4	4
29	4	4	16	16	16
30	4	5	16	25	20
31	2	1	4	1	2
32	5	6	25	36	30
33	2	3	4	9	6
34	3	3	9	9	9
35	3	4	9	16	12
36	3	4	9	16	12
$n' = 36$ $\sum\text{'s} = $	114	124	410	496	441

$$r = \frac{36(441) - (114)(124)}{\sqrt{[36(410) - (114)^2][36(496) - (124)^2]}} = .832$$

(By formula of Eq. 5.6)

4. The nine males with more than the scale average of 4.0 for V manifest average or more than average E.
5. As the values of either variate increase, so do the *average values* of the other variate, as indicated by the means of columns and of rows at the bottom and to the right of the chart. This *varying together* of the measures of two variates of a bivariate distribution is what is meant by *concomitant variation*.

Positive vs. Negative Correlation

This analysis of the bivariate distribution of Table 5.5 also signifies that the correlation is positive rather than negative. This is the case because low values of one variate are associated with low values of the other variate, average values are associated with average values, and high

Table 5.5. Correlation Chart with a Bivariate Distribution of 36 Correlation Frequencies

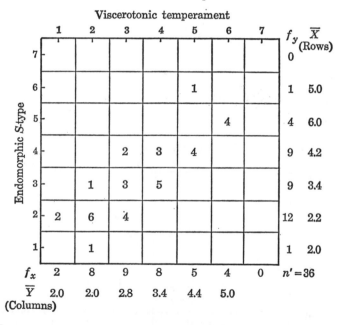

Note that the scale values of the two variables are indicated at the left and top of the chart. Frequencies for the x variable are the sums of the columns and are given at the bottom of the chart. Frequencies for the y variable are the sums of the rows and are given at the right of the chart. The *means* of the measures for the columns and the rows are given at bottom and at the right of the chart.

values with high values. Had the relation been reversed, as in Fig. 5.1, the relation would have been negative.

The Three Distributions of a Correlation Chart

Reference to Table 5.5 shows that a correlation chart generates not one but *three distributions:*

1. The bivariate distribution of the correlational frequencies in the cells of the table.
2. The univariate distribution of the frequencies of the x variable, usually summed at the bottom of each column (but sometimes summed at the tops of columns).
3. The univariate distribution of the frequencies of the y variable summed at the right of each row (sometimes summed at the left).

The marginal totals of the rows and the columns of a *correlation chart* thus give the f's of the frequency distributions of each variable considered separately. One can always obtain directly the univariate frequency distributions from a correlation chart. However, a bivariate distribution cannot be put together from only the information of two separate univariate distributions. Crosstabulating in the first instance is therefore a considerable timesaver as compared with first making separate distributions of each variate and then making the bivariate distribution.

Linearity

The question of the linearity of a bivariate distribution is considered at this point (prior to the later sections on linear regression and regression

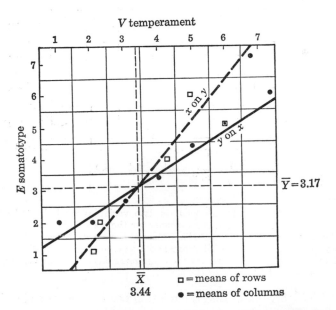

Fig. 5.3. **Straight Lines Fitted to the Average Variations of Y with Respect to X, and the Average Variations of X with Respect to Y**

estimation) in order to emphasize that the interpretation of *r* is based on the *assumption of linearity*. One might well ask, "what is linear about the scattering of correlational frequencies in Fig. 5.1? Is the relationship of Table 5.5 a linear one?" By inspection, the answer appears to be YES. The scatter of the correlational frequencies spreads somewhat elliptically around an imaginary straight line rather than a curve of some kind. However, the question of linearity is more satisfactorily answered by the graphs of Fig. 5.3. If ever in doubt about the linearity of a bivariate distribution after having used the method of inspection, one may use the method of averages, as in Fig. 5.3. If still in doubt, then a statistical test for linearity needs to be employed (p. 342).

The averages of the variation of measures of *E* for successive values of *V* are plotted in Fig. 5.3. These averages are for the variations in the *E* measures signified by each *column* of frequencies of Table 5.5 and are reported in the row at the bottom of that table. A straight line can be fitted satisfactorily to these averages, as shown by the line of "*y* on *x*." This line is called the *linear regression* of variate *y* on variate *x*. It shows the concomitance of variation, i.e., the average change in the value of the *y* variate with successive changes (increases) in the value of the *x* variate.

Similarly, the averages of the variation of the measures of *V* for successive values of *E* are shown in Fig. 5.3 by line "*x* on *y*." These averages are for the variation in the *V* measures in each row of correlational frequencies of Table 5.5 and are reported in the last column at the right of that table. A straight line can also be fitted satisfactorily to these averages. It is called the *linear regression* of variate *x* on variate *y*. It shows the covariation of *x* in relation to *y*, i.e., the average change in the value of the *x* variate (*V*) with successive changes (increases) in the value of *y* (*E*).

COMPUTATION OF PEARSON'S *r* COEFFICIENT

Pearson's correlation coefficient for distributed measurables is symbolized by the letter *r* both in descriptive and sampling statistics. The Greek letter equivalent *rho*, written as ρ, is used to symbolize parameter or population coefficients. (Note that some authors use *R* instead of rho; however, *R* will be used later for multiple correlation, p. 117). As already indicated, the idea of correlation was discovered (or invented) during the last quarter of the 19th century by *Sir Francis Galton* (1886). He developed the correlation chart for depicting and analyzing the relationship between traits of fathers and their adult sons. *Karl Pearson* (1857–1936), a student and associate of Galton, perfected the technique for the computation of correlation. Hence the coefficient is often referred to as *Pearson's r*. (See Walker, 1929.)

The numerical value of *r* may range from -1.0 through zero to $+1.0$. Both -1.0 and $+1.0$ are indicative of perfect correlation in a bivariate distribution. They signify an invariant relationship between changes in *x* and y. There is no variation or scatter around the regression lines of perfect correlation. The line for y on x coincides with the line for x on y when $r = -1.0$ or $+1.0$; hence there appears to be only one regression line in this limiting instance. It rarely, if ever, occurs in the biological and behavioral sciences. When the correlation is zero, the variation or scatter of the bivariate distribution is at its maximum.

Correlation as Relative Similarity*

As suggested at the end of the preceding chapter, the degree of correlation can be measured by obtaining the *differences* between each pair of z score measures. Such differences are *relative* to the means and standard deviations of each distribution. Taken in terms of z score measures, the original measures of both variables are transformed to equal scales with means of zero and standard deviations of 1.0. The smaller the differences within each z score pair, the greater the correlation. Thus:

Difference Method for r:

$$r = 1 - \frac{\sum\limits^{n'} (z_x - z_y)^2}{2n'} \tag{5.1}$$

The second term of Formula 5.1 thus measures the average *dissimilarity* between the two variables. Subtracted from 1.0, the remainder gives the value of r and measures the relative *similarity* between the pairs of measures of x and y.

Product-Moment r

What is the degree of correlation between E somatotype and V temperament, as sampled in Table 5.4? One method for the computation of r uses the correlation chart as a matrix for the computations. It will be developed in Table 5.6. The method used for the 36 correlational frequencies of Table 5.5 is presented in Table 5.4. It is based on the method of Table 4.2 developed in Chapter 4 for the mean, variance, and standard deviation, but works with the *products* of the original measures of each pair, rather than with differences between z scores, because of greater ease in computation. It is particularly useful for these data because:

1. All the measures are single-digit integers and are positive.
2. There are only 36 pairs of observations, or correlational frequencies.
3. Only one additional column of computations, over and beyond the two needed for the mean and standard deviation of each variable, is

---

*The writer is indebted to his colleague and friend, Dr. Alexander Mintz, for pointing to the difference formula for r as being intuitively more meaningful than the product-moment Formula 5.2.

necessary to obtain all the sums needed for the computation of r. This is the last column of XY of Table 5.4.

The products operations for Pearson's product-moment r are usually stated as in Formulas 5.2, 5.3, or 5.4.

z Score Formula:
$$r = \frac{\sum^{n'}(z_x z_y)}{n'} \tag{5.2}$$

x and y Deviate Formula:
$$r = \frac{\sum(xy)}{n'\sigma_x \sigma_y} \tag{5.3}$$

sometimes written with s's but calculated as S.D.'s for samples as well as populations:

$$r = \frac{\sum xy}{n'\ SD_x\ SD_y} \tag{5.3a}$$

or, preferably:

$$r = \frac{\sum(xy)}{\sqrt{\sum(x^2)\sum(y^2)}} \tag{5.4}$$

since the n' of the product-deviations cancels out with the $\sqrt{n_x}$ and $\sqrt{n_y}$ of the standard deviations.*

When X and Y, the original measures of a bivariate distribution, are worked with instead of the z scores or the x and y deviations, Pearson's r is equal to the following:

Original Score Formula:

$$r = \frac{\dfrac{\sum(XY)}{n'} - (\bar{X}\bar{Y})}{\sqrt{\dfrac{\sum X^2}{n_x} - (\bar{X})^2}\ \sqrt{\dfrac{\sum Y^2}{n_y} - (\bar{Y})^2}} \tag{5.5}$$

or

$$r = \frac{n'\sum(XY) - (\sum X)(\sum Y)}{\sqrt{[n_x\sum X^2 - (\sum X)^2][n_y\sum Y^2 - (\sum Y)^2]}} \tag{5.6}$$

The average of the product deviations is $\sum xy/n$, known as the *covariance*. Hence r is the ratio of covariance of a bivariate distribution to the product of the standard deviations of each variate (Formula 5.3). In the case of the data of Table 5.4, the correlation coefficient is found by Formula 5.6 to be .83. Thus the statistical measure of the relationship observed in the bivariate distribution of Table 5.5 is a value somewhat

---

*If s's had been computed with $\sqrt{n-1}$ as their divisors then the product deviations of the numerator would have $n'-1$ as their divisor.

less than 1.0 but substantially larger than zero. In view of the closeness of the relationship in Table 5.5, it may come somewhat as a surprise to find that *r* is "only .83." How high is .83? A common sense way to answer this question is to analyze the empirical bivariate distribution of Table 5.5.

Thus an analysis of the relationship between the variations in endomorphic somatotype *(E)* and viscerotonic temperament *(V)* shows the following: All four cases with most marked *V* (a value of 6 on the scale) have the same *E* (value of 5 on the scale): of the nine *V*'s above the mid-scale value of $V = 4$, five are above the mid-scale value of *E*, and the remaining four cases are at the *E* mid-scale value of 4. Of the 19 cases below the mid-scale value of *V*, and hence with little or no viscerotonic temperament, 17 are also below the mid-scale value of *E*.

This kind of descriptive analysis can also be made from the point of view of the variations in *V* as related to the scale values of *E*. Thus there are five cases *above* the mid-scale value of *E;* all five are also above the mid-scale value of *V*. There are nine cases *at* the mid-scale value of *E;* three of these are also at the mid-scale value of *V*, four are one scale interval above and two are one scale interval below the mid-value. And, finally, of the 22 cases below the mid-scale value of *E*, all but five are also below the mid-scale value of *V;* the five exceptions are at the mid-scale interval, and therefore but one scale unit removed.

The details of the preceding relationships are obscured in Fig. 5.3, where the regression lines of *x* on *y* and *y* on *x* have been fitted to the averages. The correlation of .83 is an overall index of these relationships. The best fitting straight lines describe this average relationship. Thus a value of 6 on the *E* scale is associated with a value of about 5.5 on the regression line of *V* on *E*, even though the one case has a *V* value of 5.0. From the point of view of descriptive statistics, the statistical reporter has a choice. He may describe his results in terms of the overall averages projected from the regression lines that fit his data with the minimum of error; or he may go to the correlation chart itself and give a common sense interpretation column by column or row by row, as was done above. From the point of view of sampling statistics, however, such a choice is rarely exercised. The straight line function is the average of the best fit, and the regression equations provide the best basis for the estimation of values of one variable from those of the other.

Meaning of *r* Values Between Zero and 1.00

An *r* of .83 does not signify a relationship that can be interpreted as 83/100 of perfection. The correlation coefficient is not an index of the percentage of a perfect relationship. It cannot be directly interpreted as measuring the *percentage* of association or of covariation. However, if the value of *r* is squared, a percentage or proportion can be used to give meaning to *r*.

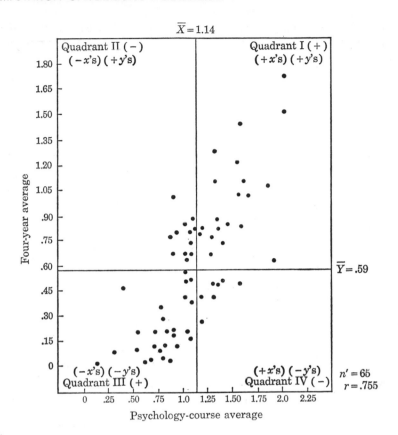

Fig. 5.4. A Scattergram: Bivariate Distribution of Students' Psychology-Course Grade Average with Their Four-Year Grade Averages
(Data from Table 5.9)

The Coefficient of Determination:

$$r^2 \tag{5.7}$$

The Coefficient of Nondetermination:

$$k^2 = 1 - r^2 \tag{5.8}$$

The square of r, r^2, gives the proportion of the variance of the one variable that is associated with the other variable. If the relationship being measured could logically be described as a direct causal one in the sense that x is a cause of y, or y a cause of x, then r^2 would literally be a coefficient of determination. It would measure the proportion of the variance of the one variate determined by the other. One may argue that temperament is a function of somatotype, in which case the square of .83 is .69; and hence 69% of the variance of the V temperament would be a function of E.

Ordinarily, in psychological measurement, causality cannot be logically assigned to either variate of a bivariate distribution. Oftentimes, however, the *co-relation* obtained between x and y is a function of (causally related to) the individual organism when it is common to each pair of measures. When causality cannot be logically assumed, the "coefficient of determination" is better interpreted as a *coefficient of association*. Thus, when r is .83, 69% of the variance of either V or E is associated with, or predictable from, measures of E or V. The difference, $1 - r^2$, symbolized by k^2, measures that proportion of the variance of one variate *not* accounted for by measures of the other variate of a bivariate distribution. Thus, for the data of Table 5.4, $1.0 - (.83)^2 = .31$; hence 31% of the variance of V (or of E) is not accounted for by the correlation of V with E.

Whether causality between two variates can be inferred or logically assumed in a given statistical problem, either directly or indirectly, depends entirely on information other than that of correlation itself.

Karl Pearson in the 3rd edition (1911) of his *Grammar of Science* inserted a new chapter (LV) entitled "Contingency and Correlation — the Insufficiency of Causation." He wrote:

Nothing in the universe repeats itself; we cannot classify by sameness, but only by likeness. Resemblance connotes variation, and variation marks limited not absolute contingency. How often when a new phenomenon has been observed, do we hear the question asked: What is the cause of it? A question which it may be absolutely impossible to answer, whereas the question: To what degree are other phenomena associated with it? may admit of easy solution and result in invaluable knowledge . . . [pp. 170–1].

Pearson goes on to advance a view of the universe, which sees all phenomena as correlated but not causally related. This is the probabilistic universe of many scientists. In this connection, Daniel Lerner writes:

Sir Charles Sherrington, reviewing the evolution of man's conceptions of himself, has shown the persistent anxiety among thoughtful men that Science should not reveal the world to be "a purely material product by Chance out of Chaos." That anxiety was not fully allayed until the development of statistics, over the past century, provided scientists with tools for observing and ordering the probabilistic universe—for clarifying the rationale that underlies events produced "by Chance out of Chaos." Nowadays, we deal efficiently with this universe, formerly so frightening even to trained minds, by randomizing Chaos and probabilizing Chance. Once an effective method for dealing with a universe codified by statistical rules was available, the idea of such a universe lost its terror. [Lerner, 1958, p. 12]

SCATTERGRAM AND CORRELATION CHART
METHOD OF COMPUTATION

When a bivariate distribution has a fairly large number of correlational frequencies and the measurable data are in fact continuous rather than discrete, a shorter method than that of Table 5.4 is usually employed,

Table 5.6. Correlation Chart for r

Subjects: Student graduates
x variable: Grades in psychology courses
y variable: Graduation grade average; all courses

Four-year average	\ Psychology grades .25	.50	.75	1.0	1.25	1.50	1.75	2.0	2.25	f	y'	fy'	fy'²	Σx'	Σx'y'
1.80									1	1	6	6	36	4	24
1.65									1	1	5	5	25	4	20
1.50							1			1	4	4	16	2	8
1.35						1	1			2	3	6	18	3	9
1.20					1	1	1			3	2	6	12	6	12
1.05			1		1	1				3	1	3	3	3	3
.90			2	6	4	1				13	0	0	0	4	0
.75		1	1	4	2					8	-1	-8	8	4	-4
.60	1			3	3	1				8	-2	-16	32	2	-4
.45			1	3	1					5	-3	-15	45	0	0
.30		1	4							9	-4	-36	144	-8	32
.15	1	1	5							11	-5	-55	275	-20	100
f	1	2	6	14	19	12	7	2	2	65		-100	614	4	200
x'	-4	-3	-2	-1	0	1	2	3	4						
fx'	-4	-6	-12	-14	0	12	14	6	8	4					
fx'²	16	18	24	14	0	12	28	18	32	162					
Σy'	-5	-7	-28	-44	-31	-6	9	1	11	-100					
Σy'x'	20	21	56	44	0	-6	18	3	44	200					

$$c_x = \frac{4}{65} = .0615$$

$$c_y = \frac{-100}{65} = -1.5385$$

COMPUTATIONS

$$r = \frac{\Sigma xy}{n'} \Big/ \sigma_x \sigma_y = \frac{\frac{\Sigma xy}{n'}}{S.D._x \cdot S.D._y}$$

$$r = \frac{\frac{\Sigma x'y'}{n'} - c_x c_y}{\sqrt{\frac{\Sigma x'^2}{n} - c_x^2}\;\sqrt{\frac{\Sigma y'^2}{n} - c_y^2}}$$

$$\frac{\Sigma x'y'}{n'} - c_x c_y = \frac{200}{65} - \left(\frac{4}{65}\right)\left(\frac{-100}{65}\right) = 3.0769 + .0946$$
$$= 3.1715$$

$$S.D._x' = \sqrt{\frac{\Sigma x'^2}{n} - c_x^2} = \sqrt{\frac{162}{65} - \left(\frac{4}{65}\right)^2} = 1.578$$

$$S.D._y' = \sqrt{\frac{\Sigma y'^2}{n} - c_y^2} = \sqrt{\frac{614}{65} - \left(\frac{-100}{65}\right)^2} = 2.661$$

$$r = \frac{3.1715}{1.578 \cdot 2.661} = .755$$

$$\bar{X} = 1.125 + .25\left(\frac{4}{65}\right) = 1.14$$

$$\bar{Y} = .825 + .15\left(\frac{-100}{65}\right) = .59$$

$$S.D._x = .25(1.578) = .3945$$

$$S.D._y = .15(2.661) = .3992$$

especially when machines are not available. It is the correlation chart method illustrated in Table 5.6.

On the other hand, if an electric calculator or an electronic computer is available, bivariate data are easily fed into the computer to give the five sums of Table 5.4, sufficient for the computation of r. One should ask, however, before the original bivariate data are fed directly into a machine, whether the assumption of linearity is satisfied. An examination of the scatter of a bivariate distribution can be readily made and should always be made, in the absence of a correlation chart, by means of a scattergram. A scattergram for the data of Table 5.6 is illustrated in Figure 5.4. Obviously, when a correlation chart is used in the computation of r, it is unnecessary to make a scattergram. As already suggested, the difference between the two is that the chart is laid off in class intervals for each variate so that the correlational frequencies are tallied into cells, whereas the scattergram substitutes points (or dots) for frequencies that are plotted against the continuous scales of each variate (rather than within class intervals).

The data of the bivariate distributions of Fig. 5.4 and Table 5.6 consist of grade indices for 65 female B.A. students who graduated as psychology majors. The scattergram of Fig. 5.3 shows three important facts about the bivariate distribution of these student's overall college average (the y variate) and their grade average in psychology courses (x variate):

1. There is a rather marked degree of correlation. The band of the scatter is fairly narrow and elliptical.
2. It is a positive correlation. Most of the cases are in the positive quadrants, marked off by the intersecting mean lines.
3. The relationship is sufficiently linear (by inspection) to warrant the use of Pearson's product-moment r to measure it. A bivariate distribution is usually judged to be linear when the scatter does not show a definite curvilinear trend.

It is to be noted that part of the correlation here is attributable to the presence in the overall four-year average of all the grades of the psychology course average. The latter grades amount to about 22% of the four-year average. The effect of this overlap will be determined in the next section.

The computations of Table 5.6 show r to be .755. The coefficient of determination, r^2, is therefore .57. Nearly three-fifths of the variance of the one variable is associated with or accounted for by the variance of the other variable. One can *see* the way this relationship works for an r of .755, by inspecting the chart in Table 5.6. If r^2 is .57, then $1.00 - r^2 =$ .43. This means that more than two-fifths of the variance of the one variate is not related to or accounted for by the other. The greatest concentration of correlational frequencies is, as expected, around the intersections of the mean lines, but there is a second area of marked concentration and that is in quadrant III. Thus, without exception, the nine students with a psychology index average below .75 have an overall index average between zero and the mean of .57 (C to B−). An inspection of quadrant I shows that all students with a general average of B or better (1.05 or more) have a psychology average of 1.25 (B+) to 2.00 (A). There are eight. An r of .755 is seen, therefore, to measure a fairly high degree of covariation: High values are associated with high values, low values with low, average values around the average.

The computation of r by the use of the correlation chart of Table 5.6 represents an adaptation of the short, coded method used for the mean and standard deviation in Table 4.4. Exactly the same procedures are used at the right of the correlation matrix, to obtain the sums for the mean and standard deviation of the y variate; and at the bottom of the chart, to obtain the sums for the mean and standard deviation of the x variate. Thus:

$$SD'^2_y = \frac{614}{65} - \left(\frac{-100}{65}\right)^2 = 9.4462 - 2.3654 = 7.0808 \qquad (5.9)$$

and $\qquad SD'_y = \sqrt{7.0808} = 2.661$ \hfill (5.10)

$$SD_y = i_y \cdot SD'_y = (.15)(2.661) = .3992 \qquad (5.11)$$

$$SD'^2_x = \frac{162}{65} - \left(\frac{4}{65}\right)^2 = 2.4323 - .0038 = 2.4885 \qquad (5.12)$$

and $\qquad SD'_x = \sqrt{2.4885} = 1.578$ \hfill (5.13)

$$SD_x = i_x \cdot SD'_x = (.25)(1.578) = .3945 \qquad (5.14)$$

The last column at the right and the last row at the bottom of Table 5.6 are the product deviations, $x'y'$, in unit interval values. The sum of the column should check with the sum of the row:

$$\frac{\Sigma x'y'}{n'} - \left(\frac{\Sigma x'}{n}\right)\left(\frac{\Sigma y'}{n}\right) = \frac{200}{65} - \left(\frac{4}{65}\right)\left(\frac{-100}{65}\right)$$

$$= 3.0769 + .0946 = 3.1715 \qquad (5.15)$$

and $\qquad \dfrac{\Sigma xy}{n'} = i_x i_y \dfrac{\Sigma x'y'}{n'} = (.25)(.15)(3.1715) = .118931$ \hfill (5.16)

Therefore $\qquad r = \dfrac{\dfrac{\Sigma xy}{n'}}{SD_x SD_y} = \dfrac{.118931}{(.3992)(.3945)} = \dfrac{.118931}{.157484} = .755$ \hfill (5.17)

Perhaps it has already been observed by the student that the computation of this ratio can be simplified by doing it in unit interval terms. The

$i_x i_y$ value in the numerator cancels out the i_x and i_y in the denominator. Therefore

$$r = \frac{\frac{\sum x'y'}{n'}}{SD'_x SD'_y} = \frac{3.1715}{(2.661)(1.578)} = .755 \qquad (5.18)$$

The product-deviation values of the last row and last column of Table 5.6 may be obtained in either one of two ways:

1. By multiplying the product-deviation value of each cell by the number of frequencies in the cell, then summing these products by rows to give the entries of the last column; and summing them by columns to give the entries of the bottom row, or

2. By getting the $\sum x'$ values for each row and entering them in the next to last column; then multiplying these successive $\sum x'$ values by the corresponding y' value of the row to give $y'(\sum x') = \sum x'y'$. And, similarly, by getting the $\sum y'$ values for each column and entering them in the next to last row; then multiplying these successive $\sum y'$ values by the corresponding x' value of the column to give $x'(\sum y') = \sum x'y'$.

Correction of Inflated r for Known Common Elements

It was indicated that part of the correlation of .755 obtained for the data of Table 5.6 represents an inflation in its value. Grades in psychology courses were correlated with grades in *all* courses (including psychology) over the four-year program leading to graduation. The correlation of the psychology grade averages with themselves, as part of the four-year average, is of course 1.00. The question therefore arises as to how much of the r of .755 is attributable to this "within correlation" of 1.00. The "how much" will be *estimated* and the value of r corrected accordingly. Then the r of Table 5.6 will be recomputed after the elimination of psychology course grades from the general four-year average.

When r is .755, the coefficient of determination, r^2, is .570. It will be recalled that this coefficient measures the proportion of the variance of x associated with y (or vice versa). If, then, 28 credits, on the average, of the 128 needed for graduation are in psychology courses, the proportionate part of psychology grades to the whole is $28/128 = .219$, or 21.9%. This value of .219 should represent the average extent to which the "within correlation" of 1.00 enters into the coefficient of determination of .570:

$$(.219)(.570) = .125$$

The value of the coefficient of determination is now corrected by the removal of that part whose value is known to be equal to 1.00:

$$.570 - .125 = .445$$

and the value of r thus corrected is the square root of .445, which is .667.

Table 5.7. Grades of Graduating Psychology Majors
(65 Women Who Received the A.B. Degree)

Code No.	Psych. Index	General Index*	Code No.	Psych. Index	General Index*
1	2.00	1.64	36	1.00	.37
2	2.00	1.37	37	1.29	.27
3	1.61	1.39	38	1.36	.25
4	1.32	1.27	39	1.56	.18
5	1.55	1.13	40	.42	.47
6	1.62	.94	41	1.33	.17
7	1.35	1.00	42	1.00	.26
8	1.84	.84	43	1.21	.20
9	.92	1.04	44	1.09	.17
10	1.63	.80	45	.77	.22
11	1.67	.79	46	.80	.15
12	1.12	.81	47	1.23	.00
13	1.31	.76	48	.93	.02
14	1.00	.82	49	1.00	—.01
15	1.47	.68	50	.57	.10
16	1.57	.62	51	.74	.05
17	1.13	.75	52	.87	.00
18	1.22	.71	53	.93	—.04
19	1.35	.66	54	1.06	—.09
20	1.06	.71	55	.81	—.05
21	.95	.73	56	.73	—.05
22	1.19	.65	57	.90	—.10
23	1.28	.61	58	.50	.00
24	.86	.73	59	.76	—.07
25	1.35	.57	60	.77	—.11
26	1.12	.63	61	.87	—.19
27	.94	.58	62	.62	—.16
28	1.09	.54	63	.16	—.04
29	1.28	.49	64	.61	—.17
30	1.00	.55	65	.26	—.07
31	1.00	.54			
32	1.90	.26			
33	1.03	.45			
34	1.06	.38			
35	1.00	.28			

*General Index does not include the grades received in psychology courses; each psychology index average has been given the same weight, viz., 28 credits.
Grade Scale: A = 2.0; B = 1.0; C = 0; D = —1.0; F = —2.0

Presented in Table 5.7 are the psychology grade averages and the overall four-year college averages minus the psychology course averages of each of the 67 graduating female psychology majors who received the Arts degree. The student may verify the correlation between these two variables as an exercise in the computation of r. He or she should find r to be approximately .667 (depending on whether the data are grouped into class intervals, or not grouped, etc., in the computation of r). The author's computations yield a value of .659 for the corrected r, obtained by the short-cut, correlation chart method of Table 5.6.

The preceding example illustrates the *role of common* elements or functions in the correlation of bivariates. Presumably any degree of correlation obtained in research is a mixture of the role of common elements (or psychological functions) and the contaminating effects of error, which are self-correlating and hence increase the value of r. The long search for the nature of the common elements or functions in people's performance on mental tests began early in this century with the publication by Charles Spearman (1904) of a paper entitled, "The Proof and Measurement of Association Between Two Things." Spearman's work has led to thousands of hours of research and speculation about the nature of man's abilities. The statistical methods used in this work are methods of correlational analysis known as *factor analysis*. The interested student is referred to J. P. Guilford's (1954) *Psychometric Methods* for an introduction to both the topic and the methods, or to Fruchter (1954).

Product–Moment *r* as the Average of $\sum(z_x z_y)$

It has already been pointed out that Pearson's r can be computed as equal to the average of the products of the pairs of z scores:

$$r = \frac{\dfrac{\sum(z_x z_y)}{n'}}{SD_{z_x}SD_{z_y}} = \frac{\sum z_x z_y}{n'} \qquad [5.2]$$

Since the product of the standard deviations of a bivariate distribution of z deviates is unity, the product of $SD_{z_x}SD_{z_y} = 1.0$ and hence need not be written in the z deviate formula for r.

This formula for r again emphasizes its meaning as a measure of concomitant variation. It also again emphasizes the *relativity* of product moment r. If a bivariate frequency has the same z deviate value on both x and y, and if such sameness within pairs is characteristic of all correlational frequencies of a bivariate distribution, the association is tantamount to perfect correlation. Subjects may take test A and then take it again a few days later. They do not have to make the same score in the second test as in the first in order for the correlation of their two performances to be perfect. It will be perfect if their respective performances remain the *same relative to* the mean and standard deviation of each variate. If their respective z deviates are the same, the value of r will be 1.0. This is illustrated in Table 5.8 with a bivariate distribution of only three correlational frequencies, where x_a represents the first testing and x_b the second.

Table 5.8. Pearson's r as the Average of z Deviate Products

Case	x_a	x_b	x_a	x_b	x_a^2	x_b^2	z_a	z_b	$z_a z_b$
1	6	8	1	1	1	1	$1/\sqrt{\tfrac{2}{3}}$	$1/\sqrt{\tfrac{2}{3}}$	$1/(\tfrac{2}{3})$
2	5	7	0	0	0	0	0	0	0
3	4	6	-1	-1	1	1	$-1/\sqrt{\tfrac{2}{3}}$	$-1/\sqrt{\tfrac{2}{3}}$	$1/(\tfrac{2}{3})$
$\Sigma = $	15	21	0	0	2	2	0	0	$2/(\tfrac{2}{3})$

$\overline{X}_a = 5 \quad \overline{X}_b = 7 \qquad SD_x = \sqrt{\tfrac{2}{3}}; \; SD_y = \sqrt{\tfrac{2}{3}}$

Thus

$$r = \frac{\Sigma(z_a z_b)}{n'} = \frac{2/(2/3)}{3} = 1.0$$

The variation is concomitant both as evidenced by inspection of the original bivariate distribution and by the measure of correlation. If the *relative* positions were maximally different, then r would be -1.0.

LINEAR REGRESSION AND PEARSON'S r

The relationship measured by r correlation is meaningfully expressed in terms of linear regression, i.e., in terms of that straight line function which fits the bivariate data with the errors of fit at a minimum. The regression lines of y on x and of x on y were illustrated in Fig. 5.3. One line represented the average variation of y with respect to successive values of $x;$ the other line, the average variation of x with respect to successive values of y.

Galton (1886) originated the symbol r for *reversion* and then later changed the word to *regression*. He noticed in his studies of the relation between heights of fathers and their adult sons that the heights of the sons tended to revert or regress toward the mean height of the fathers. In other words, the heights of the sons of tall fathers were on the average *less* and hence closer to the mean height; the heights of the sons of short fathers were on the average *more* and hence also closer to the mean height.

Only when the correlation between two variables is perfect, i.e., 1.00 or -1.00, is there no reversion or regression toward the mean. This is the case because when $r = 1.0$ or -1.0, the z deviate values of the x variable are the same as the z deviate values of the corresponding paired members of the y variate. And, as just indicated in Table 5.8, the average of the sum of the z score products is r, and when the z values within pairs are equal, $r = 1.0$.

Since r for the bivariate distributions of life situations is rarely if ever 1.0 because of the variability of life phenomena, there will always be some degree of regression toward the mean. When the correlation is zero, there is *complete* regression to the mean in that the average value of y for any particular value of x, however distant from x, is the mean of y. This is illustrated in Fig. 5.5.

When $r = $ zero, the scatter of the measures about the regression line is at a maximum. For the regression of y on x, the scatter is that of the y variates in each x score interval, and hence the variation is perpendicular

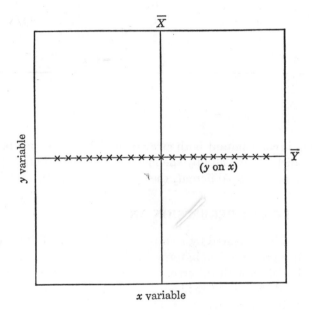

Fig. 5.5. Linearity of Zero Correlation; Slope of Zero
(Regression of y on x)

to the abscissa. The standard deviation of this scatter is called the *standard error of estimate*. When $r = $ zero, it is equal to the standard deviation of the y variable. On the other hand, when $r = 1.0$, there is no scatter or variation of measures about the regression lines, and therefore the standard error of estimate is zero.

Standard Error of Estimate, $s_{y \cdot x}$

The variance of measures about the line of linear regression can be computed from the squared deviations of the *differences* between the original Y measures and the predicted values of y, as they occur *on* the regression line, for successive values of x:

Variance of the Estimate of y on x:

$$s_{y \cdot x}{}^2 = \frac{\sum\limits^{n'} (Y - \tilde{Y})^2}{n' - 2} \tag{5.19}$$

where $\tilde{Y}$ is the predicted value of Y on the regression line associated with a particular X value. To obtain $s_{y \cdot x}{}^2$, $\tilde{Y}$ (read as Y tilde) may be computed for each X of the bivariate distributions, the differences from their corresponding Y values squared, and then averaged (with a loss of two *degrees of freedom*).* For large samples, this would require a large number of computations. Fortunately they are not necessary, since it can be shown that Formula 5.19 is equal to the following:

$$s_{y \cdot x}{}^2 = s_y{}^2 (1 - r^2) \frac{n' - 1}{n' - 2} \tag{5.20}$$

Hence the standard error of estimate is equal to

Standard Error of Estimate of y on x:

$$s_{y \cdot x} = s_y \sqrt{(1 - r^2) \cdot \frac{n' - 1}{n' - 2}} \tag{5.21}$$

Note that in large samples, since the fraction $(n' - 1)/(n' - 2)$ approaches unity, it can be ignored, and therefore

$$s_{y \cdot x} = s_y \sqrt{(1 - r^2)} \tag{5.21a}$$

Formula 5.21a, for large samples, is thus the standard deviation of the variation of measures of the y variate above and below the regression line of y on x. The usefulness of this measure in the estimation of y values from x values depends on the extent to which three conditions are satisfied:

1. Linearity of bivariate distribution.
2. Normality of bivariate distribution.
3. Homoscedasticity (equal variances) of scatter along each regression line.

Only the first condition is a prerequisite to the interpretation of Pearson's r as a measure of the correlation of a bivariate distribution of measurables. The other two conditions are supposed to be adequately satisfied when the standard error of estimate is employed to measure the *precision* with which

---

*In product-moment correlation the number of correlational frequencies that can vary freely is $n' - 2$. Two cannot vary because it requires two cases in order to fix two points for the best-fitting regression line, the mean and the slope. This restriction of two cases is aptly illustrated by the fact that $r = 1.00$, or -1.00, for any bivariate distribution of only two cases: No variation from the regression line is possible.

estimates of Y can be made from X values for varying degrees of correlation. The third assumption of equal variances along each regression line is illustrated in Fig. 5.6.

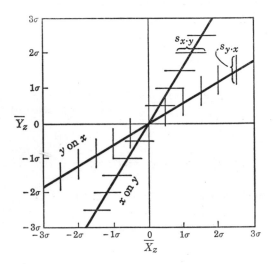

Fig. 5.6. Condition of Homoscedasticity
(Equal Variance Along the Regression Lines)

For the variations of x with respect to the y variable, the standard error of estimate of x on y is as follows:

Standard Error of Estimate of x on y:

$$s_{x \cdot y} = s_x \sqrt{(1 - r^2) \frac{n' - 1}{n' - 2}} \qquad (5.22)$$

As in Formula 5.21a, the fraction $(n' - 1)/(n' - 2)$ may be ignored when n' is large enough that the fraction is nearly 1.0.

Coefficient of Alienation (k):

$$k = \sqrt{1 - r^2} \qquad (5.23)$$

The expression $\sqrt{1 - r^2}$ is known as the coefficient of alienation and is symbolized by k. It measures noncorrelation in the way that r measures correlation. The square of k, k^2, is the coefficient of nondetermination, or nonassociation. As earlier indicated, $k^2 = 1 - r^2$ measures the proportion of the variance of the one variate *not* associated with or predictable from the variance of the other variate of a bivariate distribution. Hence the total variance of the y variable multiplied by k^2 measures nonassociation:

$$\text{Variance of nonassociation} = s_y{}^2(1 - r^2) \qquad (5.24)$$

This measures the proportion of the total variance of y that is *not* associated with x. Thus the square root of Formula 5.24, viz., $s_y\sqrt{1 - r^2}$, the standard error of estimate, measures the variation in correlation that scatters about the regression line independently of the relation of x and y.*

It has been emphasized that the relationship between two variates as described by correlation and regression is *relative* rather than absolute. Thus the heights of offspring could conceivably be several inches more, on the average, from the shortest to the tallest, than the heights of corresponding parents. In other words, the mean of each interval of the distribution of offsprings' heights could be several inches more than that of parental heights, and the value of r would be unaffected. Such a shift of one scale to higher values will not affect the z values of a variable as long as the value of the standard deviation is unaffected. The z deviate values are *relatives* in that they are taken relative to their respective means in units of s. From the point of view of the transformation of original measures to z deviate values, the phenomena of regression signifies that heights *regress* toward the mean heights; the means for both variables are z values of zero.

Linear Regression Equation

The linear regression equation is an equation of a straight line. For problems of prediction it may be set up in the following form:

$$\tilde{Y} = \bar{Y} + b_{yx}x \qquad (5.25)$$

where $\bar{Y}$ and b_{yx} are constants determining the line, x is a deviate value equal to $(X - \bar{X})$, and $\tilde{Y}$ is the regression estimate of Y, i.e., it is the value of Y on the regression line rather than the observed value of Y. Only when $r = 1.0$ or -1.0 will $\tilde{Y} = Y$. This is the case because, as already indicated, it is only under these circumstances that there is no scatter around the regression line and all correlational frequencies are *on* the regression line.

Since $x = (X - \bar{X})$, it will be generally more advantageous to *use* the regression equation in the following form:

$$\tilde{Y} = \bar{Y} + b_{yx}X - b_{yx}\bar{X} \qquad (5.26)$$

There are now visible three constants for any particular sample in a correlational problem, viz., the mean of the y variable, the mean of the x variable, and b_{yx}. This b *coefficient* is a measure of the *slope* of the regression line. As indicated in Fig. 5.6, the slope of the line for y on x is the tangent of angle a. The value of the tangent of angle a is the ratio of the side opposite that angle (viz., side y) to the side adjacent to the angle (viz., side x). Thus $\tan \sphericalangle a = y/x$.

---

*See Table G of Appendix for values of $(1 - r^2)$ and $\sqrt{1 - r^2}$ for values of r from .00 to 1.00 (p. 414).

Ordinarily in statistics the slope of a regression line is not determined by the trigonometry of the right triangle. Rather it is computed algebraically from the statistical data of the bivariate distribution. It may be calculated from data obtained in the computation of *r*.

Regression Coefficients

The coefficient *b* is a measure of the slope of the linear regression equation. Since there are the two regression lines, there are two regression coefficients. As in the case of the standard error of estimate, these coefficients can be computed from data obtained in the calculation of *r*. They are equal to the product of *r* and the ratio of the standard deviations:

Regression Coefficient of y on x:

$$b_{yx} = r_{yx} \frac{s_y}{s_x}, \quad \text{or} \quad r_{yx} \frac{SD_y}{SD_x} \tag{5.27}$$

Regression Coefficient of x on y:

$$b_{xy} = r_{xy} \frac{s_x}{s_y}, \quad \text{or} \quad r_{xy} \frac{SD_x}{SD_y} \tag{5.28}$$

When the original measures of a bivariate distribution have been transformed to *z* deviates, and consequently the two variables have equal standard deviations, the regression coefficients are equal to *r* and hence to each other:

$$b_{z_y z_x} = r_{yx} \tag{5.29}$$

$$b_{z_x z_y} = r_{xy} \tag{5.30}$$

Under these conditions, *r* measures the slope of the regression lines and is thus the tangent of the angle *a* in Fig. 5.6 for the regression of z_y on z_x, and is the tangent of the angle for the regression of z_x on z_y. Hence the regression equation of z_y on z_x simplifies to:

$$\tilde{z}_y = r_{yx} z_x \tag{5.31}$$

and that for z_x on z_y is:

$$\tilde{z}_x = r_{xy} z_y \tag{5.32}$$

A trigonometric way to determine the value of *r*, therefore, consists in (1) setting up equated scales (by *z* scores) for a bivariate distribution, as in Fig. 5.7; (2) plotting the average variation of z_y with respect to successive interval values of z_x; (3) drawing a straight line to these averages so that the errors of fit will be as small as possible; and (4) then determining the value of the tangent of angle *a*. As a check, the average variations of z_x with respect to z_y can also be plotted, the line fitted, and the tangent of angle *a'* determined.

It is to be noted that the order of the *x* and *y* subscripts for *r* may be either *xy* or *yx*; consequently, when the *r* referred to is clear by context, the subscripts are usually omitted. On the other hand, since $b_{yx} \neq b_{xy}$,

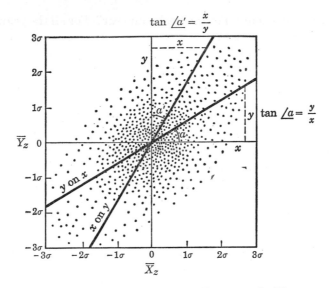

**Fig. 5.7. Slopes of the Regression Lines as the Tangents
of Their Respective Angles**

the order of the subscripts is essential to the identification of the regression
coefficients.

Finally, it may be noted that Pearson's r is the *geometric mean** of the
regression coefficients:

$$r = \sqrt{b_{yx}b_{xy}} \tag{5.33}$$

Since the product of their values in Formulas 5.27 and 5.28 is equal to r^2,
the square root of their product is r.

PREDICTION BY REGRESSION ESTIMATION

Many of the generalizations in psychometrics about the usefulness of
various measures are based on samplings of bivariate populations in which
psychological test scores are related to independent functional criteria.
Thus, test results are correlated with performance in the classroom. The
results of such correlations are in turn evaluated in terms of the precision
with which the criterion can be predicted from the test score. In other
words, the precision of a regression estimate of $\bar{Y}$ from a given value of X
brings out the predictive usefulness of test results.

An example of regression estimation is provided by an analysis of the
predictive value of college entrance examinations. How well do they pre-

---

*The geometric mean, $\bar{X}_G$, is the nth root of the product of n measures. When $n > 3$,
$\bar{X}_G$ is usually calculated most readily as equal to the antilogarithm of the mean (arithmetic) of the logarithms of the measures.

dict college achievement? For the freshman year? For all the years leading to the baccalaureate degree?

Prediction and Evaluation of College "Success"

Statistical analyses of correlation data are often handicapped by the fact that the correlations are attenuated (lowered) by the absence from the final bivariate samples of those cases (persons) who couldn't make the grade. The absence of the failures and drop-outs restricts the range of talent for the correlational analysis. Consequently these correlations usually underestimate rather than overstate the usefulness of the various predictors of "success," whether success be in terms of grades achieved during the freshman year or grades achieved over several college years.

An r of .67 Between Math Grades and "Success"

A correlation of .67 was obtained from data for 72 graduating seniors in Liberal Arts at CCNY. All had taken mathematics during their freshman year. The r of .67 was the correlation between their freshman-year mathematics grades and their general average at time of graduation. How well were their graduating averages predicted by their freshman-year math grades?

It has been indicated that there are two aspects to the estimation of $\tilde{Y}$ values from X values in the light of the regression of y on x. The first aspect is that of prediction by regression estimation, i.e., the prediction of $\tilde{Y}$ from different values of X. The second aspect is the evaluation of the precision of the estimate or prediction. Essentially these two aspects to the estimation of $\tilde{Y}$ from X consist of (1) *single value estimates* as predictions, and (2) *interval estimates*. The single value estimate is obtained with the regression equation. The interval estimate, which gives a measure of the precision of the single value estimate, is based on the standard error of the variations of Y on X.

Single Value Estimate of $\tilde{Y}$

The single value estimate of $\tilde{Y}$ corresponding to any value of X is based on Formula 5.26 for the regression equation:

$$\tilde{Y} = \overline{Y} + b_{yx}X - b_{yx}\overline{X} \qquad [5.26]$$

Since the value of b_{yx} is based on r and the standard deviations, and both means are also required, the complete set of statistics needed for the prediction of $\tilde{Y}$ from any value of X is as follows:

$$\overline{X} = 2.28 \text{ (C+)} \qquad\qquad \overline{Y} = 2.776 \text{ (B—)}$$

$$s_x = 1.11 \text{ (of a grade)} \qquad s_y = .42 \text{ (of a grade)}$$

$$n' = 72 \qquad r = .67$$

The grade scale used was as follows:

$$A = 4, \quad B = 3, \quad C = 2, \quad D = 1, \quad F = 0.$$

The regression equation is equal to:

$$\tilde{Y} = 2.776 + .67\,\frac{.42}{1.11}\,X - .67\,\frac{.42}{1.11}\,2.28$$

$$= 2.776 + .254X - .579$$

$$= 2.197 + .254X$$

Regression estimates of graduating averages will be made from freshman-year math grades of A, B, C, and D. Substituting in turn, $X_1 = 1.0$, $X_2 = 2.0$, $X_3 = 3.0$, and $X_4 = 4.0$:

When $X_1 = 1.0$ (D): $\tilde{Y} = 2.197 + .254\ (1.0) = 2.45$ (C+)

When $X_2 = 2.0$ (C): $\tilde{Y} = 2.197 + .254\ (2.0) = 2.71$ (B−)

When $X_3 = 3.0$ (B): $\tilde{Y} = 2.197 + .254\ (3.0) = 2.96$ (B)

When $X_4 = 4.0$ (A): $\tilde{Y} = 2.197 + .254\ (4.0) = 3.21$ (B+)

These regression estimates illustrate the fact of regression as Galton saw it: Freshman math A's revert or regress toward the general graduating mean of 2.78 (B−); freshman math D's also regress toward the mean of 2.78, as do the C's and the B's. Even so, however, the spread of the regression estimates is fairly broad, being a range of from C+ to B+. This is the case because of the r of .67. Had r been near zero, all these regression estimates would have converged on the mean of Y.

Standard Error of Estimate

The regression estimates of $\tilde{Y}$ are the best single estimates that can be made from the associated values of X. But each is subject to a considerable amount of sampling variation. This is the case because a correlation of .67 describes a bivariate distribution with a great deal of scatter around the regression line of y on x. The coefficient of nondetermination, $k^2 = (1 - r^2)$, indicates that 55% of the variance of y is not associated with the variance of x. The standard error of estimate is needed in order to emphasize the precision (or lack of it) with which graduating averages can be predicted from freshman math grades.

The standard error of estimate of y on x is as follows:

$$s_{y \cdot x} = .42\,\sqrt{(1 - .67^2)\,\frac{72 - 1}{72 - 2}} \qquad [5.21]$$

$$= .42\sqrt{(.55)(1.01)} = .42(.74) = .311$$

(Note that the term $(72 - 1)/(72 - 2)$ can be ignored, since its value is practically 1.00.) Thus,

$$s_{y \cdot x} = .311 \quad \text{(nearly } \tfrac{1}{3} \text{ of a grade)}$$

The standard error of estimate provides the basis for an *interval estimate* of $\bar{Y}$. It is based on the three conditions earlier mentioned, viz.:

1. Bivariate relationship is linear.
2. Bivariate distribution has a normal correlation surface.
3. Standard deviation of the scatter along the regression line of y on x (also of x on y) is equal throughout the various intervals of the regression line. (This is the condition of *homoscedasticity* [equal variances] of y along the regression line of y on x, as in Fig. 5.6.)

The first condition has been discussed. The second condition is satisfied if the two variables taken separately can be considered as normally distributed. Although the second and third conditions are not often satisfied in a literal sense, the question is whether the variations observed for a given bivariate distribution differ from the assumed conditions to no greater extent than reasonable by chance.

Emphasis is given to these conditions for two reasons. First, they are essential considerations to the precision of a regression estimate. Secondly, they emphasize a distinction often misunderstood, viz.: Pearson's r as a descriptive statistic is dependent on only the first condition (the linearity of the relationship); however, its use in regression estimation is based on the two additional conditions. It will be assumed that these conditions are sufficiently satisfied for the estimates that follow.

Precision of the Estimates of Success

The *interval* estimates of graduating averages for the four freshman-year math grades will be set up so as to cover approximately *95% of the expectancies*. Since the bivariate distribution is assumed to be normal, about 95% of the scatter of correlational frequencies along the regression line of y on x can be expected to be within the range of $\pm 2.0 s_{y \cdot x}$. The value is 2.0 because $\pm 2\sigma$ in normal variation (Table A in Appendix) includes the middle 95% of the frequencies.

Each interval estimate is therefore equal to the following, with $s_{y \cdot x} = .42\sqrt{1 - (.67)^2} = .311$:

For any value of X:

$$\hat{Y} = \bar{Y} \pm 2.0(s_{y \cdot x})$$

where $\hat{Y}$ is the interval estimate.

When $X_1 = 1.0$ (D), $\bar{Y}_1 = 2.45$:

$$\hat{Y}_1 = 2.45 \pm 2.0 (.311) = 1.83 \text{ (C}-\text{) and } 3.07 \text{ (B)}$$

When $X_2 = 2.0$ (C), $\bar{Y}_2 = 2.71$:

$\qquad \hat{Y}_2 = 2.71 \pm 2.0\ (.311) = 2.09$ (C) and 3.33 (B+)

When $X_3 = 3.0$ (B), $\bar{Y}_3 = 2.96$:

$\qquad \hat{Y}_3 = 2.96 \pm 2.0\ (.311) = 2.34$ (C+) and 3.58 (A——)

When $X_4 = 4.0$ (A), $\bar{Y}_4 = 3.21$:

$\qquad \hat{Y}_4 = 3.21 \pm 2.0\ (.311) = 2.59$ (B——) and 3.83 (A—)

These regression point estimates, $\bar{Y}$, and the interval estimates, $\hat{Y}$, taken equal to twice the standard error of estimate, should make more meaningful the predictive value of an r of .67. Furthermore, if the data for this group of 72 students could be legitimately used as an *inferential model* for current students, certain useful generalizations might be made. For approximately 95 of every 100 graduating Liberal Arts students:

1. Those earning D in freshman math would be expected to have graduating averages of between C— and B.
2. Those earning C in freshman math would be expected to have graduating averages of between C and B+.
3. Those earning B in freshman math would be expected to have graduating averages of between C+ and A——.
4. Those earning A in freshman math would be expected to have graduating averages of between B—— and A—.

Efficiency of Prediction as a Function of k

From the foregoing discussion, it is evident that the predictive implication of Pearson's r coefficient is closely related to the standard error of estimate, $s_{y \cdot x}$. As has been shown, this measures the scatter of correlational frequencies along the regression line of y on x. This scatter is at a maximum when $r = 0$; there is no scatter when $r = 1.0$. But in between these values, the efficiency of prediction varies only slightly from zero for low values of r; in fact, r needs to be .866 in order that the scatter around the regression line be reduced by 50% of the maximum scatter when r is zero. In other words, an r of .866 (rather than .50) has a predictive efficiency 50% better than a guess. This is the case because it takes an r of .866 to reduce $s_{y \cdot x}$ by 50% from its value when r is zero. Using z scores, and hence s's of 1.0,

When $r = $ zero:$\qquad s_{y \cdot x} = \sqrt{1 - r^2} = 1.0$

When $r + .866$:$\qquad s_{y \cdot x} = \sqrt{1 - r^2} = .50$

As indicated earlier, $\sqrt{1 - r^2}$ is known as the coefficient of alienation, k. Hence it should now be clear that the efficiency of regression estimates, i.e., the precision with which they can be made, is a function of k. From this fact, Clark Hull (1928) developed the following index of predictive efficiency and symbolized it as **E**.

Index of Predictive Efficiency:

$$\mathbf{E} = (1 - k)\,100\% = (1 - \sqrt{1 - r^2})\,100\% \qquad (5.34)$$

When r is .67, as in the foregoing example, $\mathbf{E} = 26\%$; in other words, such an r permits prediction of y from x (or vice versa) with an efficiency that amounts to 26% better than a guess.

Any value of k for r, and of **E** for k, can be readily obtained from Table G of the Appendix. The last two columns of values for r from zero to 1.00 are k values and **E** values.

SOME CONDITIONS THAT AFFECT THE MAGNITUDE OF *r*

The great contribution that Karl Pearson made to Galton's original measure of co-relation was to *generalize* r by equating the scales of both variables in terms of z deviates with means of zero and standard deviations of unity. The slope of best-fitting straight lines to such equated scales *is* the r coefficient:

When s's Are Equal: $\quad b_{yx} = r_{yx}\,\dfrac{s_y}{s_x} = r_{yx} \qquad (5.35)$

and $\qquad\qquad\qquad\quad b_{xy} = r_{xy}\,\dfrac{s_x}{s_y} = r_{xy} \qquad (5.36)$

Thus r coefficients equal in value signify the same degree of relationship for two or more bivariate distributions.

Pearson's r is not so *generalized*, however, as the foregoing seems to imply. This is the case because various conditions, external to or independent of its method of computation, definitely affect the value of r.

Sample Variability

Other things equal, the greater the variability of a group in the functions correlated, the larger the value of r. Thus the range or spread of intellectual abilities among a large public school population of fourth graders can be expected to be considerably greater than this range for a large college population. This is the case because of the operation of selective factors on the spread of abilities in school populations during the years between the fourth grade and college. Variability, however measured, progressively decreases. As the range of talent is constricted, the value of r is reduced. The r's are therefore not comparable. For fourth graders the r between measures of their intellectual abilities and their classroom grades may be as high as .75 or .80. For college populations such correlations may be only .40 or .50, not only because of the restricted range of ability but also because of other factors such as the changed nature of achievement at the college level.

Errors of Measurement

Since the measurables of psychology and the behavioral sciences are inexact approximations, the effect of errors of measurement on r is important to consider. They were systematically discussed by Charles Spearman (1904), who developed a method still used to "correct" r correlations for the attenuating effects of error:

Spearman's Correction for Attenuation:

$$r_c = \frac{r_{xy}}{\sqrt{r_{xx}r_{yy}}} \tag{5.37}$$

where r_c is the corrected value of r_{xy}, r_{xx} is a measure of the reliability of the x measures, and r_{yy} is a measure of the reliability of the y measures.

Various methods are employed to measure the reliability of measurables and hence obtain r reliability coefficients.

1. Test-retest, for which r_{xx} is the correlation obtained between two administrations of the same measuring instrument on the same sample of persons. Thus r_{xx} provides an index of the instrument's reliability.
2. Test results between alternative forms of a given measuring instrument, such as the two forms of the Stanford revision of the Binet test. The resulting coefficient may be symbolized as $r_{xx'}$, the prime indicating the alternative form of x.

Irrespective of the method used for the estimation of an instrument's reliability, its expression in terms of an r coefficient represents an attempt to gauge the *consistency* with which the instrument measures (differentiates) aspects of behavior or mental functioning.

If the correlation between two variables is .67, as in the earlier example, and the reliability coefficient of the x variable is an r_{xx} of .70 and that for y is an r_{yy} of .80, then the attenuating effect of measurement error on r can be judged from Spearman's formula (5.37) as follows:

$$r_c = \frac{.67}{\sqrt{(.70)(.80)}} = \frac{.67}{.75} = .89$$

Theoretically, therefore, the correlation between the two variables x and y would be expected to be about .90, were the measuring instruments free of attenuating error.

It is to be emphasized that such an "expected" r of .90 is purely theoretical. Correlations corrected for attenuation have no practical value inasmuch as they cannot be used in a regression equation in order thereby to "improve" an estimate of $\tilde{Y}$ from a given value of X.

Reliability coefficients, being r correlations, are themselves subject to the effects of restricted ranges of talent as well as restricted samplings of tasks. Hence their values also suffer from the conditions that limit the generality or comparability of r's.

Distorting Effects of a Third "Irrelevant Variant"; Partial Correlation

The quoted words are Charles Spearman's (1904). He noted that

A series of experiments was recently executed by one of our best known psychologists and ended—to his apparent satisfaction—in showing that some children's school-order was largely correlated with their height, weight, and strength. As, however, no steps had been taken to exclude the variations due to difference of age, the only reasonable conclusion seemed to be that as children grow older they both get bigger and go up in the school! Such explanation turned out in fact to probably be the true and sufficient one.

This *contaminating effect* of the age variable on the other variables was called *distortion* by Spearman. He presented the technique, now known as *partial correlation*, to rule out the effect of age heterogeneity on the correlation between other variables. The sampling units are, of course, persons. The method enables one to determine the correlation between measures of x and y variables, with the effect of age differences held constant. The effects of the latter variable are measured (not hypothesized) in terms of its correlations with x and y.

Thus, a correlation of .50 is reported between vocabulary test scores (the x variable) and arithmetic test scores (the y variable). The correlation between the subjects' ages (the a variable) and their vocabulary test results is .65; between their ages and their arithmetic test results, the correlation is .55. What would the correlation of r_{xy} be like if the effects on x and y of age differences were eliminated? The answer is .22, as follows:

Partial Correlation (Three Variables):

$$r_{xy \cdot a} = \frac{r_{xy} - r_{xa}r_{ya}}{\sqrt{1 - r_{xa}^2}\ \sqrt{1 - r_{ya}^2}}$$

$$= \frac{.50 - (.65)(.55)}{\sqrt{1 - (.65)^2}\ \sqrt{1 - (.55)^2}} = .22$$

(5.38)

where $r_{xy \cdot a}$ is read as the correlation between the x and y variables, with the effects of the a variable on x and y held constant.

Had the original x and y measurements been based on a sample fairly homogeneous in age (say, 13-year olds), r_{xy} would most likely have been much closer to the *corrected* value of .22 than to .50. If all were the same age, then the r_{xa} and r_{ya} correlations would be zero. It is only when there is some correlation between age and two other variables that the correlation of the latter is distorted. The distortion effects of the age factor are greatest during periods of growth and during maturation of intellectual functions. Thus the contaminating effects may not be so serious in adult samples as in samples of children.

MULTIPLE CORRELATION, *R*

The degree of the correlation of two or more combined variables with another variable is generally unpredictable. That is to say, correlations will not necessarily be changed, decreased, or increased by the addition of variables, as for example in a battery of psychological tests designed for the prediction of aspects of behavior. In some instances a single variable may be a better predictor of the behavior than would be a composite of several variables. The method for assessing the effectiveness of such composites is known as *multiple correlation, multiple regression,* or *multivariate correlational analysis.*

Multiple correlation is defined as the correlation between one variable (symbolized usually by a zero subscript) and the sum of two or more variables that are combined by weightings that will *maximize* the correlation. In effect, multiple *R* is a correlation coefficient that measures the relationship between *two* variables, one of which is unmodified and the other of which is a composite. Usually the variables that enter into the composite are called *independent, or predictor,* variables. They are symbolized by numerical subscripts (successive integers beginning with 1). The unmodified variable is usually known as the *dependent, or criterion,* variable.

Multiple correlation and regression are employed in psychology when the problem is one of predicting behavior in one situation (the criterion variable) from the information obtained about behavior in two or more other situations. Most commonly, perhaps, the methods of multivariate correlational analysis are employed to determine (1) the efficiency with which two or more sets of test results will predict performance in a particular setting, such as in the classroom or in a trade or occupation; and (2) the most efficient weights to assign each test variable in the composite. The statistics needed for such an analysis consist not only of the means and standard deviations of each variable but also of *all* the Pearson *r* intercorrelations between the variables. Since *r* is the correlation of a bivariate distribution, the number of such intercorrelations will be equal to the following:

Number of Intercorrelations for a Multivariate Analysis:

$$\tfrac{1}{2}k(k - 1) \tag{5.39}$$

where k signifies the number of variables (including the criterion variable).

There are three correlations to be calculated for a three-variable problem, for which $R_{0.12}$ is equal to the following:

Multiple R for a Three-Variable Problem:

$$R_{0.12} = \sqrt{\frac{r_{01}^2 + r_{02}^2 - 2r_{01}r_{02}r_{12}}{1 - r_{12}^2}} \qquad (5.40)$$

If the problem is to predict academic success in college from the information of a composite of high school graduating averages and an entrance or admission examination, the correlations between each of these variables for a suitable sample of a college population will be needed. Such correlations are frequently made, and the following values are taken as illustrative:

$r_{01} = .50$ (correlation between freshman-year college grade averages and high school graduating grade averages)

$r_{02} = .55$ (correlation between college grades and entrance examination results)

$r_{12} = .65$ (correlation between high school averages and entrance examination results)

With this information, multiple R can be calculated:

$$R_{0.12} = \sqrt{\frac{(.50)^2 + (.55)^2 - 2(.50)(.55)(.65)}{1 - (.65)^2}} = .58$$

The value of R is thus slightly larger than the value of the largest correlation between a single predictor variable and the criterion, viz., .55. The addition of high school graduating average to the entrance examination results increases the efficiency of prediction of college grades from an **E*** of 16.5% (when $r = .55$) to an **E** of 18.5%. This is not much of an increase in the efficiency of the prediction of college grades. Since high school graduating averages *alone* have a predictive efficiency of **E** = 13.4% when r is .50, the usefulness of entrance examinations has been questioned by an increasing number of college administrators. However, *more information*, not less, is needed to increase the value of **E**.

If the correlation between the predictor variables is *less than* .65, the value of R will be *increased*. If it is *more than* .65, the value of R will be *decreased*. For example, if r_{12} were .50 instead of .65, and the other two correlations were unchanged, $R_{0.12}$ would be .61; and if r_{12} were .80 instead of .65, $R_{0.12}$ would be .56. Thus the more independent the predictor variables are of each other (i.e., the lower their r's), the greater their

---

*E, the index of predictive efficiency (Formula 5.34), can be read directly from the next to last column of Table G of the Appendix.

combined effect as a single composite variable for the prediction of the criterion variable. This is based, of course, on the assumption that each predictor correlates *positively* with the criterion. It is as if a test variable were quantitatively and *qualitatively* enlarged by the addition of items or tasks that tend to correlate positively with the criterion but not with each other.

It may be apparent that the inclusion in a composite of one or more predictor variables that correlate *negatively* with a criterion may result in an R whose value is *less than* the highest r between a predictor and the criterion. Sizable negative correlations between predictor tests of abilities, achievements, or aptitudes and criteria presumably dependent on similar psychological functions occur only rarely, if at all.

The computation of R when there are more than two predictor variables is somewhat more complicated than when there are only two such variables. The interested student will find DuBois (1957) or Walker and Lev (1953) very helpful for the more advanced problems. Regardless, however, of the number of independent or predictor variables, R is a measure of Pearson correlation between a single unmodified variable and another variable that is a composite of all the independent or predictor variables. Each of the latter is weighted into the composite so that the predictive effectiveness of the *whole* will be at a maximum.

Multiple Regression

In order to predict a criterion measure from the composite variable of the predictor measures, a multiple regression equation is required. It is set up in z deviate units and regression coefficients known as *beta* (β) coefficients, as follows:

Equation of Multiple Regression:

$$\beta_1 z_1 + \beta_2 z_2 + \cdots + \beta_k z_k \tag{5.41}$$

For a three-variable problem of two predictors and one criterion, the equation is equal to:

$$\tilde{z}_0 = \frac{r_{01} - r_{02}r_{12}}{1 - r_{12}^2} z_1 + \frac{r_{02} - r_{01}r_{12}}{1 - r_{12}^2} z_2 \tag{5.42}$$

In the case of the data of the preceding example, the multiple regression works out as follows:

$$\tilde{z}_0 = \frac{.50 - (.55)(.65)}{1 - (.65)^2} z_1 + \frac{.55 - (.50)(.65)}{1 - (.65)^2} z_2$$

$$= .25 z_1 + .39 z_2$$

Note that values of $(1 - r^2)$ can be read directly from the sixth column of Table G of the Appendix.

Although the correlations between the two predictor variables and the criterion differ by only 10% (.55 is 10% larger than .50), the *beta* coefficient, .39, of the second predictor is 56% larger than the other *beta* coefficient of .25. However, it is the square of the coefficients that provides an index of the relative importance of each measure of a composite in the prediction of a criterion. Since their squared values are .1521 and .0625, respectively, the second predictor has 1.4 times the weight of the first predictor: $(.1521 - .0625)/.0625 = 1.4$.

Standard Error of Estimate of R

Except for the fact that R is always positive, it has most of the properties of a Pearson r. Thus the standard error of estimate of R is like that of r (Formula 5.21):

$$s_{0.12\cdots k} = s_0 \sqrt{1 - R_{0.12\cdots k} \frac{n' - 1}{n' - 2}} \qquad (5.43)$$

Table 5.9. Sex, Degree, and Grade Indices of 154 Graduating Psychology Majors

(Male = 1, Female = 0; Bachelor of Arts = 1, of Science = 2)

Serial No.	Sex	Degree	General Grade Index	Psychology Grade Index	Statistics-Experimental Grade Index
001	0	1	1.72	2.00	2.00
002	0	1	1.51	2.00	2.00
003	0	1	1.44	1.61	2.00
004	0	1	1.28	1.32	1.57
005	0	1	1.22	1.55	1.00
006	0	1	1.09	1.62	1.67
007	0	1	1.08	1.35	1.00
008	0	1	1.06	1.84	2.00
009	0	1	1.01	.92	1.00
010	0	1	.98	1.63	1.67
011	0	1	.98	1.67	2.00
012	0	1	.88	1.12	1.00
013	0	1	.88	1.31	1.00
014	0	1	.86	1.00	1.57
015	0	1	.85	1.47	.67
016	0	1	.83	1.57	1.57
017	0	1	.83	1.13	1.00
018	0	1	.82	1.22	1.00
019	0	1	.81	1.35	1.33
020	0	1	.79	1.06	.43

Table 5.9. Sex, Degree, and Grade Indices of 154 Graduating
Psychology Majors (Continued)
(Male = 1, Female = 0; Bachelor of Arts = 1, of Science = 2)

Serial No.	Sex	Degree	General Grade Index	Psychology Grade Index	Statistics- Experimental Grade Index
021	0	1	.78	.95	1.00
022	0	1	.77	1.19	1.00
023	0	1	.76	1.28	1.00
024	0	1	.76	.86	1.33
025	0	1	.74	1.35	1.43
026	0	1	.74	1.12	1.67
027	0	1	.66	.94	.67
028	0	1	.66	1.09	1.00
029	0	1	.66	1.28	1.00
030	0	1	.65	1.00	1.00
031	0	1	.64	1.00	1.00
032	0	1	.62	1.90	2.00
033	0	1	.58	1.03	.57
034	0	1	.53	1.06	.14
035	0	1	.53	1.41	1.57
036	0	1	.51	1.00	.33
037	0	1	.49	1.29	1.00
038	0	1	.49	1.36	1.33
039	0	1	.48	1.56	1.67
040	0	1	.46	.42	.57
041	0	1	.42	1.33	1.33
042	0	1	.42	1.00	1.00
043	0	1	.42	1.21	.67
044	0	1	.37	1.09	.67
045	0	1	.34	.77	.67
046	0	1	.29	.80	.67
047	0	1	.27	1.23	.67
048	0	1	.22	.93	1.00
049	0	1	.21	1.00	1.00
050	0	1	.20	.57	.57
051	0	1	.20	.74	.33
052	0	1	.19	.87	1.00
053	0	1	.17	.93	.14
054	0	1	.16	1.06	.43
055	0	1	.14	.81	1.00

Table 5.9. Sex, Degree, and Grade Indices of 154 Graduating Psychology Majors (*Continued*)

(Male = 1, Female = 0; Bachelor of Arts = 1, of Science = 2)

Serial No.	Sex	Degree	General Grade Index	Psychology Grade Index	Statistics-Experimental Grade Index
056	0	1	.12	.73	.57
057	0	1	.12	.90	.67
058	0	1	.11	.50	0
059	0	1	.11	.76	1.00
060	0	1	.08	.77	.57
061	0	1	.04	.87	.57
062	0	1	.01	.62	.57
063	0	1	0	.16	—1.31
064	0	1	0	.61	.43
065	0	1	0	.26	0
066	1	1	1.65	1.67	1.57
067	1	1	1.46	1.88	2.00
068	1	1	1.40	1.80	2.00
069	1	1	1.39	1.62	1.67
070	1	1	1.39	1.85	2.00
071	1	1	1.38	1.57	2.00
072	1	1	1.32	1.68	1.67
073	1	1	1.31	1.90	2.00
074	1	1	1.29	1.74	2.00
075	1	1	1.26	1.91	2.00
076	1	1	1.15	1.53	1.43
077	1	1	1.10	1.79	1.67
078	1	1	1.06	1.57	1.00
079	1	1	.97	1.50	1.67
080	1	1	.95	1.44	1.57
081	1	1	.94	1.68	1.33
082	1	1	.93	1.41	1.00
083	1	1	.91	1.16	1.00
084	1	1	.91	1.36	1.43
085	1	1	.91	1.09	1.00
086	1	1	.87	1.57	1.57
087	1	1	.84	1.26	1.14
088	1	1	.83	1.53	1.57
089	1	1	.79	1.10	1.67
090	1	1	.79	1.55	2.00

Table 5.9. Sex, Degree, and Grade Indices of 154 Graduating
Psychology Majors *(Continued)*
(Male = 1, Female = 0; Bachelor of Arts = 1, of Science = 2)

Serial No.	Sex	Degree	General Grade Index	Psychology Grade Index	Statistics- Experimental Grade Index
091	1	1	.75	1.35	1.67
092	1	1	.71	1.25	1.00
093	1	1	.70	1.07	.57
094	1	1	.69	1.34	1.57
095	1	1	.66	1.00	.67
096	1	1	.61	.56	−1.00
097	1	1	.58	1.07	1.00
098	1	1	.57	1.49	1.67
099	1	1	.57	1.12	0
100	1	1	.56	1.53	1.67
101	1	1	.52	.91	.67
102	1	1	.50	1.03	1.00
103	1	1	.45	.70	.67
104	1	1	.43	1.40	1.00
105	1	1	.42	1.50	1.67
106	1	1	.40	1.90	1.00
107	1	1	.38	.58	0
108	1	1	.21	.90	.57
109	1	1	.20	.90	.57
110	1	1	.13	.67	0
111	1	1	.12	.46	0
112	1	1	.07	.43	0
113	1	1	.04	.54	.14
114	1	1	0	.28	−1.00
115	0	2	1.66	2.00	2.00
116	0	2	1.30	1.62	2.00
117	0	2	1.15	1.40	1.00
118	0	2	1.00	1.61	1.67
119	0	2	.90	1.74	1.57
120	0	2	.65	1.47	1.43
121	0	2	.64	1.54	1.67
122	0	2	.15	.97	.86
123	1	2	1.68	1.90	2.00
124	1	2	1.52	1.83	2.00
125	1	2	1.47	1.72	1.57

**Table 5.9.   Sex, Degree, and Grade Indices of 154 Graduating
Psychology Majors**   (*Continued*)

(Male = 1, Female = 0; Bachelor of Arts = 1, of Science = 2)

Serial No.	Sex	Degree	General Grade Index	Psychology Grade Index	Statistics-Experimental Grade Index
126	1	2	1.41	1.91	2.00
127	1	2	1.24	1.38	1.00
128	1	2	1.22	1.66	2.00
129	1	2	1.10	1.60	1.00
130	1	2	1.02	1.54	1.00
131	1	2	1.01	1.76	2.00
132	1	2	.94	1.47	1.00
133	1	2	.75	1.38	1.00
134	1	2	.67	1.31	1.57
135	1	2	.57	1.10	1.00
136	1	2	.56	1.23	1.00
137	1	2	.51	1.57	2.00
138	1	2	.37	.71	.57
139	1	2	.34	1.69	2.00
140	1	2	.33	1.62	1.00
141	1	2	.27	1.17	.67
142	1	2	.25	1.73	2.00
143	1	2	.22	1.00	.67
144	1	2	.21	1.00	1.00
145	1	2	.21	.76	.43
146	1	2	.18	.26	.62
147	1	2	.13	.38	.33
148	1	2	.12	1.11	.67
149	1	2	.12	1.00	1.00
150	1	2	.10	1.57	2.00
151	1	2	.09	1.00	1.00
152	1	2	.04	.68	1.00
153	1	2	.04	−.31	−.71
154	1	2	.02	1.00	1.00

Scale for Grade Index: $F = -2.0$; $D = -1.0$; $C = 0$; $B = 1.0$; $A = 2.0$.

ADDITIONAL CORRELATION METHODS

Any one at all accustomed to original investigation must be aware how frequently phenomena will group themselves in such a manner as to convincingly suggest the existence of some law — when still more prolonged experiment reveals that the observed uniformity was due to pure hazard and has no tendency whatever to further repeat itself.

Charles Spearman

CORRELATION OF MEASURABLES WITH MEASURABLES

WHEN both variables of a bivariate are not continuously distributed, Pearson's r coefficient may nevertheless be computed for the several types of situations outlined in the preceding chapter. The methods will be described in this section. Each assumes linearity of the bivariate relationship.

Biserial Correlation, r_{bi}

When one of two measurables is dichotomized and the other is continuously distributed, biserial r may be calculated on the assumption that the dichotomized variable would be normal if it were distributed. As in the case of product moment r, no such assumption is made about the distributed variable.

Often-recurring situations for which biserial r is needed occur in the field of psychological test construction. In *item analysis*, for example, the differentiating usefulness of a test item may be determined by correlating persons' dichotomized responses of *correct* and *incorrect* with the distributed measures of an entire test result. In *validation analysis*, test results may be correlated with independently established criteria or ratings of success versus little or no success. This type of situation is illustrated by the data of Table 6.1. The usefulness of a clerical proficiency test is measured in terms of the extent to which its scores *predict* the criterion ratings of "no or some skill" and "skilled." To be useful, the correlation should be high enough to permit cut-off points such that persons scoring *above* the upper cut-off point on the test generally receive "skilled" ratings; those scoring below the lower cut-off point of the test generally receive ratings of "no skill" or only "some skill."

The clerical proficiency test consisted of 53 items of an information type designed to sample *know-how* in clerical work. In the sample of 133 stenographers, the test scores ranged from 15 to 52. As indicated by the computations at the bottom of Table 6.1, the biserial correlation is .72. As an *inferential model*, this sample result suggests that the proficiency test is useful: Persons scoring above 46 are likely to be "skilled"; persons scoring below 25 are likely to have little or no skill. Those with scores in between are unpredictable. This is essentially the usefulness of a correlation of .72 for a bivariate distribution when one of the variables is dichotomized.

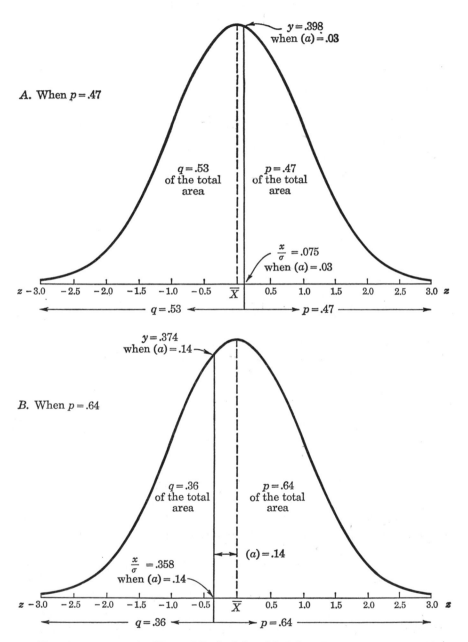

Fig. 6.1. Use of the Normal Probability Model in Biserial Correlation

Since the test variable of Table 6.1 is distributed over 19 class intervals, the correlation *chart* for the crosstabulation of the bivariate data is a 2 by 19 chart (columns 2 and 3). The marginal totals by rows (column 4) yield the frequency distribution of the distributed variable. The sums of columns 2 and 3 are the frequencies of the dichotomy.

Dunlap's (1936) simplified version of the formula for biserial r is as follows:

Biserial r, r_{bi}: $$r_{bi} = \left(\frac{(\overline{Y}_h - \overline{Y})}{SD_y}\right)\left(\frac{p_h}{y'}\right) \tag{6.1}$$

where $\overline{Y}$ is the mean of the distributed measures of the y variable, $\overline{Y}_h$ is the mean of those cases crosstabulated with the higher (skilled) group (column 2), SD_y is the standard deviation of the y variable, p_h is the proportion of cases in the higher group, and y' is the value of the ordinate of the normal distribution at the point of dichotomy of the x variable. This point is located from the p_h value taken in relation to the area values of Table A of the Appendix. Since for the data of Table 6.1, $p_h = .47$, the point of dichotomy is located *above* the mean of the normal distribution. This is illustrated in Fig. 6.1. The value of y' at this point is found to be .398 in Table A.

The mean and standard deviations of the y variable are calculated in Table 6.1 by the simplified, coded method (columns 5, 6, and 7). The mean of that part of the y variable associated with the higher group of the x variable is computed in the last two columns of Table 6.1. (See Fig. 6.1.)

The magnitude of biserial r derives from the slope of a straight line whose value is determined from two points, the mean of y with respect to x and the mean of y_h with respect to x. The greater the difference between these two means, the greater the slope and consequently the higher the value of r_{bi}. If the mean of y for the higher part of x is *less* than the mean of y, then the correlation is negative.

Triserial Correlation, r_{tri}

Validation criteria are often trichotomized rather than dichotomized. If the other variable is distributed, then its correlation with the trichotomized measurable can be obtained by means of triserial r (Jaspen, 1946):

Triserial r: $$r_{tri} = \frac{y'_h \overline{Y}_h + (y'_c - y'_h)\overline{Y}_c - y'_c \overline{Y}_l}{SD_y\left[\frac{y'^2_h}{p_h} + \frac{(y'_c - y'_h)^2}{p_c} + \frac{y'^2_c}{p_l}\right]} \tag{6.2}$$

where the symbols are as in Formula 6.1, plus the additional subscripts c and l; $\overline{Y}_c$ being the mean of those cases of the y variable crosstabulated with

Table 6.1. Biserial Correlation of Clerical Proficiency Test Results with Criterion Ratings

Test Scores	Criterion Ratings Some Skill and No Skill	Skilled	Total Group	t'	$f_t t'$	ft'^2	h'	$f_h h'$
	f_l	f_h	f_t					
(1)	(2)	(3)	(4)	(5)	(6)	(7)	(8)	(9)
51–52	0	1	1	9	9	81	6	6
49–50	1	5	6	8	48	384	5	25
47–48	0	7	7	7	49	343	4	28
45–46	3	8	11	6	66	396	3	24
43–44	2	4	6	5	30	150	2	8
41–42	2	8	10	4	40	160	1	8
39–40	1	9	10	3	30	90	0	0
37–38	6	7	13	2	26	52	−1	−7
35–36	7	2	9	1	9	9	−2	−4
33–34	6	3	9	0	0	0	−3	−9
31–32	4	2	6	−1	−6	6	−4	−8
29–30	8	4	12	−2	−24	48	−5	−20
27–28	6	1	7	−3	−21	63	−6	−6
25–26	9	2	11	−4	−44	176	−7	−14
23–24	3		3	−5	−15	75		
21–22	1		1	−6	−6	36		
19–20	6		6	−7	−42	294		
17–18	4		4	−8	−32	256		
15–16	1		1	−9	−9	81		
	$n_l = 70$	$n_h = 63$	$n_t = 133$		307	2700		99
					−199			−68
					$\Sigma = 108$			31

$$\overline{Y} = 33.5 + 2(108/133) = 35.12$$

$$SD_y = 2\sqrt{2700/133 - (108/133)^2} = 8.86$$

$$\overline{Y}_h = 39.5 + 2(31/63) = 40.48$$

$$p_h = 63/133 = .474$$

$$y' = .398 \text{ (from Table A, when area from mean} = .03)$$

$$r_{bi} = \left(\frac{40.48 - 35.12}{8.86}\right)\left(\frac{.474}{.398}\right) = (.605)(1.191) = .72$$

SOURCE: Courtesy E. E. Cureton.

the *central* (or middle) class of the trichotomized x variable, and $\overline{Y}_l$ being the mean of those cases in the *lowest* class of x.

Jaspen also gives formulas for quadriserial r, quintiserial r, and generalizes for any number of classes. With five or six classes, however, Pearson's product moment r should give a satisfactory measure of correlation *when* the relationship is linear.

Jenkins (1956) has developed a simplified version of Formula 6.2. It can be used when the n's of the high and low groups of the trichotomized x variable are *approximately equal* (i.e., do not differ in their proportionate values by more than 0.10):

$$r_{tri}, \text{ when } n_h \cong n_l: \quad r_{tri} = \frac{\overline{Y}_h - \overline{Y}_l}{sD_y} \cdot \frac{\dfrac{p_h + p_l}{2}}{2y'_{h \text{ and } l}} \tag{6.3}$$

where the symbols are as in Formula 6.2 and the ordinate value of y' is located at a point beyond which the *average area* of p_h and p_l is subtended, that is, the area beyond p_h is averaged with the area below p_l and the ordinate of y' is a value from Table A that will subtend the average amount of the two areas.

Tetrachoric Correlation, r_t

When *both* sets of measurables of a bivariate distribution are dichotomized, their r correlation can be obtained by a method developed by Karl Pearson (1901) and known as *tetrachoric* (four-celled) *correlation*. The method is based on the assumptions that both measurables if continuously distributed would be normal and the relationship would be linear. However, the coefficient is somewhat laborious to compute, and r_t is thus ordinarily used only when computing diagrams or when tables are available, such as the diagrams by Cheshire, Saffir, and Thurstone (1933), or the table by Davidoff-Goheen (1953). The latter is available in Table D of the Appendix, p. 404.

Perhaps the most likely situation to arise for an extensive need of tetrachoric r's is in the correlational analysis of many variables. Such analysis requires all the correlations between *all* variables, taken two at a time. If, for example, a battery of ten test variables to predict a criterion variable is being developed, the number of *intercorrelations* is equal to $\frac{1}{2}k(k-1) = 5.5(10) = 55$. If the use of punch cards and the IBM type of machine computers is not feasible, the 55 intercorrelations can be fairly quickly obtained by dichotomizing the variables at their means (or medians), *crosstabulating* each set of bivariate data into a 2 by 2 correlation chart (55 in all), and then estimating r with the aid of the Davidoff-Goheen table (Table D).

This has been done in Table 6.2 for the data of Table 6.1, with the continuous variable dichotomized at the mean. The ratio of the products of the *frequencies* of cells bc to ad is first computed from the results of the bivariate distribution in the chart.

Ratio for r_t (Table D): $\qquad \dfrac{bc}{ad} \qquad$ (when $bc > ad$) $\hfill$ (6.4)

or $\qquad\qquad\qquad \dfrac{1}{(bc)/(ad)} \qquad$ (when $ad > bc$) $\hfill$ (6.5)

For the data of Table 6.2, the product of the frequencies in cells $bc =$ $(52)(50) = 2600$; and the product of the frequencies in cells $ad =$ $(18)(13) = 234$. Therefore

$$\frac{bc}{ad} = \frac{2600}{234} = 11.1$$

Table D of the Appendix is entered with this ratio value of 11.1; r_t is .75. Reference to the computing diagrams of Cheshire, Saffir and Thurstone also gives a value of .75 for r_t.

The Davidoff-Goheen table is developed from Pearson's cosine approximation method for tetrachoric correlation:

Pearson's Cosine Method for Tetrachoric Correlation:

$$r_t = \cos\left(\frac{180°}{1 + \sqrt{\dfrac{bc}{ad}}}\right) \hfill (6.6)$$

Table 6.2. Tetrachoric Correlation of Data of Table 6.1

		CRITERION RATINGS			
		Little or No Skill	Skilled		
TEST SCORES ($\overline{Y} = 35.12$)	*Above the Mean:*	a 18	b 50	68	(.51)
	Below the Mean:	c 52	d 13	65	(.49)
		70 (.52)	63 (.48)	133	

$$\frac{bc}{ad} = \frac{2600}{234} = 11.1$$

The value of r_t from the Davidoff-Goheen table (Appendix, Table D) is .75.

where a, b, c, and d are the frequencies of the corresponding cells. The cosine of an angle is the horizontal side of a right-angled triangle divided by its hypotenuse. When there are no frequencies in cells a and d, the correlation is seen to be perfect. By Formula 6.6 it is 1.0, since the cosine of a zero angle is 1.0. (When $ad = 0$, the value of $\sqrt{(bc)(ad)}$ approaches an infinitely large magnitude, and hence $r_t = \cos 0° = 1.0$). Where $ad = bc$, there is no correlation, and $r_t = 0$; i.e., ($\sqrt{ab/cd} = 1.0$ and $r_t = \cos 90° = 0$, since the cosine of a 90° angle is zero).

For the data of Table 6.2,

$$r_t = \cos \frac{180°}{1 + \sqrt{11.1}} = \cos 41.6° = .75$$

Reference to a trigonometric table will show the cosine of a 41.6° angle to be .75.

Correlation of Bivariates Not Linearly Associated (*Eta* Correlation)

When the condition of a linear relationship is not sufficiently satisfied to warrant the use of Pearson's r, then the degree of correlation can be measured in terms of the *eta* coefficient, η. In fact *eta* is useful to measure the correlation not only between two measurables (only one of which needs to be fully distributed) but also between an unordered countable and a distributed measurable.

A problem of the first kind would be analogous to serial correlation except that no assumption of the linearity of relationship need be made, nor is it necessary to assume that the variable with only a few classes would be normal if distributed.

An example with fictional data is given in Table 6.3. *Eta* is based on the ratio of two different sums of squared deviations:

Eta Correlation: $$\eta = \sqrt{\frac{\sum y_a^2}{\sum y_t^2}}$$ (6.7)

These two sums of squared deviations can be calculated directly from the various means, or the short method of computation may be used. The latter method is employed in Table 6.3. The sum of the squared deviations for the total group is equal to the following:

Sum of Squared Deviations from Mean of All Measures:

$$\sum y_t^2 = \sum Y_1^2 + Y_2^2 + \cdots + Y_n^2 - \frac{(\sum Y)^2}{n}$$ (6.8)

$$\sum y_t^2 = \overset{n}{\sum} (Y^2) - \frac{(\sum Y)^2}{n}$$ (6.9)

where the subscripts 1 through n refer to the individual measures of the y variable. This is the same as Formula 4.9 for the sum of squares.

The sum of the squared deviations among means is as follows:

$$\Sigma y_a{}^2 = \frac{(\Sigma Y_l)^2}{n_l} + \frac{(\Sigma Y_c)^2}{n_c} + \frac{(\Sigma Y_h)^2}{n_h} - \frac{(\Sigma Y)^2}{n} \qquad (6.10)$$

where the subscripts identify the sum of the measures of the y variable in the lowest, central or middle, and highest groups.

As indicated at the bottom of Table 6.3, these sums of squared deviations

Table 6.3.   Computation of *Eta* Correlation
(By Method of Sums of Squared Deviations)*

Measures Y	Validity Criteria Low	Validity Criteria Average	Validity Criteria High	Total f	fY	$f(Y^2)$
7	–	–	4	4	28	196
6	–	5	3	8	48	288
5	1	5	2	8	40	200
4	1	–	–	1	4	16
3	4	–	–	4	12	36
2	4	–	–	4	8	16
1	1	–	–	1	1	1
	$n_l = 11$	$n_c = 10$	$n_h = 9$	$n' = 30$	141	753

$$\Sigma Y_l = 30 \quad \Sigma Y_c = 55 \quad \Sigma Y_h = 56 \qquad\qquad (\Sigma Y) \quad (\Sigma Y^2)$$

$$\overline{Y}_l = 2.7 \qquad \overline{Y}_c = 5.5 \qquad \overline{Y}_h = 6.2$$

$$\Sigma y_t{}^2 = [5^2 + 4^2 + 4(3^2) + 4(2^2) + 1 + 5(6^2) + 5(5^2) + 4(7^2) + 3(6^2) + 2(5^2)]$$
$$- \frac{(141)^2}{30}$$

$$= 753 - 662.7 = 90.3$$

$$\Sigma y_a{}^2 = \left[\frac{(30)^2}{11} + \frac{(55)^2}{10} + \frac{(56)^2}{9}\right] - \frac{(141)^2}{30} = 732.7 - 662.7 = 70.0$$

$$\eta = \sqrt{\frac{\Sigma y_a{}^2}{\Sigma y_t{}^2}} = \sqrt{\frac{70.0}{90.3}} = \sqrt{.78} = .88$$

*Note that the body of this table consists of the frequencies of the crosstabulations between the measures and the trichotomy. Each *measure* is squared. Thus the first squared measure is 5, which has one frequency, being the first of the "Low" column. The third measure squared has a value of 3; its square is multiplied by 4, since it occurs four times; etc. The sum of the squares of each Y measure is most easily obtained in the last column.

are 90.3 and 70.0, respectively. The value of the *eta* coefficient is therefore:

$$\eta = \sqrt{\frac{70.0}{90.3}} = \sqrt{.78} = .88$$

Since this *eta* coefficient is not a Pearson's r, it is somewhat difficult to interpret. That the correlation is fairly high for predictive purposes is indicated by a study of the crosstabulated data of Table 6.3. However, it is to be noted that the differentiation is mainly between the low members of the criterion group and the remainder. That is to say, only one member of the low group scores as high as members in the average and high groups. The mean difference between the measures of the low and average groups is nearly as large as the mean difference between the measures of the low and high groups.

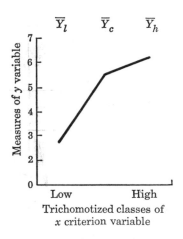

Fig. 6.2. Nonlinear Correlation of Trichotomized Criterion with a Continuously Distributed Measurable

The nonlinearity of the data is graphically illustrated in Fig. 6.2 (made on the assumption of equally spaced intervals on variable x). Although the $\overline{Y}$ average of each class of the trichotomy is based on about the same number of cases, the samples are small, and consequently the nonlinearity characteristic of the result may not hold for the population sampled. The possible significance of mean differences of this kind and a test for linearity of a bivariate distribution are evaluated in Chapter 11 by the technique of sampling-inferential statistics known as *analysis of variance* (see p. 342).

CORRELATION OF COUNTABLES WITH COUNTABLES (UNORDERED)

The correlation of unordered countables involves dichotomous variables such as sex, categorial classifications such as different college degrees, or hybrid classifications that sometime occur in attitude studies or in opinion polls such as "like, dislike, and indifferent," or "yes, no, and don't-knows." These are not orderable inasmuch as there are no properties inherent in their characteristics such that one category is first and another second, etc. Male-female can be just as well crosstabulated female-male with another variable. Arts degree, science degree, engineering degree, etc., comprise characteristics that have no inherent order of arrangement. The three categories of yes, no, and don't-know are not orderable; they can be meaningfully stated in any order. The categories of like, dislike, and indifferent are sometimes treated as if they could be ordered from like through indifferent to dislike, or vice versa. But this is really a hybrid classification of two variables, with one variable consisting of the dichotomy, "having or *not* having an attitude." The other variable for those having an attitude is also dichotomized: attitudes of *like* and of *dislike*.

Two methods are used to measure the correlation of unordered countables. Both are related to a very important statistic, viz., *chi-square*. The first method is for 2 by 2 crosstabulations and yields the *phi* coefficient, ϕ. The second may be used for all other crosstabulations of unordered countables (2 by 3, 3 by 3, etc.) and yields the contingency coefficient C. Neither of these coefficients is directly comparable with r correlation unless their values are at or near zero. They do not have genuine negative values, since there is no *order* or direction of differences characteristic of either of the crosstabulated variables.

Phi Coefficient, ϕ

This coefficient is based on the ratio of the difference between the products of the frequencies in the diagonal cells of the 2 by 2 crosstabulation to the square root of the products of the marginal frequencies of the columns and rows.

The ϕ Coefficient,

When bc > ad:

$$\phi = \frac{bc - ad}{\sqrt{(a + b)(c + d)(a + c)(b + d)}} \tag{6.11}$$

When bc < ad:

$$\phi = \frac{ad - bc}{\sqrt{(a + b)(c + d)(a + c)(b + d)}} \tag{6.12}$$

This method can be used to measure the correlation of the 2 by 2 crosstabulation of the data of Table 5.1, where sex was one attribute of the bivariate and attitude toward baseball was the other. The correlation is found to be .60 as follows:

$$\phi = \frac{(40)(40) - (10)(10)}{\sqrt{(50)(50)(50)(50)}} = \frac{1500}{2500} = .60$$

About the best way to give meaning to a ϕ coefficient of .60 is to go back to the bivariate distribution of the 2 by 2 correlation chart and verbalize the eight correlative propositions as was done on pp. 84–85. The usefulness of having a correlation value is mainly for comparative purposes with other ϕ coefficients but not with r's (unless the coefficients are near zero).

The relation of ϕ to chi-square, symbolized as χ^2, is as follows:

ϕ and χ^2:
$$\phi = \sqrt{\frac{\chi^2}{n'}} \qquad (6.13)$$

and

$$\chi^2 = n'\phi^2 \qquad (6.14)$$

where n' is the number of paired observations crosstabulated in the bivariate 2 by 2 distribution.

Contingency Coefficient, C

When the bivariate distribution of unordered countables is other than a 2 by 2 relationship, the contingency coefficient is used to measure the magnitude of possible correlation.

The Contingency Coefficient:
$$C = \sqrt{\frac{\chi^2}{\chi^2 + n'}} \qquad (6.15)$$

Although this measure can be used for a 2 by 2 crosstabulation, and although both C and ϕ are related to χ^2, they are not equivalent measures of a 2 by 2 bivariate distribution (as a comparison of Formulas 6.13 and 6.15 will show). For 2 by 2 distributions, ϕ is preferred because it does not suffer as C does for higher values of correlation. The maximum possible value that C can take is equal to the following, when the number of row categories is equal to the number of column categories:

Maximum Value of C: $$C_{\max} = \sqrt{\frac{k-1}{k}} \qquad (6.16)$$

where k signifies the number of categories per row (or column). Therefore, for a 2 by 2 bivariate distribution,

$$C_{\max} = \sqrt{\tfrac{1}{2}} = 0.71$$

The ϕ coefficient is not thus handicapped *if* the marginal frequencies for each dichotomy are equal (as in Table 5.1 where they are 50 and 50): the maximum value ϕ can take is 1.0. However, as the marginal frequencies of *either* dichotomized variable become increasingly unequal, the maximum value for ϕ will be increasingly less than 1.0. Had ϕ been used with the data of Table 6.2, the correlation would have been only .54 instead of the r_t of .75.

Correlation of a 3 by 3 Bivariate (Unordered Countables)

The fictional data of Table 6.4 represent a 3 by 3 bivariate distribution of two unordered countables. There is apparently some correlation between war experience and personality status. It can be stated perhaps more meaningfully by a verbalization of the correlative relationships observable in the table than by a C coefficient. In fact the former is needed to give meaning to the value of C. *Normals* are mostly those of the group not in a battle area during the war. *Neurotics* are mostly those who fought in a battle area but were not taken prisoner. *Psychotics* are mostly those who fought in a battle area and were also prisoners of war.

The Computation of Chi-square, χ^2

Chi-square as a measure of contingency between two variates consists essentially in a comparison of the obtained crosstabulated distribution with what the bivariate distribution would be, cell by cell, if there were absolutely no contingency; in other words, zero correlation. In order to calculate what such a theoretical crosstabulation would be like for a given set of information, as in Table 6.4, it will be necessary to anticipate a probability theorem of the next chapter.

Table 6.4.   Crosstabulation of Personality Status with War Experience

WAR EXPERIENCE OF A GROUP OF WAR VETERANS	PERSONALITY STATUS			n_r
	Psychotic	Neurotic	Normal	f_r
Fought in war area but not taken prisoner:	a 5	b 20	c 5	30
Not in battle area and not taken prisoner:	d 5	e 5	f 20	30
A prisoner of war:	g 20	h 5	i 5	30
$n_c = f_c =$	30	30	30	$N' = 90$

If the fictional group of 90 war veterans of Table 6.4 were treated as a miniature population, and if a small sample of persons were drawn from it by means of a randomizing process and then replaced, and if this process of sampling randomly and by replacement were repeated indefinitely, it may be apparent that the long-run odds of *psychotics*, for example, showing up in these randomized samples would be 30 in 90:

$$\text{Odds for psychotics in randomized samples} = \frac{30}{90} = \frac{1}{3}$$

And, by the same randomizing process, the odds of getting P.W.'s would also be 30 in 90:

$$\text{Odds for prisoners of war in randomized samples} = \frac{30}{90} = \frac{1}{3}$$

Question: What are the odds in such randomized sampling of drawing persons who are *both* psychotic and P.W.'s? In other words, what are the odds for the joint occurrence of the two attributes showing up in the same persons in the repeated samples? The answer to this question is provided by *the product theorem of probability.* It states, in effect, that in randomized, indefinitely prolonged sampling by replacement, the odds for the joint occurrence of independent (noncorrelated) events are equal to the product of the odds for each. Hence,

$$\text{Odds for psychotics who were P.W.'s} = \tfrac{1}{3} \cdot \tfrac{1}{3} = \tfrac{1}{9}$$

The number of frequencies to be expected in cell a when there is absolutely no contingency (zero correlation) between the two variates is therefore:

$$\text{Expected } \mathbf{F}_a = \tfrac{1}{9}(N') = \tfrac{1}{9}(90) = 10$$

Since cell a has only five frequencies, there are five fewer frequencies in this cell than *on the average* would be expected if the two variates were not correlated, i.e., if the two attributes were absolutely independent of each other.

To summarize this *estimation of expectancies* and generalize it for the determination of the number of frequencies for any cell when the correlation is assumed to be zero, the symbols $\mathbf{F}$ and k will be used:

Hypothesized Frequencies for No Contingency:

$$\mathbf{F}_k = \frac{n_r}{N'} \cdot \frac{n_c}{N'} \cdot N' = \frac{n_r n_c}{N'} \tag{6.17}$$

where $\mathbf{F}_k$ represents the expected frequencies for any cell; n_r is the number of frequencies for the row of the kth cell; n_c is the number of frequencies for the column of the kth cell; and N' is the total number of correlational frequencies. Thus, for cell b,

$$\mathbf{F}_b = \frac{(30)(30)}{90} = 10$$

It may be noticed (without this computation of $\mathbf{F}_b$) that when the correlation is hypothesized as zero, the expected number of frequencies for each of the nine cells of Table 6.4 is 10 inasmuch as the frequencies of both variates are evenly divided: 30, 30, and 30 for both rows and columns.

Chi-square may now be computed. Since the differences between f and $\mathbf{F}$ of each cell sum to zero, each difference is squared and taken as a ratio of its $\mathbf{F}$. Thus,

Chi-Square:

$$\chi^2 = \frac{(f_a - \mathbf{F}_a)^2}{\mathbf{F}_a} + \frac{(f_b - \mathbf{F}_b)^2}{\mathbf{F}_b} + \cdots + \frac{(f_k - \mathbf{F}_k)^2}{\mathbf{F}_k} \qquad (6.18)$$

As usually written: $\qquad \chi^2 = \sum^k \frac{(f - \mathbf{F})^2}{\mathbf{F}} \qquad (6.19)$

Each of the nine ratios for the cells of Table 6.4 is obtained in Table 6.5, and the value of chi-square is found to be 45. The contingency coefficient, the measure of correlation, is equal to .57, as follows:

$$C = \sqrt{\frac{\chi^2}{\chi^2 + n'}} = \sqrt{\frac{45}{45 + 90}} = \sqrt{.3333} = .57$$

Compared with an r correlation, this value of .57 for C is somewhat less in its implications inasmuch as the maximum value that C can take for 3 by 3 bivariate distributions is

$$C_{\max} = \sqrt{\tfrac{2}{3}} = .82$$

Table 6.5.   Computation of Chi-Square for the Data of Table 6.4

Cell	f	$\mathbf{F}$	$(f - \mathbf{F})$	$(f - \mathbf{F})^2$	$(f - \mathbf{F})^2/\mathbf{F}$
a	5	10	-5	25	$25/10 = 2.5$
b	20	10	10	100	$100/10 = 10.0$
c	5	10	-5	25	$25/10 = 2.5$
d	5	10	-5	25	$25/10 = 2.5$
e	5	10	-5	25	$25/10 = 2.5$
f	20	10	10	100	$100/10 = 10.0$
g	20	10	10	100	$100/10 = 10.0$
h	5	10	-5	25	$25/10 = 2.5$
i	5	10	-5	25	$25/10 = 2.5$
			$\sum = 0$ (Check)		$\chi^2 = \sum = 45.0$

CORRELATION OF RANKABLES WITH RANKABLES

Pearson's r may be used to correlate a bivariate distribution composed of two ordered series of ranks from 1 to n. This fact emphasizes again the single condition that needs to be satisfied for the use of r, viz., *linearity* of the relationship. The assumption of a normal distribution enters *not* into the *calculation* of r but into correlation theory, regression estimation of y on x, the estimation of parameter r's, significance tests for r's, and differences between r's, etc. The use of product-moment r for the correlation of two series of ordered ranks perfectly correlated with each other is illustrated in Table 6.6. However, Pearson's r by the *method of differences*

Table 6.6.   Correlation of Ranks by the Product-Moment Method

Subject	X	Y	X^2	Y^2	YX
1	5	5	25	25	25
2	4	4	16	16	16
3	3	3	9	9	9
4	2	2	4	4	4
5	1	1	1	1	1
$\sum$'s	15	15	55	55	55
Means	3	3	11	11	11

$$r = \frac{\overline{XY} - (\overline{X})(\overline{Y})}{\sqrt{\overline{X^2} - (\overline{X})^2}\sqrt{\overline{Y^2} - (\overline{Y})^2}} \tag{5.5}$$

$$= \frac{11 - (3)(3)}{\sqrt{11 - (3)^2}\sqrt{11 - (3)^2}} = \frac{2}{\sqrt{2}\sqrt{2}} = 1.0$$

is easier to use than the product-moment method. Spearman (1904) showed that Pearson's difference method for r simplifies to the following formulation when both variables are ordered series of ranks from 1 to n.

Spearman's Rank Difference Method, r_r

$$r_r = 1 - \frac{6\sum_{}^{n'} D^2}{n'(n'^2 - 1)} \tag{6.20}$$

where $\sum^{n'} D^2$ is the sum of the square of the differences between each pair of ranks. Since the differences between each pair of ranks of the data of Table 6.6 sum to zero, by Formula 6.20 r_r is seen to be 1.0, without the need of further computation.

Pearson's *difference* formula for r is equal to the following:

Pearson's r by Differences:

$$r = \frac{s_x^2 + s_y^2 - s_d^2}{2s_x s_y} \tag{6.21}$$

where $s_d{}^2$ is the standard deviation of the differences between the deviates of each pair of observations:

$$s_d{}^2 = \frac{\sum\limits^{n'}(x - y)^2}{n' - 1} \tag{6.22}$$

When the means and standard deviations of both variables of a bivariate distribution are equal, Formula 6.21 can be simplified for measurables as well as for ranks:

Difference Formula for Measurables When Means and Variances Are Equal:

$$r = 1 - \frac{\sum\limits^{n'}(D^2)}{2n'\sigma^2} \tag{6.23}$$

Stated in terms of z deviates, Formula 6.23 becomes simply Formula 5.1:

$$r = 1 - \frac{\sum\limits^{n'}(z_x - z_y)^2}{2n'} \tag{5.1}$$

since the standard deviations of z deviate distributions are unity.

Stated for ordered series of ranks, Formula 6.23 becomes Formula 6.20 inasmuch as the variance of a series of ranks from 1 to n is equal to

$$V = \frac{n^2 - 1}{12} \tag{4.27}$$

The substitution of Formula 4.27 for σ^2 of Formula 6.23 gives Spearman's difference formula for ranks (Formula 6.20).

The *use* as well as the computation of Spearman's method for the correlation of rankables is free of the assumption that the correlated variates are normally distributed. This is doubtless apparent, since the method is designed for ordered series of ranks whose distributions are therefore rectangular. The method is consequently sometimes referred to as one of the *distribution-free* types of methods. (See Chapter 12.) The technique is also often referred to as *nonparametric* inasmuch as there are no parameters for r_r. (Note that some authors symbolize this coefficient by *rho*.)

During the first half of this century, Spearman's rank-difference method was often employed with measurables by their conversion to an ordered series of ranks. This was done as a short-cut procedure for Pearson's r, and conversion tables for r_r to r were published. Such a substitution of r_r for the Pearson r correlation of measurables has, however, little or nothing to recommend it. The rank-difference method can best be used when either one of or both the variables of a bivariate distribution consists of an ordered series of ranks, 1 to n, or when a distribution-free method is needed for measures. (See Chapter 12.)

Statistical information of countables can often be most satisfactorily correlated by their conversion to ordered series of ranks. Such series, for example, can be set up for the various Liberal Arts fields according to the number of doctoral degrees conferred on men and on women over an interval of time. *The World Almanac* reports such information currently. The ordered series for men and women in Table 6.7 are for such a set of information. The Liberal Arts field conferring the most doctoral degrees was ranked highest (given a rank of n) and that field conferring the fewest was given a rank of 1.

Table 6.7. Rank Correlation of the Sexes with Respect to the Number of Doctoral Degrees Awarded in Liberal Arts Fields
(For the U.S., 1958–1959)

Field	No. of Doctorates Awarded Men	Women	Ranks Men	Women	D	D^2
1. Biological Sciences	933	112	8	9	−1	1
2. Education	1297	317	10	11	−1	1
3. English and Journalism	317	65	6	6	0	0
4. Fine and Applied Arts	233	43	4	4	0	0
5. Foreign Language and Literature	182	59	3	5	−2	4
6. Geography	43	8	1	1	0	0
7. Mathematics	267	15	5	3	2	4
8. Philosophy	90	10	2	2	0	0
9. Physical Sciences	1743	69	11	7	4	16
10. Psychology	537	98	7	8	−1	1
11. Social Sciences	1058	129	9	10	−1	1
	6700	925			$\sum = 0$ (Check)	28

$$r_r = 1 - \frac{6(28)}{11(121 - 1)} = 1 - \frac{168}{1320} = 1 - .127 = .87$$

SOURCE: *The World Almanac*, 1961, p. 508.

An r_r of .87 signifies a high correlation between the sexes with respect to the order of the frequency of doctoral degrees for the 11 fields received during the one year. This r_r of .87 can be given meaning by an examination of the actual differences in the next to last column of Table 6.7. In 4 of the 11 cases, the differences are zero, and thus the rank positions (not the frequencies) of the men and women recipients of doctoral degrees were the same. There are four differences of only one-rank position; two of two-rank positions; and the largest differences is in the Physical Sciences, where the men considerably outrank the women.

The correlation is high even though the number of doctoral degrees awarded within the various Liberal Arts groups vary considerably between the sexes as well as between each other. Note that conversion of each series of information from frequencies to proportions or percentages would be another way to compare a dichotomy crosstabulated with a countable. Thus 8% of all these degrees awarded went to males who were psychologists as against 11% to women. Generally the percentage differences are small (as implied by $r_r = .87$), but the absolute differences are large. Such comparisons of percentages give added meaning to the implications of r_r for such bivariate distributions.

CORRELATION OF UNORDERED COUNTABLES WITH MEASURABLES

There are three methods, one or the other of which may be employed to measure the degree of correlation between an unordered countable and a measurable. Which to use depends on (1) how many categories the countable has and (2) whether or not the measurable is distributed or consists of only two or a few classes. The three methods are:

1. Point biserial correlation, r_{pb}.
2. *Eta* correlation, η.
3. The contingency coefficient, C.

Since the latter two methods have already been described, the first method will be developed in this section.

Point Biserial Correlation, r_{pb}

When the members of a dichotomized variate, such as males and females, or those who die and those who survive, are measured in relation to a distributed measurable, such as distribution of grades, or of test scores, or of weights in pounds, four pertinent questions may be asked:

1. Is there a mean difference between the measurable results of the two subgroups of the dichotomy?
2. Is there a variance difference between the measurable results of the two subgroups?
3. Is there any correlation between the dichotomized attribute and the measurable?
4. Are any of the preceding differences *"significant"*?

The first and third of these questions can be answered simultaneously, since a difference between the mean results of the subgroups will be indicative of some degree of correlation; *how much* will depend on the extent of the mean difference *relative* to the size of the standard deviation of the measurable as a whole. Both the first and second question, as well as the fourth question, will be considered in Chapter 10. The third question will be answered here.

Table 6.8. Birth Weights of Premature Infants Correlated with Survival

(A 2 by 17 Crosstabulation for Point Biserial Correlation)

Birth Weight in Grams	Expired (0)	Survived (1)	n_r
2100–(2268⁻)	0	6	6
2000–2099	2	6	8
1900–1999	0	11	11
1800–1899	3	21	24
1700–1799	2	22	24
1600–1699	1	22	23
1500–1599	4	16	20
1400–1499	5	12	17
1300–1399	3	24	27
1200–1299	4	16	20
1100–1199	3	12	15
1000–1099	6	8	14
900–999	8	4	12
800–899	11	2	13
700–799	8	0	8
600–699	4	0	4
500–599	3	0	3

$$n_c \qquad 67 \qquad\qquad 182 \qquad n' = 249$$

$$\overline{Y}_0 = 1108, \ \overline{Y}_1 = 1553, \qquad \overline{Y} = 1433$$

$$s_y = 385.6$$

SOURCE: Data by courtesy of Miss Ann Sprayregen who examined the records for one calendar year of all infants of the premature nursery of an urban hospital.

Table 6.8 presents *survival* data for 249 infants prematurely born. The dichotomy of the unordered countable variable consists of those who *expired* in the premature nursery and those who *survived* the premature nursery situation and were discharged as healthy babies weighing at least 2268 grams (5 pounds). Only those infants were brought to the premature nursery who (1) survived delivery and (2) had a birth weight of less than 2268 grams.

It is apparent that this dichotomy is in a class different from that of Table 6.1. Survival and death are clear-cut dichotomies. No assumption of a continuously distributed normal variable can be made for these disjunctive alternatives. Hence biserial correlation cannot be used to measure the relationship. *Point biserial r* is, however, specifically designed to obtain Pearson's *r* correlation for this type of bivariate distribution: a true dichotomy with a measurable.

The measurable variable consists of the distribution of the birth weights in grams of the 249 prematures. The mean birth weight of the 67 prematures who expired was 1108 grams. For the 182 who survived, it was 1553 grams. The mean birth weight of the entire group was 1433 grams. The greater the z deviate difference between the two subgroup means, the greater is the slope of a straight line function fitted to them, and thus the closer the value of r_{pb} is to 1.0 as a limit.

Point Biserial r: $$r_{pb} = \frac{\overline{Y}_1 - \overline{Y}_0}{s_y} \sqrt{\frac{n_1 n_0}{n'(n'-1)}} \qquad (6.24)$$

(*An Alternate Formulation*):

$$r_{pb} = \frac{\overline{Y}_1 - \overline{Y}_0}{\sqrt{\Sigma y^2}} \sqrt{n'pq} \qquad (6.25)$$

where the subscripts 0 and 1 designate the subgroups of the dichotomy and p is the proportion of n_1/n' and q is the proportion of n_0/n'.

For the data of Table 6.8, $r_{pb} = .51$, as follows:

(*By Formula 6.24*):

$$r_{pb} = \frac{1553 - 1108}{385.6} \cdot \sqrt{\frac{67(182)}{249(248)}} = 1.154(.444) = .51$$

The correlation coefficient is .51. It may be treated as a Pearson's *r*, since r_{pb} is a special case of product moment *r*, provided:

1. The y variate for both subgroups of the dichotomy is normally distributed.
2. The respective population variances of the subgroups of y are equal.

As will be seen on p. 296, this second requirement is not satisfied for the data of Table 6.8. Hence r_{pb} for these data is a *descriptive statistic* and should not be generalized as a Pearson's *r* to be used, for example, with other *r*'s in multiple correlation problems. In view of unequal variances, the better procedure for the analysis of the significance of the data of Table 6.8 is a direct comparison of the mean birth weights of the two subgroups, as is done on p. 297 ff.

CORRELATION OF RANKABLES WITH MEASURABLES

It sometimes happens that a bivariate distribution consists of one variate in the form of a rankable and the other in the form of a measurable. When the measurable is well distributed, it can be converted to a rankable and the correlation between the two variates obtained by means of Spearman's rank difference method. In effect, this sort of conversion was made with both variables in Table 6.7. Both variates, however, were originally countables, the number of doctorates awarded to males and females for each category. They were ordered and hence ranked.

Averaging of Ranks

A difficulty that sometimes arises in the conversion of a measurable to a rankable is the problem of what to do with repeated measures. A series of ordered ranks from 1 to n has no duplicated values. When, however, there are duplicates in a series of measurables to be converted to ranks, the duplicates are given average ranks as follows:

Original Measures	Order	Ranks
73	1	1
75	2	3.0
75	3	3.0
75	4	3.0
78	5	5
80	6	6.5
80	7	6.5
84	8	8
etc.	etc.	etc.

Rank Difference Correlation as a Distribution-Free Method

It was pointed out in the first chapter that for significance testing and inferential statistics, some statistical techniques are based on the assumption of samples *of measures* drawn randomly from normally distributed populations and populations whose variances are also equal. If the results for a particular bivariate distribution of measurables appear to contradict or be out of harmony with these conditions, then both variates may be converted to rankables and their correlation obtained by Spearman's rank difference method. Essentially this was done with the original data of Table 6.7. Although both variables were in the first instance *countables*, they could have been ordered countables treated as measurables. But their "distributions" were far from normal in form. Hence their conversion to rankables and the use of Spearman's method to measure their correlation was indicated. Even though the *computation* of Pearson's r is free of the condition of normally distributed populations, the *use* of r in sampling-inferential statistics is based on this assumption. When it is apparently not satisfied, Spearman's rank difference method provides a distribution-free or nonparametric method for measuring correlation between the distributed variables of a bivariate.

It is to be emphasized, however, that when there is a *choice* of techniques, as between Spearman's *rank* method and Pearson's product-moment method, the decision is made in favor of the latter. This is generally true when there is a choice between a distribution-free method and a parametric method. The disadvantage of methods that convert the data of measurables to ranks (or counts, as in the sign test) lies in the fact that some information is being discarded. Thus, in rank difference correlation, all measures lose their original magnitudes of differences and differ successively only by unit ranks.

CHAPTER 7

PROBABILITY, SAMPLING, AND INFERENTIAL STATISTICS

Philosophy goes no further than probabilities,
and in every assertion keeps a doubt in reserve.

J. A. Froude

INFERENTIAL statistics are based on logic and implications of probability theory. Hence it is essential that the student of statistics have some insight into and knowledge of probability theory. As a matter of interest, it is a fascinating topic in its own right. It can become doubly so when the attempt is made to use various models of probability theory with the great variety and wealth of empirical observation and measurement. The student needs to be cautioned, however, lest he blithely assume that a given probability model, such as the Laplace-Gaussian normal curve of error, will apply to his data. Quételet and Galton "canonized" the normal curve. Galton applied its properties to grade distributions, and ever since, students have been treated to the unhappy prospect of some teachers "grading them on the curve." That such a short-cut approach to the problem of assembling grades may but rarely be warranted by the facts does not seem to deter young and old enthusiasts of the "easy way out." Absolute standards of excellence in a course may be difficult to establish, but when attempted, as is commonly done in mathematics and statistics courses, there is the rationale of what experience has taught. That is to say, the teacher can benefit from a knowledge of what bright students have accomplished.

Gamblers and Chance

In Chapter 1 it was indicated that the wish to know the odds of winning at games of chance was instrumental to the early development of probability theory. Consider, for example, the casting of a pair of dice. Many generations of gamblers had been aware that certain combinations (or sum of pips) of a pair of dice turn up more frequently than others. However, the emergence of science and developments in mathematics during the 16th century led to questions such as: Can the probability of each type of result be determined? Can the behavior of the dice be predicted? The Newtonian science of mechanics led to the development and application of scientific method in many fields. It led to the view of strict determinism in the affairs of science. Could the indeterministic quality of chance behavior also be dealt with as a mathematical-scientific phenomenon? Mathematicians like Pascal, Fermat, Bernoulli, de Moivre and Laplace turned their attention to problems of probability and developed a theory and calculus of probabilities. Once the probabilities have been worked out for the chance behavior of a pair of dice, it is possible deductively to infer, within limits, the expected behavior of fair dice when tossed by a randomizing method. Such inferences are subject to sampling variation and, most important, it is possible to calculate the expected variation, which decreases as the series of tosses is increased. It was found that the sampling variation under certain conditions decreases not in direct proportion to the increase in number of tosses but to the square root of the number of tosses (size of sample).

Probability theory is based on certain assumptions. It defines the field of chance behavior. With respect to the behavior of a pair of dice, the following assumptions are made:

1. A method of randomization of the behavior of the dice is used in their casting.
2. The dice are fair; i.e., perfectly balanced.

In other words, the behavior of tossed dice is not purposive nor, from the point of view of probability theory, is such behavior controlled by purposive forces. The gambler, of course, has a purpose, viz., to win. If he is honest, however, the behavior of the dice is not manipulated by him to his advantage or by a confederate. The dice are thoroughly shaken and their roll broken so that the result is a function of "pure chance." The dice themselves, to be fair, have to be constructed very carefully so as to be in perfect balance. *Empirically*, no one face of each die should have a greater frequency of appearing over a long series of tosses than any other face. Dice are considered to be fair if by such test the relative frequency of each face of each die equals $\frac{1}{6}$ as a limit and continues to hold at this limit as the series of tosses is prolonged. In the *mathematical* development of probability theory, dice are *assumed* to be fair. This assumption is built into the conceptual structure for deductive inference.

PROBABILITY DEFINED

Mathematical (a priori) Probability

Let n be the number of (1) *exhaustive*, (2) *mutually exclusive*, and (3) *equally likely* cases of an event under a given set of conditions. If m of these cases are known as event A, then the probability of event A under the given set of conditions is

$$\mathbf{P}\,(A) = \frac{m}{n} \tag{7.1}$$

Thus the probability of drawing a red die (A) from a box containing 3 red dice and 4 green dice is $\frac{3}{7}$. Given the assumed conditions of 3 red and 4 green dice, the number of exhaustive, mutually exclusive, and equally likely cases is 7. Under the condition of randomized drawings, m (red dice) equals 3. Hence,

$$\mathbf{P}\,(A) = \frac{m}{n} = \frac{3}{7} \tag{7.2}$$

The probability $\mathbf{P}$ of A equals $\frac{3}{7}$, or .429.

It may be apparent that this definition of a priori, mathematical probability is circular, since "equally likely" signifies or means "equally probable." Nevertheless the definition is useful in that it gives intuitive meaning to the concept of probability.

Statistical Probability: P as a Limiting Value

If, in a random series of n trials, m of which are favorable to event A, the ratio m/n has the limit of $\mathbf{P}$ as n increases indefinitely, then the ratio m/n is the probability of the event.

This is a further definition of a priori, or deductive, probability, but the concept of a limiting value may be used also to establish a definition of empirical-inductive probability.

Empirical (a posteriori) Probability

If in a series of trials an event A has occurred m times and failed m' times, then

$$\mathbf{P}\ (A) = \frac{m}{m + m'} = \frac{m}{n} \tag{7.3}$$

Thus the value of $\mathbf{P}$ is a ratio based on empirical information. If the value of $\mathbf{P}$ stabilizes after many observations or trials, this value will be taken as the probability value of the event A. However, such empirical $\mathbf{P}$ values do not have the universal character of a priori, deductive $\mathbf{P}$ values. Empirical probability is tricky not only because conditions may change but also because they do change. Actuaries are painfully aware of this at times. Thus the increases in longevity in this country have been costly to certain kinds of insurance, such as pensions or annuities. On the other hand, these changes have produced financial windfalls to those specializing in death insurance. The probability of death by violence for a given time and place is the ratio of the number of deaths by violence (m) to this number, m, plus m', the number of deaths by conditions other than violence. During hot wars, the probability of death by violence may be higher than in other periods. Obviously an unambiguous definition of violence is essential to these distinctions. Is death in a collision of two cars defined as death by violence?

The probability of an event may thus be calculated in either one or two ways:

1. Deductively, by mathematical-logical processes.
2. Inductively, by sampling information derived from empirical observations and measurements.

Deductively, the probability of an event is equal to expectancies under defined conditions. Thus the randomized behavior of a fair die has a probability of $\frac{1}{6}$ for each face. A $\mathbf{P}$ of $\frac{1}{6}$, or .1667, is inferred from the assumed conditions. On the other hand, inductive probability of a die is

Table 7.1. Subsets and Their Combinations

Subset (Type of Result)	Combinations (Number of)	Dice A B
2 pips	1	1 and 1
3 pips	2	1 and 2 2 and 1
4 pips	3	1 and 3 2 and 2 3 and 1
5 pips	4	1 and 4 2 and 3 3 and 2 4 and 1
6 pips	5	1 and 5 2 and 4 3 and 3 4 and 2 5 and 1
7 pips	6	1 and 6 2 and 5 3 and 4 4 and 3 5 and 2 6 and 1
8 pips	5	2 and 6 3 and 5 4 and 4 5 and 3 6 and 2
9 pips	4	3 and 6 4 and 5 5 and 4 6 and 3
10 pips	3	4 and 6 5 and 5 6 and 4
11 pips	2	5 and 6 6 and 5
12 pips	1	6 and 6

$$\sum = 36$$

There is thus a total of 11 different subsets and 36 combinations. Since the faces of the dice are equiprobable, the probability value, P, for any particular subset of pips is the ratio of the number of combinations for that subset to the total number of combinations. Thus, for two pips, $P(S_2) = 1/36$.

based on the empirical results obtained from many throws. **P** should approach a relative frequency of $\frac{1}{6}$ as a limit for each face of the die, if the die is fair and its behavior has been randomized in the casting. If **P** does not approach a limit of $\frac{1}{6}$, then either the die is not in perfect balance, and hence not a "fair" die, or the method of tossing is not truly random, or both conditions may operate concurrently.

CALCULATION OF A PRIORI PROBABILITIES

How are the probabilities of events calculated? If the events are hypothesized as indefinitely repetitive, independent of each other and equally likely, their **P** values are based on their possible ways of behaving; i.e., on the number of *permutations* of the various types of results. Thus a single die can behave in but six different ways, and each way is a different type of result (a different number of pips). Hence each way is hypothesized as being equiprobable with every other way when a die is fair and the tossing is randomized:

$$\mathbf{P} \text{ (of any face)} = \frac{m}{m + m'} = \frac{1}{1 + 5} = \frac{1}{6} = .1667 \qquad (7.4)$$

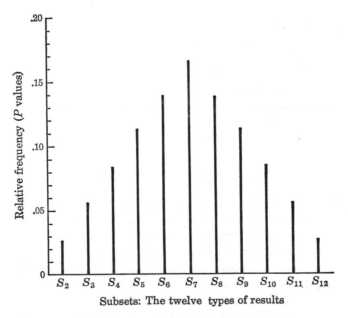

Fig. 7.1. **Hypothesized Probability Model Describing the Randomized Behavior of a Pair of Dice** (*n* Indefinitely Large)

where m is the number of ways any one face may show, and m' is the remaining number of permutations, or ways of showing. This is simple enough.

The situation is immediately complicated, however, when two or more dice are tossed, as is usually done. This is the case because certain results (counts of the pips) may occur in more than one way. In other words, for some types of results there are two or more combinations, as indicated in Table 7.1. Each type of result will be denoted as a subset, with *all* possible results or elements being the set.

Table 7.2.   A Priori Probability of Each Subset in the Randomized Behavior of a Pair of Fair Dice

Type of Subset	Number of Combinations	Probability Ratio	**P**
S_2	1	1/36	.0278
S_3	2	2/36 (1/18)	.0556
S_4	3	3/36 (1/12)	.0833
S_5	4	4/36 (1/9)	.1111
S_6	5	5/36	.1389
S_7	6	6/36 (1/6)	.1667
S_8	5	5/36	.1389
S_9	4	4/36 (1/9)	.1111
S_{10}	3	3/36 (1/12)	.0833
S_{11}	2	2/36 (1/18)	.0556
S_{12}	1	1/36	.0278
$(k = 11)$ $\sum = 36$		36/36 = 1	1.0000

The **P** distribution of the last column *is* the *probability model* for a pair of fair dice whose behavior is randomized over an infinite number of trials.

Addition Theorem of Probability

The probability of the occurrence of mutually exclusive, disjunctive events is equal to the sum of their respective probabilities. Two or more disjunctive events are alternative events that are mutually exclusive in the sense that they cannot occur simultaneously. They are "either-or" events; or "or-or-or $\cdots$ or" events. Thus each combination of a given subset is disjunctive, and the probability of any subset of dice results is equal to the sum of the probabilities of each combination that will yield the subset. Since the probability of any single combination is 1/36, the probability of subset S_7 with six combinations is

$$\mathbf{P}(S_7) = \tfrac{1}{36} + \tfrac{1}{36} + \tfrac{1}{36} + \tfrac{1}{36} + \tfrac{1}{36} + \tfrac{1}{36} = \tfrac{6}{36} = \tfrac{1}{6} \qquad (7.5)$$

Similarly the probability of the occurrence of several mutually exclusive, alternative *subsets* is equal to the sum of their respective probabilities:

$$\mathbf{P} \ (S_7 \ \text{or} \ S_8) = \mathbf{P} \ (S_7) + \mathbf{P} \ (S_8) = \tfrac{6}{36} + \tfrac{5}{36} = \tfrac{11}{36}$$

and

$$\mathbf{P} \ (\text{at least 10 pips}) = \mathbf{P}(S_{10}) + \mathbf{P}(S_{11}) + \mathbf{P}(S_{12})$$
$$= \tfrac{3}{36} + \tfrac{2}{36} + \tfrac{1}{36} = \tfrac{6}{36} = \tfrac{1}{6}$$

Thus "at least 10 pips" has the same probability as 7 pips, as does also the "or, or, or" of a 2, 3, 11, or 12:

$$\mathbf{P}(S_2 \ \text{or} \ S_3 \ \text{or} \ S_{11} \ \text{or} \ S_{12}) = \mathbf{P}(S_2) + \mathbf{P}(S_3) + \mathbf{P}(S_{11}) + \mathbf{P}(S_{12})$$
$$= \tfrac{1}{36} + \tfrac{2}{36} + \tfrac{2}{36} + \tfrac{1}{36} = \tfrac{1}{6}$$

Product Theorem of Probability

In the preceding chapter this probability theorem was used in the calculation of the contingency coefficient. The probability of the joint occurrence of two or more independent events is equal to the product of their respective probabilities. "Joint occurrence" may be interpreted as having either temporal dimension of simultaneity or of succession. Applied to the behavior of a pair of dice, this product theorem gives the probability of any successive combination of results.

In casting a single die, the probability of a single pip twice in succession is equal to the product of the probability of each result:

$$\mathbf{P}(S_1) \ \text{and} \ \mathbf{P}(S_1) = \tfrac{1}{6} \times \tfrac{1}{6} = \tfrac{1}{36}$$

In casting a pair of dice, the probability of two pips twice in succession is equal to

$$\mathbf{P}(S_2) \ \text{and} \ \mathbf{P}(S_2) = \tfrac{1}{36} \times \tfrac{1}{36} = \tfrac{1}{1296}$$

whereas the probability of casting 7's twice in succession is

$$\mathbf{P}(S_7) \ \text{and} \ \mathbf{P}(S_7) = \tfrac{1}{6} \times \tfrac{1}{6} = \tfrac{1}{36}$$

This result is in the long run 36 times more likely to occur than are two pips twice in succession.

From the foregoing, it is seen that both the addition theorem and the product theorem underlie the determination of the $\mathbf{P}$ values for the various combinations of results in the casting of dice. By generalizing, it will be seen that these two theorems are essential to mathematical (a priori) probability theory.

Permutations and Combinations

Since the probability of an event A is usually defined for statistics as the relative frequency of A to all events of the set or population of events of which A is a member, the a priori calculation of probabilities is considerably facilitated by a knowledge of some basic theorems of permutations and combinations.

A permutation, P, is an ordered arrangement or sequence of all or part of a set of objects or things. A combination of a set of objects is any selection of one or more of the objects without regard to order.

A permutation of n things taken *all at a time* is an ordered arrangement of all the members of the set. All possible permutations of a set of three objects, A, B, and C, are the following six arrangements without repetitions:

ABC, ACB, BAC, BCA, CAB, and CBA

If order is disregarded, then there is but one combination of this set of three objects, viz., the combination ABC (which can, of course, be written in any one of the six ways).

THEOREM I: The number of permutations, P, of n different objects is

$$P_n = n!$$

The exclamation point to denote n *factorial* doubtless arises from the amazing increase in the number of permutations as n is increased only slightly. Thus the members of a class of 5 students can be seated in a row in 120 different ways or orders:

$$P_5 = 5! = 5 \times 4 \times 3 \times 2 \times 1 = 120$$

Any one of the 5 can be in the first seat, any one of the remaining 4 in the second seat, any one of the remaining 3 in the third seat, either one of the remaining 2 in the fourth seat, and the remaining 1 in the fifth seat.

Thus, when the arrangements are by chance and assumed to be equiprobable, the odds for any particular seating arrangement are but $\frac{1}{120}$:

$$\mathbf{P} = \frac{m}{n} = \frac{1}{120}$$

where m is the number of permutations that will give the particular order and n is the total number of permutations.

A class of only 13 students can be seated in more than 6 billion different ways, since

$$P_{13} = 13! = 6,227,020,800*$$

---

*Herbert E. Salzer (1961). See Table EEE of the Appendix (p. 407) for the factorials of integers 0 to 20.

The odds of any one particular arrangement occurring, such as A B C D E F G H I J K L M, are infinitesimal.

THEOREM II: The number of permutations of n things r at a time is

$$_nP_r = \frac{n!}{(n-r)!} \tag{7.6}$$

If in an experiment with 10 different persons, A to J, any 5 are to be selected at random from the 10 and arranged in a random order, the odds are but 1/151,200 that a particular order of a particular subset of 5 of the 10 persons will occur:

$$_{10}P_5 = \frac{10!}{5!} = \frac{10 \times 9 \times 8 \times 7 \times 6 \times 5!}{5!} = 151,200$$

THEOREM III: The number of combinations that will give a particular subset in a given n set is

$$\binom{n}{r} = \frac{n!}{r!(n-r)!} \tag{7.7}$$

From a class of 20 students, a subset of 5 is to be selected at random as a sample to serve as subjects in an experiment. The odds for any combination of 5 particular students showing up in the sample are only 1/15,504, since

$$\binom{20}{5} = \frac{20!}{5!15!} = \frac{20 \times 19 \times 18 \times 17 \times 16 \times 15!}{5 \times 4 \times 3 \times 2 \times 1(15!)}$$
$$= 15,504$$

Note the difference between Theorems II and III. In II the number of permutations (arrangements or order) of 5 objects at a time is relevant. In III the order of the 5 students within a sample (the subset) doesn't matter. It is the combination of any 5 students, the subset, that counts.

A standard deck of ESP (extrasensory perception) cards contains 25 cards, 5 each of 5 different symbols, viz., a cross, a circle, a wavy equal sign, a square, and a star. This is the set, or universe. How many different combinations (samples) of 5 cards each are possible from such a deck? Answer:

$$\binom{n}{r} = \frac{n!}{r!(n-r)!} = \frac{25!}{5!20!} = \frac{25 \times 24 \times 23 \times 22 \times 21 \times 20!}{5 \times 4 \times 3 \times 2 \times 1(20!)} = 53,130$$

Therefore the odds in random dealing of any particular subset of 5 cards of the same design (such as 5 circles) from such a deck are only 1/53,130 since **P** (the probability) will be the ratio of the number of combinations for a given subset to the total number of combinations.

Use of a Probability Model

Students may well ask what the preceding discussion has to do with their field of major interest, which may be psychology, or sociology, or education, but not probability theory. This is a real question and not easily answered. Perhaps the most immediate way to approach the question is to relate the mathematical model of chance variation in dice behavior (Table 7.2) with an experimental research problem.

It has been contended, for example, that it is possible to influence the behavior of a pair of dice by *mental concentration* on certain combinations of results. This is known as the hypothesis of psychokinesis. In order to explore the possible truth of this contention, an experiment will need to be designed that will prevent any chicanery in the tossing of the dice, and at the same time will give the contender of this mental concentration hypothesis an opportunity to demonstrate his contention. The dice used will have to be measured for fairness, i.e., for cubic exactness, and tested for perfect balance.

The contention can then be tested by obtaining a sample of many randomized tosses from the contender. The results are carefully recorded, the frequency of each combination of pips is determined, and the proportion of each result is compared with the probability model of Table 7.2, i.e., with the corresponding probability values of each combination. The mathematical probability model gives the relative frequencies for *an indefinitely prolonged series* of tosses.

It may be apparent that in any finite series of tosses, variations from the mathematical values of the probability model will occur because of the role of chance variations in sampling. *Chance variation* is to be expected in any finite sampling of randomized castings of a pair of fair dice. Therefore the statistical question to be considered and treated is this:

Are the differences between the p values of the obtained results and the **P** values of the probability model of Table 7.2 greater than those expected as the result of the role of chance variations in the empirical results?

One way to tackle this question is to enlist the aid of chi-square, the statistical technique used in the preceding chapter to obtain the contingency coefficient. (It will be seen that chi-square is useful for many kinds of statistical problems.) Its application to this kind of problem is presented on p. 255, to test the "goodness of fit" of an empirical, sampling distribution with a hypothetical probability distribution.

Another way to tackle the question is to deal with particular combinations of results rather than with the whole distribution of results. The contender will doubtless have concentrated on a particular combination or combinations. He might have concentrated on "snake eyes" (2 pips) or on "box cars" (12 pips). In such instances the problem is to determine whether the difference between the obtained and the expected (by the mathematical probability model) results differ by amounts greater than those *considered likely* for chance variation alone. (Note that a *decision* will have to be made; the *statistical results are not self-interpreting*.)

Even though the distribution of all results might not be found to differ significantly from the mathematical model for chance variation, a given combination may nevertheless be "out of line"; i.e., it may differ from theoretical expectancy by an amount greater than that ordinarily ascribed to chance variation. Assume that the contender concentrated on getting 10 or more pips per toss. Table 7.2 gives the probability of 10 or more pips as .1667. If in 1000 tosses the contender obtains 190 results with 10 or more pips, the p (proportion) of these results to all possible results is

$$p = \tfrac{190}{1000} = .190$$

The statistical problem therefore has essentially two aspects:

1. The establishment by mathematical probability (deductive) of the sampling variation to be expected by chance for 10 or more pips with a **P** value of .1667.

2. A *decision* as to whether the obtained p of .190 is within the range of the "normal sampling variation" or beyond that range. Obviously this decision is crucial. If the empirical result of .190 is judged to be within the range of normal sampling variation, then in effect the contention of mental influence (psychokinesis) is disallowed or rejected. On the other hand, if the result is judged to be outside the range of normal sampling variation, then presumably the nonchance factors operating in the result were a consequence of the role of mental concentration.

The first question will be dealt with in this chapter; the second, at more length in Chapter 9. At this point the answer will be anticipated by indicating that for large samplings such as 1000 tosses ($n = 1000$), the expected sampling variations are measured against another mathematical probability model, viz., the model characteristic of the normal probability distribution. The result, a p of .190 (Fig. 7.2), is related to this normal probability model by means of the standard deviation of a sampling distribution of proportions. The mean of this sampling distribution of proportions is the theoretical proportion of the first probability model, viz., a **P** of .1667 for 10 or more pips.

As usual, the measure of variation is the standard deviation. The expected variation for an infinite number of tossings is described *approximately* by the probability (area) values of Table A (Appendix) for the normal distribution. When the mean of this distribution is a parameter proportion of .1667, the standard deviation is calculated to be, as follows, where $Q = 1 - P$.

$$\sigma_p = \sqrt{\frac{PQ}{n}} = \sqrt{\frac{(.1667)(.8333)}{1000}} = .0118 \qquad (7.8)$$

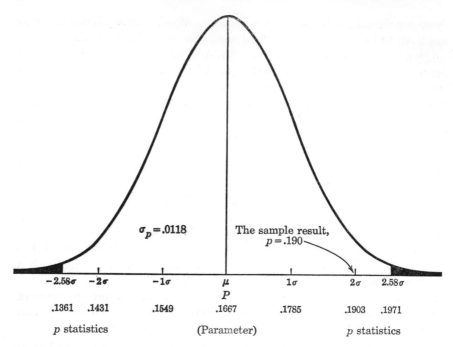

Fig. 7.2. Location of a p Statistic of .190 on the Hypothesized Probability Model for a Parameter Proportion of .1667 and n of 1000 (Approximately Normal)

The mean of the hypothetical sampling distribution of proportions is the *parameter proportion*. When the mean of a sampling distribution of proportions departs considerably from .50, the sampling distribution is skewed, becoming increasingly so as P approaches zero and 1.00. However, if the sample is very large, as for example $n = 1000$, the bulk of the middle range of the sampling variation is fairly symmetrical and of normal proportions even when P is as small as .1667. Consequently the form of the variation characteristic of the normal probability model fairly well describes the variation to be expected within the range of plus and minus two standard deviations from the parameter mean of .1667. (Note that this parameter mean proportion P of .1667 is also the a priori **P** probability value of the result under consideration, viz., 10 or more pips.)

This is illustrated in Fig. 7.2 with the sample result of $p = .190$ located on the base line of the distribution. The range of the middle 99% of the normal distribution is given approximately by the mean $\pm 2.58\sigma$. Under the conditions described,* this range is therefore as follows:

$$P \pm 2.58\sigma = .1667 \pm 2.58(.0118) = .1667 + .0304 = .1971$$
and $$.1667 - .0304 = .1363$$

---

*When $n = 1000$, there is no need to make the correction for discontinuity, since the scale value of a half of a discrete interval is nearly a vanishing value. (p. 167)

When the sampling variation is purely a matter of chance, 99% of the time the expected variation of sample results (when $n = 1000$) is within the range of .1363 and .1971. In only 1% of the time would chance be expected to yield sample results of less than .1363 and greater than .1971. It is to be emphasized that these percentages indicate what would be expected on the average in the long run over an indefinitely prolonged series of samples under the defined conditions of fair dice and randomization.

Since the contender's result is .190, well within the 99% range, the decision ordinarily is made to the effect that .190 signifies a result that is *within the range* of chance expectancy for a single sample result. If .190 is the best the contender can do, his contention is rejected, since the value does not deviate far enough from the parameter proportion of .1667 to warrant any inference other than that of random variation as characteristic of the result.

In Chapter 9 the student will see that the decision-making process just illustrated is related to one of the general problems of inferential statistics, viz., significance testing. The problem is one of reasoning from the information at hand, viz., a sample result, to the theoretical values of a mathematical probability model such as that of Fig. 7.2. If the conditions of experimentation are rigorous, sample results with values within the middle 99% range of the probability model are often inferred to be within the range of chance variation for the parameter mean of the distribution. On the other hand, if the sample result is a value equal to one that would occur in the hypothesized mathematical model less than 1% of the time, a different decision may be called for.

Probability and Certainty (Probability Paradox of Birthdays)

As long as there are alternative possibilities to the occurrence of a particular event, the prediction of its occurrence will be *conditional* rather than necessary or certain. However, the sometime nearness of what may be *but probable* to what is *certain* is aptly illustrated by the probability paradox of birthdays (Gardner, 1959).

Although there are 365 days in a year (not counting leap years), the odds that at least 2 people in *any* group of 60 people will have *the same birthdays (not birth dates)* are better than 99 in 100. *As a matter of probability*, at least half the time one may count on finding 2 people with the same birthdays in any classroom or social gathering of more than 23 persons. This paradox may be readily tested by asking each person of groups of 23 or more to write the date of his birthday on a slip of paper. Then all slips can be arranged in order of calendar dates and compared for *coincidences*. Or names can be drawn randomly from *Who's Who* and the birthdays compared. Over many such samples, coincidences should occur somewhat more than half the time.

The odds for a coincidence of 2 persons with the same birthday can be determined for any size sample of from 2 to 365 by the use of the product theorem of probability for the joint occurrence of independent events. Since there is but 1 chance in 365 that one person's birthday will coincide with another, the probability that the birthdays of any 2 people are *not* the same is $1 - (1/365) = (364/365)$ (exclusive of February 29). The probability that a 3rd person's birthday will differ from the other two is $363/365 \cdots$ etc., the probability that the 24th person's birthday will differ from the other 23 being $342/365$. The product of all these respective probabilities is $23/50$; hence the odds that any 2 persons of a group of 24 will have birthdays on the same calendar date (exclusive of February 29) are $1 - (23/50) = 27/50$, or .54. Carried to samples of 60 persons, the odds are better than 99 in 100 for such a coincidence. Thus one can be *practically certain*, but *not absolutely* certain, of finding a coincidence of birthdays among at least 2 of 60 persons. Absolute certainty would, of course, require a sample of 367 cases (1 more than a leap year of 366 days).

The same reasoning applies to dates of death. Perhaps one of the most remarkable examples of the "death day" paradox is the fact that three of the first five Presidents of the United States died on July 4, the date of the Independence Day that two of them helped create. These were John Adams and Thomas Jefferson, who died on the same *day*, July 4, 1826. James Monroe died on July 4, 1831. The birthday paradox is illustrated by Presidents Polk and Harding, whose birthdays were November 2.

BERNOULLI PROBABILITY DISTRIBUTION

Perhaps the most important *discrete* probability distribution for inferential statistics is the binomial distribution. This was investigated originally by the great Swiss mathematician, Jacques Bernoulli (1654–1705), whose work was published posthumously at Basle in 1713 under the editorship of his nephew, Nicholas Bernoulli (1695–1726). This distribution is called the *point binomial*, as well as the Bernoulli probability distribution, because a variable so distributed can assume only integer values from zero to n. Consequently the probabilities are concentrated at the point values of the integers (as in Figs. 7.3 and 7.5).

An a priori binomial probability distribution can be set up for any number of mutually exclusive and exhaustive events with postulated probability values. Such events may be drawn from a two-class population, such as a population of head events and tail events of n elements (coins). And just as the calculation of the probabilities of dice behavior becomes less simple when several dice are used, so the calculation of the probabilities of coin behavior becomes less simple when the number of coins in a sample is many rather than only a few. It can readily be inferred, when a coin is assumed to be fair, that the probability of a head is $\frac{1}{2}$, and the probability of a tail is also $\frac{1}{2}$. When two coins are tossed, or the same coin is tossed twice, then one subset of results, viz., the head-tail combination, may occur in either of two ways:

Subset		Probability
1. Head and Head	1	1/4 = .25
2. Head and Tail	$\left.\begin{array}{c}1\\1\end{array}\right\} = 2$	1/2 = .50
Tail and Head		
3. Tail and Tail	$\dfrac{1}{4}$	1/4 = .25

The number of different subsets will be equal to the number of coins in the sample (or elements) plus one. The number of combinations, i.e., the different ways of obtaining each subset, will rapidly increase as the number of elements (coins) increases. The total number of combinations for any number of elements, n, equals a^n, where a represents the number of different kinds of events possible. When there are only two, as in the heads and tails events of coin behavior, $a = 2$; and for 10 elements, the number of combinations equals $2^{10} = 1024$. (With two dice the total number of combinations was seen to be 36, or 6^2.)

The number of different combinations for each type of result or subset is given by the coefficient of each term in the expansion of the binomial for a given n. These coefficients may be calculated for any number of elements, n, taken r at a time, by the use of the algebra of *factorials*. Thus factorial 10, written as 10! is

$$10! = 10 \times 9 \times 8 \times 7 \times 6 \times 5 \times 4 \times 3 \times 2 \times 1 = 3,628,800$$

Factorials and Binomial Expansion

The number of ways of obtaining any particular combination of r heads (or successes) and $n - r$ tails (failures) for n coins (elements) was given by Formula 7.7:

$$\binom{n}{r} = \frac{n!}{r!(n-r)!} \tag{7.7}$$

For 10 heads, when the number of coins is 10,

$$\binom{n}{r} = \binom{10}{10} = \frac{10!}{10!(10-10)!} = \frac{10!}{10!} = 1$$

since zero factorial is 1.

For 9 heads, when $n = 10$,

$$\binom{10}{9} = \frac{10!}{9!(10-9)!} = \frac{10!}{9!} = 10$$

For 8 heads, when $n = 10$,

$$\binom{10}{8} = \frac{10!}{8!(10-8)!} = \frac{10!}{8!2!} = \frac{10 \times 9}{2 \times 1} = 45$$

For 5 heads, when $n = 10$,

$$\binom{10}{5} = \frac{10!}{5!(10-5)!} = \frac{10 \times 9 \times 8 \times 7 \times 6}{5 \times 4 \times 3 \times 2 \times 1} = 252$$

It should be apparent that the computation of factorials is considerably simplified by the cancellation of values in the numerator and denominator.

These then are the coefficients of terms in the binomial $(p + q)^{10}$, regardless of the values of p and q. In the case of coin elements, heads and tails are assumed for a priori probability to be equiprobable. The probability of p, the expected relative frequency of heads, equals $\frac{1}{2}$. The probability of q, which always equals $1 - p$, is $1 - \frac{1}{2} = \frac{1}{2}$. The probability of tails is therefore $\frac{1}{2}$.

It may be difficult to "see" that the subset of 5 heads and 5 tails (or 5 successes and 5 failures) can be obtained from 10 elements in 252 ways. The fact can be self-demonstrated by systematically writing out all the 252 combinations of 5 heads and 5 tails, with each coin identified either by position or by a different letter. Thus, by position, one may begin with: HHHHH TTTTT, and end with TTTTT HHHHH.

The *a priori probability* of any subset of r successes in n trials is as follows:

$$\binom{n}{r} p^r q^{n-r} \tag{7.9}$$

For 5 successes, the probability is therefore

$$\mathbf{P}(\text{5 successes}) = \frac{10!}{5!(10-5)!} \left(\frac{1}{2}\right)^5 \left(\frac{1}{2}\right)^{(10-5)} = \frac{252}{1024} = .246$$

The binomial expansion can be generalized as follows:

$$(p + q)^n = p^n + \frac{n}{1} p^{(n-1)}q + \frac{n(n-1)}{2 \times 1} p^{n-2}q^2$$

$$+ \frac{n(n-1)(n-2)}{3 \times 2 \times 1} p^{(n-3)}q^3 + \cdots + q^n \tag{7.10}$$

For 10 elements:

$$(p + q)^{10} = \left(\frac{1}{2}\right)^{10} + 10\left(\frac{1}{2}\right)^{9}\left(\frac{1}{2}\right) + \cdots + \left(\frac{1}{2}\right)^{10}$$

$$= \frac{1}{1024} + 10\frac{1}{1024} + 45\frac{1}{1024} + \cdots + \frac{1}{1024}$$

(as in the fourth column of Table 7.3).

It is evident that when $P = Q = \frac{1}{2}$, as in the case of the postulated behavior of the fair coins, the a priori probability of each combination is the ratio of its number of different ways of occurring (combinations regardless of the order of occurrences) to all possible combinations. Since the total number of different combinations is equal to a^n, where a equals the number of mutually exclusive alternatives of an element (coin) and n is the number of elements

Total Combinations: $\quad a^n = 2^{10} = 1024$ $\hfill$ (7.11)

Relation of Bernoulli Distribution to Normal Distribution

The probability distribution in the last column of Table 7.3 is illustrated in Fig. 7.3. It will be observed that this distribution is similar in form to the normal distribution, except that it is discrete. If it were converted from a discrete distribution to a smoothed curve, it would hardly differ from the normal. This can be illustrated by a calculation of the normal curve equivalent of the probability value of any interval or combination of intervals of the discrete binomial distribution. The area values of Table A (Appendix) are the equivalent of probability values, since they represent the fraction of the area from the mean to the total area, which is taken as unity.

For example, the probability of 8 or more successes (head events in the case of coins) is equal to the sum of the probabilities of 8, 9, and 10 successes:

$$\mathbf{P}(S \text{ at least } 8) = \mathbf{P}(S_8) + \mathbf{P}(S_9) + \mathbf{P}(S_{10}) \qquad (7.12)$$

$$= .0439453 + .0097656 + .0009766 = .0546875$$

If the value of any integer in the discrete binomial distribution is interpreted as occupying a unit interval, then these 8 successes occupy an interval that ranges from 7.5 to 8.5, and 10 successes occupy an interval ranging from 9.5 to 10.5. Consequently the problem for comparison is that of the exact probability value of .0546875 with the normal curve approximation for an equivalent interval. The equivalent interval will be defined in terms of the z deviate values marking off the range of 7.5 to 10.5.

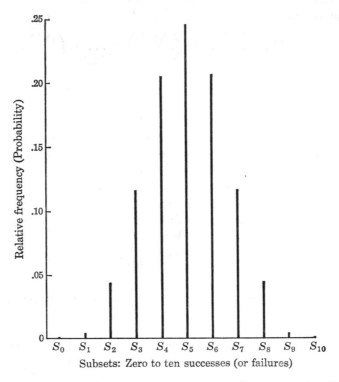

Fig. 7.3. Bernoulli Probability Model for the p Statistics of a Two-Class Population (p = Successes and q = Failures) when n = 10 and P = Q = .50 (Data from Table 7.3)

Table 7.3.   Probability of Each Subset in the Randomized Behavior of an Equiprobable Two-Class Population

Subsets		Combinations	Probability Ratio =	P*
10 Successes:	S_{10}	1	1/1024	.0009766
9 Successes:	S_9	10	10/1024	.0097656
8 Successes:	S_8	45	45/1024	.0439453
7 Successes:	S_7	120	120/1024	.1171875
6 Successes:	S_6	210	210/1024	.2050781
5 Successes:	S_5	252	252/1024	.2460938
4 Successes:	S_4	210	210/1024	.2050781
3 Successes:	S_3	120	120/1024	.1171875
2 Successes:	S_2	45	45/1024	.0439453
1 Success:	S_1	10	10/1024	.0097656
No Success:	S_0	1	1/1024	.0009766
$n_S = n+1 = 11$		$\sum = 1024$	$\sum = 1024/1024$	$\sum = 1.0000000$

*Probability values to seven decimal places from, "Tables of the Binomial Probability Distribution," National Bureau of Standards, Anon., 1952.

Correction for Continuity

The mean of a binomial distribution equals $n\mathbf{P}$, where n is the number of elements and $\mathbf{P}$ is the a priori probability of successes for any element of a subset. Therefore the mean of the distribution of Table 7.3 $= 10(\frac{1}{2}) = 5.0$. (Here $\mathbf{P}$ is usually symbolized as P, the parameter proportion of successes.)

$$\overline{X} = nP = 10(\tfrac{1}{2}) = 5.0 \tag{7.13}$$

The standard deviation of a binomial distribution equals $\sqrt{nPQ}$. Therefore σ for the distribution of Table 7.3:

$$\sigma = \sqrt{nPQ} \tag{7.14}$$

$$= \sqrt{10(\tfrac{1}{2})(\tfrac{1}{2})} = 1.5811388$$

The z deviate values of 7.5 and 10.5, which correct for the discontinuity or discreteness of the binomial point values of 8 and 10, are therefore equal to the following:

z for 7.5: $\qquad \dfrac{7.5 - 5.0}{1.5811388} = \dfrac{2.5}{1.5811388} = 1.5811388$

z for 10.5: $\qquad \dfrac{10.5 - 5.0}{1.5811588} = \dfrac{5.5}{1.5811388} = 2.8335499$

Table A shows (by interpolation) that .9430 of the area of the normal curve is below a z deviate of 1.5811; and .9977 of the area is below a z deviate of 3.4785. Hence the difference gives the area (probabilities) for the interval of 7.5 to 10.5:

Normal curve approximation of 7.5 to 10.5: $\quad$ .9977 − .9430 = .0547

This value of .0547 does not differ from the exact probability value of .0546875, obtained for the discrete binomial probability distribution of Fig. 7.2, when the latter is rounded off to four decimal places.

From the above, with the correction for continuity, it will be observed:

1. Even when n is as small as 10 and $P = Q = \frac{1}{2}$, the probability implications of the discrete model differ only slightly from those of the continuous probability model of the normal curve. Hence the implications of the latter are often used for inferential statistics about two-class populations (successes and failures; p and q). When, however, an exact statement of probabilities is needed for very small samples, then the probability value of the binomial should be used. The tables cited (National Bureau of Standards) give these probability values for n elements from 2 through 49, and for p values from .01 to .50 (when p is greater than .50, the value of q can, of course, be used, since $q = 1 - p$).

2. As the number of elements, n, approach infinity, the discrete binomial becomes one with the normal, continuous distribution.

3. Ordinarily probability values are expressed to only two or three decimal places. The computations above were carried to more places for the purpose of the comparison with the normal approximation.

Use of Binomial Probability Model When $P = Q = \frac{1}{2}$

The probability model given by the binomial for n elements and equiprobable values of $\frac{1}{2}$ for P and Q is very useful in applied statistics. This is especially the case when:

1. The number of elements, n, is small and exact probabilities are essential and therefore the approximations of the normal distribution may not be satisfactory.
2. A *distribution-free method* of analysis for inferential statistics is desired because it may not be reasonable to assume that the measures obtained are randomly drawn from a population of normally distributed measures or scores. The use of the binomial probability model is free of the normal distribution assumption.

Sign Test

The husband and wives of a sample of ten married couples are given "what-to-do tests" on child care. Their respective scores are as follows:

Couples:	A	B	C	D	E	F	G	H	I	J
Husbands' Scores:	10	12	13	16	18	21	30	31	34	36
Wives' Scores:	16	13	24	17	19	40	35	32	36	15
Signs	+	+	+	+	+	+	+	+	+	−

The signs give the direction of the difference between the scores of each wife and husband pair. In all cases but one the direction of the difference of each pair favors the distaff member. Only one husband, J, knows more of the answers than his wife does.

If the direction of the differences were just a matter of chance for a very large population of husband-wife pairs, then in the long run for such comparisons, the average difference by chance should be five plus signs and five minus signs. So, the question raised about data of this kind is whether the nine differences in the same direction, favoring the wives, may represent but a chance variation from a population model with an equal number of +'s and −'s.

The probability model of the binomial distribution in Table 7.3 will serve as a mathematical basis for an inference about the statistical significance of the result. The exact probability of obtaining at least nine plus signs, purely on the basis of chance, is equal to the sum of the probabilities for nine successes and ten successes. (Success here is defined as a plus sign.) From Table 7.3:

$$\mathbf{P}(S_9) + \mathbf{P}(S_{10}) = .0097656 + .0009766 = .0107422 \quad \text{or} \quad .011$$

Thus, in randomized sampling, for 10 pairs at a time from a two-class population evenly divided between *plus differences* and *minus differences*, the odds are about 1 in 100 that *at least* 9 plus differences will occur; i.e., the **P** of .011 indicates that in the long run, 9 or 10 plus differences will occur by chance 11 times in 1000 (or about 1 in 100). The relations involved here are illustrated in the graphs of Fig. 7.4. Fig. 7.4*a* is the hy-

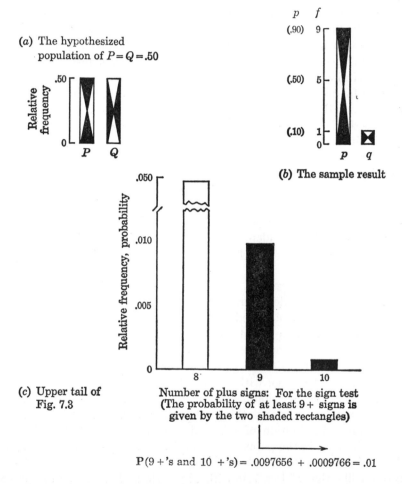

P(9 +'s and 10 +'s) = .0097656 + .0009766 = .01

Fig. 7.4.   Three Distributions: Hypothesized Population, the Sample Result, and the Upper Tail of the Bernoulli Sampling Distribution of Fig. 7.3

pothesized population in which $P = Q$; i.e., in which the *relative frequency* of plus signs = .50 = the relative frequency of minus signs = .50. (Note that *relative frequency* is *proportionate* frequency.) Fig. 7.4*b* portrays the empirical information, viz., the two-class result consisting of 9 plus signs (.90) and 1 minus sign (.10). Figure 7.4c is the upper tail, enlarged, of the hypothesized sampling distribution of Fig. 7.3 with the particular area of significance indicated. That is, the probability of a sample result equal to or greater than the one obtained and portrayed in Fig. 7.4b is marked off at the upper end of the sampling distribution of Fig. 7.4c.

One *identification* and one *decision* are now called for. First, it becomes necessary to identify the affairs of people with the implications of the cold and hard facts of probability theory. Unlike the experiment in "psychokinesis," the behavior now observed is not of dice (plus a person casting them) but of people, of a sample of husbands' and wives' test results. Their behavior of nine paired differences favoring the wives and only one paired difference favoring the husbands is now identified with the substance of Fig. 7.4a and the randomized behavior (of fair coins, for example) that generates the lawful and ordered variations portrayed in Fig. 7.3. It is *as if* this bit of human behavior is a sample result obtained from a two-class population like that of Fig. 7.4a. But is it? The answer to this question is the decision called for. If the behavior is so identified, then the relative frequency with which it may be expected to occur *on repeats*, in the long run, is the **P** value for nine pluses, .0097656. But the fact is that this particular result did not occur "in the long run." It occurred here and now and but once. Thus the identification of this "unique," single result with the mathematical models of Figs. 7.4a and 7.4b is for purposes of the argument.

With the argument set up, can it now be inferred that the result of nine pluses is but a random variation from a two-class population like that of Fig. 7.4a? It will be observed that some of the plus differences are based on test score differences of but one unit, as in the cases of couples B, D, E, and H. Should any measures of similar couples show up in another random sample, the direction of their differences may very well be minus instead of plus. Even so, with odds of but about 1 in 100 for *9 or more* plus differences, the decision is often made that a result of this kind is *not* to be explained entirely as nothing other than a random variation from a purely chance distribution of +'s and −'s; i.e., +'s half the time and −'s half the time in the population sampled. The argument is made that odds of 1 in 100 are too much of a long shot to warrant the identification of a result like that of Fig. 7.4b with Figs. 7.4a and c. Hence the population model of Fig. 7.4a and the particular sampling distribution of Fig. 7.4c are both rejected as unsuitable models for the data of this little experiment. It might therefore be concluded that at least some of the superior test performance of wives over that of their husbands is not just a matter of chance. It may be that, on the average, they really do know more about child care, but further research would be needed in order really to confirm this alternative hypothesis. (See the analysis of these data on p. 375.)

It is suggested, however, that students not be satisfied with results like the foregoing inasmuch as the sample is too small to begin with. Probability theory and the creditability of the logic involved in the preceding decision are being strained to the utmost, so to speak. Consequently it is better to give the facts greater opportunity to prove themselves than it is to rely on only such few observations. The student should at least replicate his experiment before contemplating the incorporation in an article or book of the dubious generality that wives are generally superior to their husbands on test X. The main value of a small experiment like the foregoing is exploratory rather than definitive. Had the results appeared to be purely a matter of chance, as would have been the case if there were only six or seven plus differences, then there might not ensue much enthusiasm or incentive for further research on such differences. But with the results as indicated, the leverage for further research is excellent.

BINOMIAL DISTRIBUTION WHEN $P \neq Q$

Not all two-class populations are composed of equiprobable results. Thus such a population might consist of one black ball and four white balls. Or a two-class population of successes, P, and failures, Q, might consist of five *different* elements, such as five differently colored balls, each of which is mutually exclusive and equiprobable. By chance, then, the probability of obtaining any particular ball in a random sample of one would be $\frac{1}{5}$. Also, the probability of successfully guessing which one of the five is drawn would be $\frac{1}{5}$ (**P** for success $= \frac{1}{5}$), and the probability of failing to guess correctly would be $\frac{4}{5}$ (**P** for failure $= \frac{4}{5}$). So, even though there are five different kinds of elements in the basic structure of the phenomena whose behavior is being analyzed, the population sampled is in effect a two-class behavioral population consisting of 20% successes and 80% failures. Instead of head successes and tail failures, each equiprobable, there are the two classes of results from guessing: successes and failures with **P** (*success*) $= \frac{1}{5}$ and **P** (*failure*) $= \frac{4}{5}$.

If the set of five different elements is doubled so that there are two of each kind for a total of ten elements, the binomial $(p + q)^{10}$ can again be expanded to give the mathematical, a priori probability model of the chance behavior to be expected in the long run for successful and unsuccessful guessing.

The a priori probability distribution of Table 7.4 is a very skewed distribution. Its form is portrayed in Fig. 7.5. The mean, $nP = 10(\frac{1}{5}) = 2.0$. The mean of two successes with a probability value of .302 has the highest **P** value of any of the 11 combinations of successes and failures. Thus, even though the distribution is skewed, the mean is at the modal interval. The odds of correctly guessing the character of all ten elements are only 1 in 10 million.

Table 7.4.   Probability of Successful Guessing when
$$P = \tfrac{1}{5} \text{ and } n = 10$$

Subset, Successes	Binomial Term*		Probability Ratio	P
10	p^{10} =	$\left(\dfrac{1}{5}\right)^{10}$ =	$\dfrac{1}{9765625}$ =	.0000001
9	$10p^9 q$ =	$10\left(\dfrac{1}{5}\right)^{9}\dfrac{4}{5}$ =	$10\,\dfrac{1}{1953125}\dfrac{4}{5}$ =	.0000041
8	$45p^8 q^2$ =	$45\left(\dfrac{1}{5}\right)^{8}\left(\dfrac{4}{5}\right)^{2}$ =	$45\,\dfrac{1}{390625}\dfrac{16}{25}$ =	.0000737
7	$120p^7 q^3$ =	$120\left(\dfrac{1}{5}\right)^{7}\left(\dfrac{4}{5}\right)^{3}$ =	$120\,\dfrac{1}{78125}\dfrac{64}{125}$ =	.0007864
6	$210p^6 q^4$ =	$210\left(\dfrac{1}{5}\right)^{6}\left(\dfrac{4}{5}\right)^{4}$ =	$210\,\dfrac{1}{15625}\dfrac{256}{625}$ =	.0055050
5	$252p^5 q^5$ =	$252\left(\dfrac{1}{5}\right)^{5}\left(\dfrac{4}{5}\right)^{5}$ =	$252\,\dfrac{1}{3125}\dfrac{1024}{3125}$ =	.0264241
4	$210p^4 q^6$ =	$210\left(\dfrac{1}{5}\right)^{4}\left(\dfrac{4}{5}\right)^{6}$ =	$210\,\dfrac{1}{625}\dfrac{4096}{15625}$ =	.0880804
3	$120p^3 q^7$ =	$120\left(\dfrac{1}{5}\right)^{3}\left(\dfrac{4}{5}\right)^{7}$ =	$120\,\dfrac{1}{125}\dfrac{16384}{78125}$ =	.2013265
2	$45p^2 q^8$ =	$45\left(\dfrac{1}{5}\right)^{2}\left(\dfrac{4}{5}\right)^{8}$ =	$45\,\dfrac{1}{25}\dfrac{65536}{390625}$ =	.3019899
1	$10pq^9$ =	$10\left(\dfrac{1}{5}\right)\left(\dfrac{4}{5}\right)^{9}$ =	$10\,\dfrac{1}{5}\dfrac{262144}{1953125}$ =	.2684355
None	q^{10} =	$\left(\dfrac{4}{5}\right)^{10}$ =	$\dfrac{1048576}{9765625}$ =	.1073742
			Σ =	1.000000

*See Table KK, p. 423, for coefficients of binomials.

From the probability model of Table 7.4, it is evident that on the average, simply by guessing, two successes out of ten guesses would be expected 30% of the time. All such a priori **P** values are deductively descriptive of long-run results. It is to be noted also that *only one correct guess* would be expected 27% of the time, and *no* correct guesses, 11% of the time. Thus, about two-thirds (68%) of the time, two or less successes would be expected by chance, since .302 + .268 + .107 = .677.

Use of Binomial Probability Model When $P = \tfrac{1}{5}$

The probability model of Table 7.4, illustrated in Fig. 7.5, can be directly applied to test the claim of a person who asserts he has ESP (extrasensory

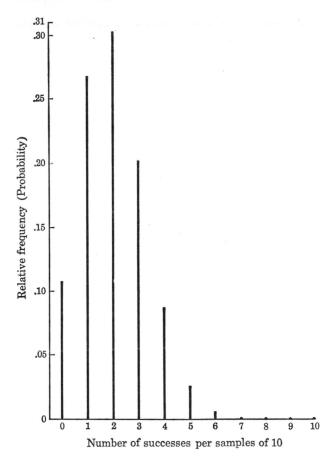

Fig. 7.5. Bernoulli Probability Model for the _p_ Statistic of a Two-Class Population (_p_ = Successes and _q_ = Failures) when _n_ = 10 and _P_ = $\frac{1}{5}$ and _Q_ = $\frac{4}{5}$
(Data of Table 7.4)

perceptual powers). Although he may not consider a series of only 10 cards, drawn randomly from a standard ESP deck of 25 cards, to be sufficient for a test of his powers, it nevertheless may be very suggestive if the claimant should achieve correct results for all ten trys. It is not possible to _prove_ a hypothesis, but it is possible to reject one as unreasonable. If the purely chance hypothesis is not disclaimed in consequence of the results of ten trials, then the claimant should be given more trials. Given enough trials but failing to produce a large enough proportion of successes to warrant the rejection of the purely chance hypothesis, the latter hypothesis wins by default.

Within the framework of ten elements (ten ESP cards), a result of only three or four successes has a **P** value too high to warrant the statistical inference that something other than chance is operating. On the other hand, if the claimant has at least six successes out of ten, the **P** value is equal to less than 1 in 100. From Table 7.4,

$$\mathbf{P}(6 + 7 + 8 + 9 + 10) = .0063693 \quad (\mathbf{P} \text{ of at least 6 successes})$$

In the long run, such a result as six or more successes may be expected to occur by chance about 6 times in 1000. Hence a result of this order might lead some researchers to decide in favor of the claimant. Certainly, if the claimant should have at least eight successes, the **P** value of which is only 8 in 100,000, there might be some question about the adequacy of the chance hypothesis to "explain" the result. The skeptic might argue, on the other hand, that this was after all an occurrence of a "long shot." He would therefore replicate the experiment, i.e., test the claimant again with another series of ten cards, etc. If the "long shot" performance could not be repeated, then the skeptic would enjoy his decision in favor of chance.

LAPLACE-GAUSSIAN NORMAL DISTRIBUTION

This distribution was described in Chapter 4 as a hypothesized mathematical model of the variation characteristic of many attributes or traits. It is also relevant and essential as a model of the variation that is characteristic of certain statistics calculated from random samples of various populations. It has already been indicated that the normal curve satisfactorily describes the behavior of the proportions (p) of successes or favorable events of random samples of two-class populations, when n is large and P is .50. Even, however, when n is as small as 10 and P is .50, the normal probability model serves as a close approximation of the discrete distribution. As n increases, P may take values somewhat less than or somewhat more than .50, and the variation in random sampling will still be satisfactorily described by the normal distribution.

Normal Distribution Function

The equation of the normal curve of Laplace and Gauss may be expressed, following Karl Pearson, in the following familiar mathematical and statistical terms:

$$y = \frac{N}{\sigma\sqrt{2\pi}} e^{-x^2/2\sigma^2} \tag{7.15}$$

where y represents the ordinate (frequency or relative frequency) for any value of the x variable, N is the number of cases, σ is the standard deviation of the x variable, x is a deviation from the mean of x, $(X - \overline{X})$, and pi and e (the base of Naperian system of logarithms) are mathematical constants whose values are 3.1416 and 2.7183, respectively.

With the total area of the normal distribution taken as unity, N of the above formula is 1.0. The deviate values may be expressed in terms of z transformations, in which case σ of Formula 7.15 becomes 1.0, and the function simplifies to the following:

$$y = \frac{1}{\sqrt{2\pi}} \, e^{-z^2/2} \qquad (7.16)$$

It may already have been observed in Table A (Appendix), which gives the probabilities for z deviate values in terms of the fractions of total area of the distribution, that the value of y at the mean is .3989. This is the curve at its maximum ordinate value and is derived from the preceding formula for a z deviate of zero (since this is the mean):

$$y = \frac{1}{\sqrt{2\pi}} = .3989 \qquad (7.16a)$$

Normal Curve of Error

It was indicated in Chapter 1 that the normal distribution originated as the normal curve of error. As applied to random sampling, the "errors" referred to are not mistakes. Rather, they are the *variations* that are expected to occur in sampling when the method of sampling is random. These errors may also include chance variations that occur in measurement and in the making of observations. The basic factor of significance for applied statistics is that the *behavior of random variation is lawful*. The effect of random variation on the statistics of sample results is describable, either deductively or inductively, by various types of distributions. Just what type will be descriptive of a particular statistic depends on the:

1. Nature of its parameter in the parent population.
2. Nature of the distribution of the parent population.
3. Size of the randomized sample.

Distributions of the *means* of randomized samples of a given size drawn from normally distributed, infinitely large populations can be inferred as approximating the form of the Laplace-Gaussian normal curve of error.

Law of Large Numbers and Central Limit Theorem

The law of large numbers states that the mean of means (or of proportions) of random samples tends to approach the value of the parameter mean as the number of observations is increased. Thus this law implies that in the random tossing of a fair coin, the ratio of m/n approaches 1/2 as a limit, with probability of 1 as a limit.

The law of large numbers, however, gives no information about the *distribution* of mean values; it tells nothing about how the sample results cluster around the mean of means. For this the central limit law is needed. Two theorems of this law are particularly essential to the development of inferential statistics.

THEOREM I: If a variable possesses a normal distribution, then the means of random samples of size n will also possess a normal distribution whose mean will equal the parameter mean and whose standard deviation will be equal to the parameter standard deviation divided by the square root of the size of the sample. Thus the expectation of $\overline{X}$ is μ, and the expectation of $\sigma_{\bar{x}}$ is $\sigma/\sqrt{n}$.

$$E(\overline{X}) = \mu \qquad (7.17)$$

$$E(\sigma_{\bar{x}}) = \frac{\sigma}{\sqrt{n}} \qquad (7.18)$$

THEOREM II: If a variable possesses a distribution with a parameter mean μ and standard deviation σ, then the means of random samples of size n will possess an *approximately* normal distribution with a mean of μ and standard deviation of $\sigma/\sqrt{n}$, the approximation becoming increasingly good as n increases.

These theorems of the central limit law are indispensable to the study of populations from the data of random samples. They provide the foundation for parametric statistics, for the estimation of parameters from statistics, as $E(\overline{X}) = \mu$. Even though parent populations may not be normally distributed, if the samples are large enough, the distribution of the means of random samples will be approximately normal and hence the mean of means is the expected value of the parameter mean. Given the information about the size of the expected variance of a distribution of sample means, it is also possible to estimate the probability that a particular sample mean or proportion will differ from the parameter mean or parameter proportion by any given amount, the amount being usually measured in terms of a normal z deviate. But in samples of means (*not* proportions) of size less than 25, the amount is usually measured in terms of "Student's t statistic" (see p. 209 and Table B, Appendix) because s is increasingly unsatisfactory as a point estimate of σ as n becomes very small.

PROBABILITY SAMPLING*

In order that the a priori probability distributions of mathematical statistics may be utilized as models for inferential statistics with empirical data, the methods used to obtain cases for observation and measurement have to follow certain ground rules. These rules are designed to yield a representative sample of instances. They will be *representative* in the sta-

---

*The term *probability sampling* originated with W. E. Deming (1950).

tistical sense of differing from the distribution of the parent population only because of *random variations* arising out of the sampling procedure itself. Thus, if inferences are to be made from the statistics of samples about the parameters of populations, as in the next chapter, the sample has to be drawn by a method that will yield a probability sample.

A probability sample is one drawn from a population in such a way that implications of probability theory can be applied to the results. Thus the best single estimate of a population mean from a sample result is provided by the mean of a sample drawn *randomly* from that population. Probability samples are obtained by carefully executed methods of randomization. They are *not* haphazard samples. Note, also: It is the *method* of sampling that is random, not the sample result. The sample result should be representative of the population in the sense that it differs from the population only by virtue of the effects of chance variation when probability sampling has been employed.

Consider, for example, the representativeness of the mean ages in months of 16 samples of 10 cases each, *drawn randomly and with replacement* from a population consisting of 34 elements. (The 34 elements are the ages in months of 34 students of an undergraduate statistics course.) Figure 7.6 illustrates the variation from sample to sample to be expected simply on the basis of randomization, which in effect is the result of chance. Sometimes the sample mean is less than, sometimes more than, the parameter mean μ. Interestingly the greatest differences happen to be for the first sample and the last sample. Regardless of their divergence from the parameter mean, each sample mean is *by definition* representative of μ. This is the case because each is based on a randomly drawn sample. Some are, of course, more representative than others in the sense that they differ less from μ. But note: When the value of μ is unknown, as is usually the case in research, it is impossible in the comparison of any two means based on samples of the same size to infer which is the more representative.

The average value of all 16 sample means is a mean of 242.22 months of age, which is very close to the parameter mean age of 242.21 months. In effect the mean of the 16 means is a mean of a random sample of $16 \times 10 = 160$ observations. It is obvious that a much more *accurate* estimate of a parameter mean is obtainable from a random sample of 160 observations than from a sample of only 10.

Frame and Sampling with Replacement

The 16 samples of 10 observations each whose means are given in Fig. 7.6 can be considered a single randomized sample of 160 observations because each sample of the population of 34 elements was drawn randomly and with replacement. Sampling with replacement signifies that each sampling unit is "put back" into the *frame* as soon as it has been observed and its value or characteristic recorded. The frame is the complete roster of all

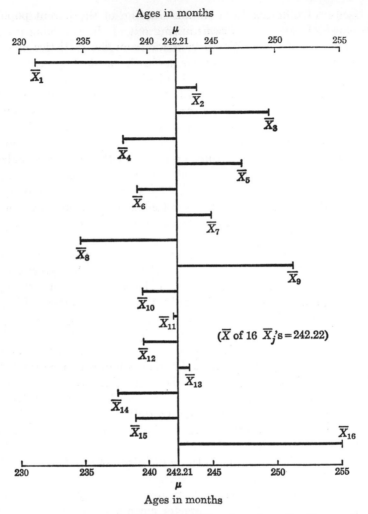

Fig. 7.6.   Sampling Variation of Means of Random Samples (k samples $=$ 15)
(Data from Table 7.5)

the sampling units of the population to be sampled; here it consists of the 34 ages in months of the 34 students.

Sampling units may be the various faces of a die, the numbers of a telephone directory, a file of index cards with names, persons, households, classes, schools, city blocks, counties, etc.   As each unit shows up in a sample, its characteristics are observed, enumerated or measured, and recorded.   In experimental psychology, the identification of sampling units is ordinarily fairly easy; they are the persons used as subjects in the investigation.   But the frame often leaves much to be desired because it is vague rather than definitive.

Table 7.5. Randomized Sampling with Replacement from a Frame of 34 Units

(Ages of a Class of College Students, in Months; $n_j = 10$)*

THE FRAME		RANDOMIZED SAMPLES**					
Code No. of Student	Age to the Nearest Month	SAMPLE NO. 1		SAMPLE NO. 2		SAMPLE NO. 3	
		Code No.	Age (−200)	Code No.	Age (−200)	Code No.	Age (−200)
1	221	3	31	5	33	10	80
2	233	22	31	23	42	14	57
3	231	25	37	19	94	33	31
4	277	12	30	13	29	32	70
5	233	13	29	21	55	11	28
6	223	31	35	15	40	10	80
7	260	12	30	30	44	13	29
8	229	1	21	24	28	9	26
9	226	22	31	10	80	21	55
10	280	25	37	11	28	20	57

$$\sum = 312 \qquad \sum = 473 \qquad \sum = 513$$

$$\overline{X}'_1 = 31.2 \qquad \overline{X}'_2 = 47.3 \qquad \overline{X}'_3 = 51.3$$
$$+200$$
$$\overline{X}_1 = 231.2 \qquad \overline{X}_2 = 247.3 \qquad \overline{X}_3 = 251.3$$

11	228
12	230
13	229
14	257
15	240

16	228
17	241
18	248
19	294
20	257

SAMPLE NO. 4   SAMPLE NO. 5   SAMPLE NO. 6

$$\sum = 431 \qquad \sum = 438 \qquad \sum = 391$$
$$\overline{X}'_4 = 43.1 \qquad \overline{X}'_5 = 43.8 \qquad \overline{X}'_6 = 39.1$$
$$+200$$
$$\overline{X}_4 = 243.1 \qquad \overline{X}_5 = 243.8 \qquad \overline{X}_6 = 239.1$$

21	255
22	231
23	242
24	228
25	237

SAMPLE NO. 7   SAMPLE NO. 8   SAMPLE NO. 9

$$\overline{X}_7 = 239.5 \qquad \overline{X}_8 = 237.5 \qquad \overline{X}_9 = 249.6$$

26	238
27	261
28	239
29	225
30	244

SAMPLE NO. 10   SAMPLE NO. 11   SAMPLE NO. 12

$$\overline{X}_{10} = 244.9 \qquad \overline{X}_{11} = 242.0 \qquad \overline{X}_{12} = 238.9$$

31	235
32	270
33	231
34	234

SAMPLE NO. 13   SAMPLE NO. 14   SAMPLE NO. 15

$$\overline{X}_{13} = 238.0 \qquad \overline{X}_{14} = 234.7 \qquad \overline{X}_{15} = 239.6$$

$$N = 34 \quad \sum = 1435$$
$$\mu = 242.21$$

SAMPLE NO. 16

$$\overline{X}_{16} = 255.0$$

*All 34 students of the same sex from a larger group of 90 males and females.

**Ages were coded to two-place numbers by the subtraction of 200 from each. Two-place random numbers of Table L, pp. 424–425, were used for the selection of 10 cases per sample.

Initially, sampling units may serve to identify the unit of investigation; thus a telephone number may serve to identify a household or a person. In large-scale surveys of peoples' attitudes, or opinions, or habits, etc., the initial or *primary sampling units* may be the 5000-odd counties of the United States, and the *secondary* and *tertiary sampling units* may be geographic sections and then households within each county. This would be an example of a *multistage* sampling procedure: If the frame of the primary sampling units were randomly sampled, and if the consequent sample of counties were randomly subsampled for smaller geographic units such as sections or assembly districts, then the districts in turn would be randomly sampled for dwelling units, from which the basic sampling units of *persons* would be obtained. The frame of the primary sampling units could be easily established, since it would consist of a roster of all counties of the 50 states, but the frame of the second-level sampling units might require maps by aerial surveys, or rosters of political subdivisions such as assembly districts, or geographic subdivisions such as city blocks. Sometimes a frame will not include all sampling units of a population because many sampling units of a population cannot be identified: for example, the ubiquitous sophomore subjects of experimental psychology, or the psychoneurotics studied in clinical psychology.

Unrestricted Randomized Sampling

A probability sample is *by definition* one obtained from a population by a process known as *randomized selection*. Unless randomization enters into the drawing of samples, the models of probability theory will not be applicable to sample results and hence sound inferential statistics cannot be had. The most commonly drawn probability sample is the unrestricted randomized sample. This is a sample selected in such a way that every sampling unit or element of the population sampled has an equal chance of being selected. In general, *probability sampling* consists in randomized selection of sampling units, each of which has a known probability of selection, but not necessarily equiprobable. In a fair die, the faces are by definition equiprobable. In a *loaded* die, the faces are not equiprobable, but a dishonest gambler who is statistically sophisticated, can work out the probability of each face empirically and work to his advantage the implications of probability sampling for his profession.

Generally the frames to be sampled are such that either an unrestricted randomized sample or a series of randomized interdependent subsamples* may be drawn. How is randomization accomplished in the drawing of a sample? Generally, either one of two resources is employed: a lottery technique or a table of random numbers. A lottery technique was used in the order of drawing Selective Service numbers at the beginning of

---

*See p. 204.

World War II. Each of 800-odd numbers from 1 to n was printed on uniform-size slips of paper, rolled and placed in uniform capsules. All were placed in a large bowl, thoroughly mixed, and then drawn one at a time, with thorough mixing between each drawing. Since lottery devices are not always at hand, *the results of lottery devices* in the form of tables of random numbers are more frequently used. One such table is presented in the Appendix (Table L) and is based on the order of the Selective Service numbers obtained by the lottery procedure just described.*

Use of Table of Random Numbers

When all sampling units of a population are known and can be given serial numbers of from 1 to n, it is relatively easy to draw an unrestricted random sample with the aid of a table of random numbers. If N, the number of sampling units in the frame, is 100 or less, two-place numbers are used. Two-place numbers can be obtained from Table L by (1) combining adjoining columns, or (2) combining adjoining rows, or (3) combining adjoining numbers by pairs in either a row or a column. Number 100 would be 00. Similarly, three-place numbers can be obtained by combining three adjacent columns or rows, etc. Number 1000 would be 000.

The 16 samples of 10 observations each whose means are given in Fig. 7.6 were obtained by the use of Table L. As already indicated, the sampling was with replacement. This procedure was used in order to achieve the effect of drawing randomized samples indefinitely from a small population consisting of 34 elements. Each separate element was, by the technique used, equiprobable, and therefore with odds of 1 in 34 of being selected. However not all *age values* in the frame were equiprobable because some ages in months were duplicated. (Most of the duplication could have been avoided if necessary by taking age to the nearest day.) Nevertheless the results consist of a series of 16 samples obtained by unrestricted randomization.

In experimental research and in survey research, sampling is usually done without replacement, since each sampling unit (person or household, etc.) is usually a subject for investigation with unduplicable, irreversible biological and psychological processes. Hence it is ordinarily neither feasible nor desirable to have the same sampling unit enter more than once into such research samples. Therefore, when sampling without replacement with a table of random numbers, any serial number that recurs is ignored.

Stratified Randomized Samples

If a population is subdivided into several subpopulations, the total sample may be obtained as a series of random samplings drawn from each

---

*See also R. A. Fisher, and F. Yates (1938); Kendall and Smith (1938); or Rand Corporation (1955).

subclassified stratum. If the criteria used for such subclassifications are in fact correlated with the population characteristic(s) being sampled for study, then the variance of the results will be reduced. A reduction in the variance will make possible a more *precise* estimation of the population characteristic (as will be shown in the next chapter). Thus, if sex and education are correlated to a significant degree with voters' preferences for political candidates, a more precise estimate of population preferences can be made from the information of random samplings stratified for sex and education than could be from unrestricted randomized samples from the whole, the size of the total sample being the same in both methods. If educational status were trichotomized, there would be six subpopulations to sample randomly: each of the three educational groups of each sex. Population estimates are then made from the combined results of the samples of the six subpopulations, with each sample result weighted proportionately to the size of its parent subpopulation in the total population. Sometimes the samples are in the first instance drawn of a size that will be proportionate to the ratio of the subpopulation to the total population. But this is not essential as long as the results for each stratum are treated and combined in their proper proportions.

Stratified randomized samples are often referred to as representative samples or proportional samples because of the way they are constructed. One or more characteristics, such as the two already mentioned, or age, type of residence or dwelling unit, economic status, and place of residence (urban vs. rural, or eastern states vs. western states, etc.) are sampled proportionately so that the make-up of the whole sample is in its parts proportionate to the make-up of the population as a whole. Thus it is the *structure* of *known characteristics* of the sample that is representative of or proportionate to the population, *not* the results of observations or measurements made on the members of the sample. However, if the method of randomization has been properly used within each structure, then the sample result should be *representative* in the sense already defined, and with less variance than in unrestricted random sampling. In other words, the representativeness of the sample result is a matter of differences (between the statistics and the population parameters) that are a function of random variations only. Naturally there will be differences. Stratified random sampling reduces the differences, as measured by the variance, whenever the characteristics stratified for are significantly correlated with the characteristics to be observed and studied. If there is no such correlation, then stratification has not increased the efficiency of the result over what would have been obtained with an unrestricted randomized sample of the whole population.

The examples of Table 7.6 illustrate situations (a) and (b); in (a), stratification should reduce the variance and hence increase the precision or efficiency of the results for estimating parameter values; in (b), stratification would be of no help toward a more efficient result.

Table 7.6.   Relevant and Irrelevant Situations for Stratification of Sex in the Study of Preferences for A and B

(Population of Males and Females = 100%)

a. TO STRATIFY FOR SEX

	Males	Females	
Preference for A:	40%	15%	55%
Preference for B:	10%	35%	45%
	50%	50%	100%

b. NOT TO STRATIFY FOR SEX

	Males	Females	
Preference for A:	27.5%	27.5%	55%
Preference for B:	22.5%	22.5%	45%
	50%	50%	100%

In Table 7.6a, an unrestricted random sample of a given size would not be as efficient as the same number of observations divided 50-50 between two samples of the subpopulations of males and females. This is the case because of the marked correlation between sex difference and A and B preferences: The males prefer A by 4 to 1; the females prefer B by $2\frac{1}{3}$ to 1. Also, the smaller the population difference in percentages for A and B preferences, the more important stratification may be in order that a sample result of a given size will be significant.

In Table 7.6b, it should be apparent that stratification will not increase the efficiency of the result. Here there is no correlation between sex and preference. Unrestricted random sampling of the whole population will be just as efficient as stratification.

In field surveys, the researcher usually does not know whether a significant correlation exists between characteristics of his respondents and the attitudes or opinions, etc., he may wish to learn about. In such cases he usually stratifies for one or two characteristics which past experience has shown to be significant in analogous situations. At least no harm will be done when stratification can be properly employed, and it may help.*

Unbiased Inference

The purpose of sampling is to obtain a result that will mirror characteristics of a population (and as closely as possible) subject only to the effects

---

*Perhaps the most useful survey method in which stratification can be employed easily and effectively is the zonal method of interpenetrating subsamples, described on p. 204 ff.

of random variation, which will vary with the size of the sample. Two types of sampling errors may occur in the process of sampling:

1. Those arising from biased selections of sampling units of a population.
2. Those arising from chance differences between members of the population in the sample and those not in the sample.

The first kind of error is a *constant* source of difference between the members of the sample and the members of the population not in the sample. Consequently this type of error is not eliminated simply by increasing the size of the sample.

When only errors of the second kind, viz., random sampling errors, are present, then *unbiased estimates* of population parameters can be made. The effects of sampling error *can be reduced* by increasing the size of the randomized samples. Significant stratification of populations into subpopulations for random sampling will, as already indicated, also reduce random sampling errors.

Variable Sampling Fractions

Variable sampling fractions can also be used with stratification to assist in the reduction of the effects of random sampling error. The sampling fraction is the ratio of n/N, where n is the size of the sample and N is the size of the population. Some characteristics are easier to sample than others because of their greater frequency of occurrence in a population. Thus a small random sample of households in an urban population like Kansas City will doubtless include members with the prevailing cultural attitudes toward non-Christian religions but will probably miss the inclusion of members of small religious groups in Kansas City, such as the Moslems and Buddhists, who may live there. The laws of chance are such that very large random samples may be required in order to give the very few of a large population an opportunity to show up in the sample. If it is important to have the views of such small subpopulations, then stratification can be used, and the sampling fractions of each subpopulation varied, i.e., increased for the small subpopulations and held at the original proportion or even decreased for the very large subpopulations. Whereas a sampling fraction of 1% may be quite adequate for the study of the attitudes of Protestant Christians in Kansas City, a sampling fraction of 10% may be necessary to obtain reliable information from the subpopulation of Moslems.

When variable sampling fractions are used in order to obtain more reliable unbiased information from small subpopulations, the overall sample results can be combined by reweighting the results of each substratum proportionately to its relative size in the population. If the statistic obtained were a mean, the procedure would be exactly analogous to the computation of a properly weighted mean from a series of means. (See p. 63.)

Large vs. Small Samples

The student who is learning statistics will come across two contrasting expressions, viz., "large samples" and "small samples." It would be quite natural therefore if he should inquire: "How large is *large* and how small is *small?*" The answer to this question depends on which of several sets of circumstances is uppermost for consideration. One set is from the point of view of probability theory and the behavior of the statistics of randomized samples. A second set is concerned with the complexity of the characteristics of a population to be studied. A third set is concerned with the precision desired for or required by an investigation.

The first set of circumstances has an amazing and somewhat unbelievable quality. Samples of less than 25 or 30 observations are considered small samples and those of around 30 or more are considered large samples. Why? Because the behavior of some statistics of very small samples vary noticeably and significantly from the behavior of statistics of samples whose size is around 30 or more. Thus the sampling distributions of mean statistics of very small samples have a form noticeably different from the form of the sampling distributions of mean statistics of samples whose n is around 30 or more. Paradoxically, the forms of the latter are approximately the same, and usually sufficiently so, regardless of whether n is 30 or 3000. In the case of the latter, approximately 34% of the area of the sampling distributions is between the mean and $\pm 1\sigma$. The form of such distributions approximate that of the Laplace-Gaussian. If, however, the means are based on the smallest possible statistical samples, viz., $n = 2$, then only 25% of the area of the sampling distribution of means is between the mean and $\pm 1\sigma$. Such distributions are extremely leptokurtic. (See probability Table B of Appendix for small samples.)

Secondly, the effective size of a sample is also related to the nature and complexity of the characteristics to be studied. A vocabulary test-sample of ten multiple-choice word items may be sufficient to differentiate reliably the feeble-minded from the bright, but it may take a sample of 100 items to differentiate reliably the very bright from the just bright. Similarly, if one wishes to ascertain the state of public opinion on complex issues for which attitudes have not polarized into black (B) and white (W) but range through many shadings of gray, then to have respondents with all the various shadings represented, larger samples will be required than would be necessary for a two-class population with either B or W opinions.

Thirdly, sample size is necessarily geared to precision requirements as well as to the cost of sampling. Preliminary, exploratory studies may not require the precision that definitive investigations demand. Thus pilot research oriented toward teasing out those factors possibly relevant to the development and maintenance of efficient study habits among high school students of City X would not require so large a sample of students as would a definitive investigation of the relative importance of the various factors found to play a role in efficient study habits. Increasing the size of randomized samples or of stratified-randomized samples will increase the precision with which estimates of the relative importance of factors can be made.

Accuracy vs. Precision in Sampling

The difference between accuracy and precision in sampling is analogous to differences that may occur in shooting at a target. Given the same number of shots (size sample), one person will have a precise but inaccurate result if his hits are grouped closely together on the target at 4 o'clock in the nine-ring, whereas another person may be accurate in that he always hits the bull's-eye but is less precise because his shots scatter much more. Increasing the size of samples should increase the precision of the result, but it won't help the accuracy of the result if there is a constant error (bias) operating throughout. Randomization of errors in sampling populations or subpopulations is the built-in requirement for precision in sampling. By increasing the size of samples fourfold, the precision of parameter mean estimates will be approximately doubled, provided the errors are randomized. But the accuracy of parameter mean estimates derives mainly from well-designed experiments and field studies, provided the sample is not too small to begin with. The difficulty that researchers must face up to lies in the fact that usually there is not available independent information about the accuracy of an inferred parameter value, which may nevertheless be estimated with great precision. Unfortunately constant errors in sampling and in measurement cannot be relied upon to stand up and announce themselves.

Importance of Random Selection in Sampling

Sampling methods comprise a study in itself, as was pointed out in Chapter 1. It is beyond the scope of this introductory work in applied statistics to go into further detail about sampling techniques. However, the importance of random selection in sampling cannot be overemphasized. *Purposive selection* is sometimes used in research for special problems, but results based on purposive selection are not amenable to sampling theory. There has to be the element of random selection in sampling if the implications of sampling theory are to be utilized for inferential statistics, such as those developed in the remaining chapters of this book.

Sampling Distributions and Standard Errors

The standard deviation of the sampling distribution of a given statistic is called the *standard error of that statistic*. Thus the means of many random samples form a sampling distribution of means, provided n, the size of each sample, remains constant. The statistics of Fig. 7.6 comprise a small sampling distribution of 16 means. The standard deviation of a sampling distribution of means is called the *standard error of the mean*, which is an elision of "the standard deviation of a sampling distribution of means whose variation is a function of randomized sampling error."

It was earlier indicated that the *mean* of any single randomized sample affords an unbiased estimate of the parameter mean of the parent population. It is the *best single estimate* that can be made. But it is fallible in the sense that its value is affected by the randomized effects of sampling variation.

The *standard error* of a sampling distribution of means provides a basis for *estimating the variation* in sample means to be expected in random sampling. Hence it serves as the basis for parameter estimation, the objective of a great deal of modern inferential statistics. Such estimation is the subject of the next chapter.

RANDOMIZATION IN EXPERIMENTAL DESIGNS

It was pointed out in the first chapter that randomization is perhaps the most important characteristic added during this century to the design of an experiment. The purpose of randomization in experimental work is to avoid biases. A technique is needed that will prevent one experimental variable (treatment or method) from being continually favored over another, or continually disfavored over another. Psychologists have long been aware of the importance of avoiding this kind of bias because of the obvious roles of adaptation and learning on performance (usually favorable bias) and of fatigue or boredom (usually unfavorable bias).

Two kinds of randomization are available for research, viz., *simple* (*unrestricted*) randomization and *restricted* randomization. Simple randomization is often satisfactory when large numbers of observations or measurements are to be made. Restricted randomization may be more desirable for shorter series. Thus, if a random sample of a specified population is to serve as its own control and the problem is to determine the possible effects of drugs A, B, and C, and placebo D (the control) on mental alertness, the order of the three experimental treatments and one control treatment can be randomized in either a restricted or an unrestricted way by the use of an ordinary well-shuffled deck of playing cards. Each suit would represent a treatment, A, B, C, or D. If the randomization were unrestricted, then the odds would be against a series of four treatments containing each mode of treatment. But over 13 such series, the number of treatments for each would work out equally, since there are 13 cards of each suit in the 52-card deck. In practice, however, restricted randomization is used for such a situation because each series of four trials is an experimental unit (or block), and it is therefore better to have each treatment represented. Hence the drawing of cards would continue with no suit used twice and until each suit was represented in the series of four (only the first three have to be determined, since there are only three degrees of freedom here).

Randomization in some form is a statistical technique that thus applies both to the selection of sampling units (persons or things) and to the procedures of observation and measurement. As Cochran and Cox (1957, p. 8) have pointed out, "randomization is somewhat analogous to insurance, in that it is a precaution against disturbances that may or may not occur and that may or may not be serious if they do occur." It is also to be emphasized that the way in which research is conducted not only affects the quality of statistical inference but also the kind of statistical calculations needed for such inference. (See Chapter 11.)

ESTIMATION OF PARAMETERS

> *The mark of an educated man is the ability
> to make a reasoned guess on the basis of
> insufficient information.*
>
> ## A. Lawrence Lowell

THE estimation of parameters and the testing of statistical hypotheses represent two aspects of inferential statistics. In this chapter, procedures for the estimation of parameters are developed. It will be seen that such estimates have a twofold usefulness:

1. *In experimental research*, the reliability or precision of a result can be specified, provided the information is based on a probability sample of a defined population.
2. *In survey research*, parameter values such as means or proportions can be estimated with a high degree of confidence, provided the sample data are derived from probability samples of the parent populations.

The estimation of parameters from the data of samples is one of the most important uses of probability statistics. Parameters are estimated by a process that relates information about the part (the sample) to the whole (the population, or the *frame of sampling units* of the population). The estimation of parameters takes two forms:

1. *A single value* or point estimate of the parameter.
2. *An interval estimate* that is inferred, with varying levels of confidence, to include the value of the parameter. The wider this interval, or band of possible values, the more likely that it includes the value of the parameter sought.

Single Value Estimates of Parameters

Single value or point estimates of parameters are based on the statistics of randomized probability samples, which may or may not be stratified. This is true also of interval estimates. In fact the interval estimate is a measure of the *reliability* of the single value estimate. The single value estimate is the best estimate of a parameter that can be made from the statistics of the sample results. The interval estimate takes into account the margin of sampling error to be expected in randomized sampling. That is to say, it is a measure of the margin of expected difference between the sample result and what the result would have been had *all* instances of the frame, or parent population, been observed and counted, or measured.

Single value estimates may be for total **F**'s as well as for parameter means, variances, correlation coefficients, and proportions or percentages. Thus, if the *sampling fraction n/N* is 1/50 for a population whose preferences for X are studied, and a randomized 2% sample shows that 263 persons prefer X, then the single value estimate of **F** for the parent population is

Estimate of F: $\quad \mathbf{F} = \dfrac{N}{n} \cdot (f) = \dfrac{50}{1}\, (263) = 13{,}150$ (8.1)

Thus the multiplier for f is N/n, the inverse of the sampling fraction n/N.

The arithmetic mean of a randomized sample is the point estimate of the parameter mean of the parent population of measurables:

$$E(\overline{X}) = \mu \qquad (8.2)$$

The expected value of the mean of a random sample is the parameter mean. All such single value or point estimates are, however, subject to the randomized errors of sampling variation. Hence their reliability is measured by means of an interval estimate of the parameter.

Reliability of Parameter Estimates

Single value estimates of parameters do not in themselves reveal the precision or reliability with which such estimates can be made. Such precision or reliability is dependent on:

1. n, the size of the randomized sample.
2. The size of the sampling fraction when *finite* populations are being studied.

In unbiased, randomized sampling, the margin of expected sampling error decreases both with increases in sample size and in the proportionate size of the sampling fraction.

Interval Estimation of Parameters

The interval estimation of parameters consists essentially of the following steps:

1. A decision about the *level of significance* or about the *confidence criterion* to be employed is made initially. This is a decision that affects the degree of sampling variation that will be accepted as *reasonable* for the ex-

perimental or the survey problem. It is made initially lest the character of the sample results bias this decision.

2. The designing of an appropriate sampling procedure and the assembly of the sample(s) of observations are accomplished by probability sampling. The observations take the form of countables or measurables. The sampling units (persons, for example) have to be drawn randomly, with or without stratification, from identifiable and accessible instances of the parent population (i.e., the frame). Each sampling unit has to be capable of being identified by a serial number. As mentioned before, the randomized sampling is best accomplished by the use of a table of random numbers. If all members of a finite universe are identifiable and accessible, then there is no gap between the entire population and the *parent population*, or frame. To the extent to which there may be a gap, the generality of any statistical inferences about parameters is limited; i.e., limited to the parent population (or frame) actually sampled.

3. Postulation is made of a probability distribution appropriate to the size of the randomized sample(s) and the measure whose parameter value is to be estimated. This step asserts the probability model that most likely will portray the *pattern* or form of sampling variation to be expected in the particular study. The pattern ordinarily most appropriate for means and proportions of large samples is the Laplace-Gaussian normal probability distribution.

4. The computation or calculated estimate of the expected sampling variation is usually made in terms of the standard deviation, using a formula appropriate to the probability model hypothesized in the preceding step. This measure, the standard deviation of the sampling variation, is known as the *standard error* of the sampling distribution of the particular statistic whose parameter is to be estimated. Thus the standard error of the mean measures *the expected margin of difference* between the sample mean and the parameter mean of the parent population.

5. The estimate is made of the interval or range of possible values that is inferred to include the value of the parameter sought. This is the *confidence interval*. It is the *interval estimate* of the parameter. It is the statistical inference, and it is inferred with a very high level of confidence when the margin of error is set wide enough to include most values that reasonably may be expected to include the value of the parameter.

The interval estimate, or range of values, is determined by relating the significance level or confidence criterion of the first step to the value of the standard error obtained in the fourth step.

ESTIMATION OF PARAMETER MEANS

The arithmetic mean of *an empirical distribution of means* is an unbiased estimate of the parameter mean of a parent population, provided the samples (all of size n_j) are drawn randomly from the parent population, either with or without stratification. The results of a single randomized sample also may give an unbiased estimate of the parameter mean. In both cases the estimates are point estimates of the parameter. If the several samples are combined, or the single sample is sufficiently large so that the expected sampling variation is small enough to be insignificant to the characteristic being counted or measured, then the single value or point estimate of the parameter mean may be sufficient in itself. That is to say, the interval estimate of the parameter mean may not be required. However, when samples are not very large and sampling fractions are small, the individual means of randomized samples may be expected to vary appreciably from the mean of the parent population. Hence, the interval estimate, as well as the single value estimate, is needed. As already indicated, it is given by the confidence interval.

Confidence Interval and Standard Error of the Mean

The reliability or precision of a single value estimate of a parameter mean is made in terms of a range of possible values, one of which, it is *reasonably expected*, will be the parameter value sought. The size of this range, which is the confidence interval, is based on the calculated standard error of the mean multiplied by the initially selected confidence criterion.

The standard deviation of a sampling distribution of means, known as the *standard error* of the mean, is equal to:*

$$\sigma_{\bar{x}} = \frac{\sigma}{\sqrt{n}} \qquad (8.3)$$

Ordinarily, however, the value of σ, the standard deviation of the distribution of the parent population and hence a parameter value, is unknown. Fortunately the standard error of the mean can be estimated from any one of the following three sets of information:

1. Standard deviation and n_j, the size of a particular randomized sample.
2. Variation of the means of two or more randomized samples (size n_j) about the mean of these sample means, of course drawn from the same parent population (or frame).
3. Range of the maximum mean and the minimum mean of several randomized samples (size n_j) drawn from the same parent population.

The latter two methods for the estimation of the standard error of the mean will be presented later in this chapter. At this point, the first and perhaps the most frequently used method will be described.

---

*When populations are infinitely large, or (approximately) when the sampling fraction n/N of a finite population is less than 1/20, or 5%.

Estimate of Standard Error of the Mean:

$$\hat{\sigma}_{\bar{x}} = \frac{s}{\sqrt{n}} = \sqrt{\frac{\sum x^2}{n-1}} \cdot \frac{1}{\sqrt{n}} = \sqrt{\frac{\sum x^2}{n(n-1)}} \qquad (8.4)$$

where the circumflex over the *sigma* denotes that the measure is an *estimate;* in this case an estimate of the standard error of the mean as signified by the subscript $\bar{x}$. The standard deviation of the distribution of the sample data is symbolized by s and is calculated, as indicated, by dividing the sum of squared deviations by the number of degrees of freedom (d.f.'s), which in this case equals $(n-1)$; as in Formula 4.6, p. 52.

The use of this estimated standard error of the mean for the estimation of the parameter mean of the parent population is based on the assumption that $\hat{\sigma}_{\bar{x}}$ is a satisfactory estimate of the sampling variation for the hypothesized sampling distribution of means. When the size of randomized samples is about 30 or more, this assumption is usually considered to be well enough satisfied when parent populations are normally distributed. And if the randomized samples are sufficiently large, $\hat{\sigma}_{\bar{x}}$ is usually considered a satisfactory estimate of sampling variation even though the parent population may not be normally distributed.

When, however, a sample is small in size, with n of less than 30, the standard error of the mean estimated from s and n, as in Formula 8.4, is increasingly unsatisfactory as n decreases. Therefore the estimation of parameter means from a small sample is done by reference to a special family of probability distributions, known as "Student's" distributions of the t statistic. Their use is described on p. 209 ff.

For "large" samples, i.e., samples whose n's are 30 or more, implications of the Laplace-Gaussian normal curve of error are used not only to describe the *pattern or form of expected sampling variation* but also the *extent* of such expected variation for given size randomized samples. Once the desired *level of significance, alpha,* has been chosen, the normal probability model is used to establish:

1. A *confidence criterion* (c.c.) in order to set up
2. *Confidence limits* that will mark off the
3. *Confidence interval,* the scale range of whose values is inferred with some degree of confidence to include the value of the parameter mean. The confidence interval *conditionally,* not certainly, is presumed to contain the value of the parameter sought.

Estimate of a Parameter Mean

The estimation of a parameter mean may be illustrated by a sample of measurements of simple reaction time to sound.* Given 36 trials, a sub-

---

*Reaction time in milliseconds is a measurable whose sample distributions are often highly skewed; consequently the estimate of the *parameter median* of such measures, by

ject's mean is found to be 150 milliseconds, and the standard deviation of the variation is 15 milliseconds. These results are a measure of what the subject can do under the conditions of the test. The mean of the sample of 36 measures is subject to errors, both in the *sampling* of his behavior and in the *measurement* of his behavior. The estimate of his parameter mean reaction time will be made on the assumption that the conditions of measurement were such that the errors, both of sampling and of measurement, are randomized over the series of 36 trials. The parent population thus sampled consists of the subject's hypothesized, indefinitely repeated reactions under the same controlled conditions of observation and measurement.

How *reliable* is this sample mean of 150 milliseconds? In other words, what is the subject's parameter mean reaction time under the conditions of the test? What would his mean reaction time be if the measurements were continued "indefinitely" within the *frame* of the specified controls for the sample of results?

Single Value Estimate. The single value estimate of the subject's parameter mean reaction time to sound, under the assumed conditions, is 150 milliseconds, this being the value of the sample mean result. The reliability of this estimate is measured by the range of a confidence interval.

Interval Estimate. The confidence interval for a mean can be stated in either one of two ways:

Interval Estimate of μ: $\overline{X} \pm \text{c.c.} \cdot \hat{\sigma}_{\bar{x}}$ (8.5)

This estimate is thus equal to the value of the sample mean plus or minus the product of the value of the confidence criterion and the estimate of the standard error of the mean.

Interval Estimate of μ:

$$\overline{X} - \text{c.c.} \cdot \hat{\sigma}_{\bar{x}} < \mu < \overline{X} + \text{c.c.} \cdot \hat{\sigma}_{\bar{x}}$$ (8.5a)

This way of estimation signifies exactly the same interval of possible values for the parameter as does Formula 8.5. The reason for the two modes of statement lies in the fact that the first formulation (8.5) is limited to those estimates whose confidence limits are *equidistant* from the point or single value estimate of the parameter. The second statement (8.5a), by inequalities, is generally more useful because the confidence limits of some parameters are *not* equidistant from the single value estimate.

Alpha Level of Significance and Confidence Criterion

The significance level, which determines the value of c.c. (the confidence criterion) of a probability model, is designated as *alpha* and symbolized

---

the distribution-free method of p. 221 ff., perhaps involves less risk of having a confidence interval that does *not* include the value of the parameter.

by α. *Alpha* is a measure of the proportion of extreme sampling variations
that will be ignored in the making of an interval estimate of a parameter.
If *alpha* is written as a proportion equal to .01, as it often is, then 1% of
the hypothesized sampling variations will be judged as so extreme, *and
hence unlikely*, that they will be disregarded.

Sampling variation with respect to a parameter mean may be either *plus*
or *minus*. Hence an *alpha* level of significance of .01 (or 1%) refers to subtended areas in the tails of the probability model of the sampling distribution such that one half of 1% are in one tail and the other half of 1% are
in the other tail. The remaining 99% of the sampling distribution signifies
a range of sampling variations that will be considered as *likely of occurrence*
even though only one can occur in a single sample result.

The relation of the *alpha* significance level to the normal probability
model is illustrated in Fig. 8.1.

The confidence criterion is *a critical value* on the scale of values of the
probability model that conforms to the implications of *alpha*. When

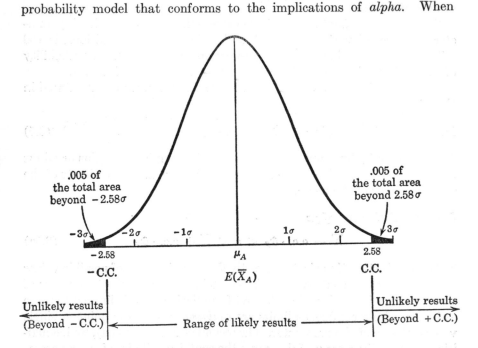

**Fig. 8.1. Use of the Normal Hypothetico-Deductive Probability Model with
the Empirical-Inductive Statistics of Sample Results in the Estimation of a
Parameter Mean**

Since the sample result is an empirical datum (a fact, so to speak) rather than an estimate, the interval of parameter estimation includes only those hypothesized possible
values whose statistics (sample results) are WITHIN the range of plus and minus c.c.
Thus the value of μ_A will be within the confidence interval estimate IF the sample result
is within the range of ±c.c. But the value of μ_A may not be within the range of the
confidence interval estimate IF the sample result is beyond *either plus or minus* c.c.

$\alpha = .01$ (or 1%) and the probability model is the normal distribution, the value of c.c. can be obtained from Table A (Appendix) in terms of a *z deviate* that subtends .005 (0.5%) of the area at either tail. The area values of Table A are therefore scanned for one equal to .005 in column C (area in the smaller portion) and one equal to .995 in column B (area in the larger portion). They are found to be at a *z* deviate distance from the mean of 2.58. Hence in interval estimates of parameters, with the normal probability model and $\alpha = .01$, the confidence criterion, c.c., is a *z* deviate value of 2.58.

The estimate of a parameter mean for α of .01 may now be stated as follows:

$$\overline{X} - z_{.005} \cdot \sigma_{\bar{x}} < \mu < \overline{X} + z_{.995} \cdot \sigma_{\bar{x}}$$

$$150 - 2.58 \cdot \sigma_{\bar{x}} < \mu < 150 + 2.58 \cdot \sigma_{\bar{x}}$$

The estimate of the standard error of the sampling distribution of mean reaction times is as follows (Formula 8.4):

$$\hat{\sigma}_{\bar{x}} = \frac{s}{\sqrt{n}} = \frac{15}{\sqrt{36}} = 2.5 \text{ msec}$$

Therefore the interval estimate of the subject's parameter mean reaction time is

Estimate of μ:

$$150 - 2.58(2.5) < \mu < 150 + 2.58(2.5)$$

$$150 - 6.45 < \mu < 150 + 6.45$$

$$143.6 \text{ msec} < \mu < 156.4 \text{ msec}$$

This estimate may also be stated by the mode of Formula 8.5:

Estimate of μ:

$$150 \pm 2.58(2.5) = 150 - 6.45 \quad \text{and} \quad 150 + 6.45$$

$$= 143.6 \quad \text{and} \quad 156.4$$

Statistical Inference Is Uncertain Inference

There are reasonable expectancies but no certainties in inferential statistics. The preceding inference about the subject's parameter mean reaction time cannot be made with certainty. On the assumption of a normally distributed population of O's reaction times, it is, however, reasonable to infer *with considerable confidence* that his parameter mean is a value somewhere along a continuum of value possibilities ranging from 144 to 156 milliseconds. In the light of the assumption, the information available, and the significance level of 1%, this is the most precise statement that can be made with a high degree of confidence.

A less precise estimate can be made with even a greater degree of confidence. Under proper conditions of sampling and measurement, it is quite reasonable to expect with "practical certainty" that a confidence interval set up with the "3σ criterion" will include the value of the parameter sought. For the normal probability model, the 3σ confidence criterion is equivalent to an *alpha* level of significance of .0027 (or about 0.3%, three-tenths of 1%).

Nevertheless an inference about the value of a parameter from the information of a sample, or even several samples, cannot be made with certainty. Being *practically certain* is logically quite different from *certainty* in that the former allows for the possible very rare exceptions inherent to the implications of probability theory. The concept of *certainty* has no such margin of tolerance for the exception.

Some authors interpret estimates of parameters as made with *99% confidence* when an *alpha* significance level of .01 is employed. This author prefers nonquantitative expressions of confidence such as "highly confident" (when $\alpha = .01$) and "practically certain" (when $\alpha = .0027$ or less). Quantitative statements such as "99% confidence" have relevance to the *deductive* implications of probability theory. They do not have demonstrated applicability to the inductive implications of any particular research result.

As an exercise in probability, one can doubtless demonstrate by repeated sampling—under certain defined conditions of sampling, of sample size, and of known characteristics of a population—that approximately 1% of the means of sample results will diverge more than $\pm 2.58\sigma$ from the known mean of the population, and that about 99% of the sample means will vary within the range of $\mu \pm 2.58$. But the practical problem of utilizing implications of probability theory for the estimation of parameters is not an exercise in repeated sampling with populations whose mean and other characteristics are known. Rather, it is a search for unknown parameters with the aid of the information of only one or a few sample results. The inferences made are empirical-inductive with the very helpful guidance of mathematical-deductive probability models, as illustrated in Figs. 8.1 and 8.2.

The odds, so to speak, may reasonably be inferred as favoring the correctness of an interval estimate, but the exact odds are not computable. The calculus of probabilities can be used in a priori deductive inference but not with an inductive inference such as the estimate of an unknown parameter from only sample information. Either the interval estimate is correct, in that it includes the parameter, or it is incorrect. Thus the probability, **P**, of a correct inference is either zero or 1.0. But there is no way with only the sample information to ascertain which of these disjunctive alternatives is the correct one.

Coefficient of Risk and *Alpha*

The student who expects to distill absolute truths from the empirical mix of sampling statistics should be prepared to be disappointed. The basic "absolutes" in statistics, if there are any, are the VARIABILITY of phenomena and the fact that statistical inference is CONDITIONAL rather than necessary. The student can assume certain risks of error and nevertheless arrive at reasonably sound inferences. The *alpha* significance level is in effect a *coefficient of risk of error*. When $\alpha = .01$, the risk of an incorrect inference in interval estimation is low; when $\alpha = .0027$, the risk is even less. If $\alpha = .05$ is employed, as it sometimes is, then the risk of an incorrect inference is fairly high, too high to be recommended in the estimation of parameters but not too high for certain purposes in hypothesis testing, as in the subsequent chapters.

Whatever the numerical symbol of the coefficient of risk may be, as signified by *alpha*, the extent or degree of confidence to be put on the result is not measurable. A high degree of confidence is a lot of confidence but how much is indeterminate.

Argument Against an Extreme Parameter Value

With respect to the mean reaction time problem, what is to be said and inferred about the possibility of a parameter mean value beyond the limits of 144 and 156 milliseconds? For example, in the light of the facts available, is a mean of 175 ruled out as the subject's parameter mean? The answer is YES from the point of view of the implications of the decision to use the 1% significance level. The answer is NO from the point of view of the full implications of probability theory.

If, for the argument, a priori mathematical probability is hypothesized, it should be agreed that, deductively, 175 milliseconds is a highly unlikely possibility. Although deductive logic is not inductive logic, the atmosphere engendered by the hypothesized situation can legitimately lead to a psychological feeling of great confidence and the very reasonable inference that 175 milliseconds is a most unlikely value. The reasons are developed in the following paragraphs.

The z deviate value of a sample mean of 150 milliseconds for a subject whose parameter mean is hypothesized at 175 milliseconds is as follows, when the size of the sample is 36 and its standard deviation is 15:

z Deviates for Hypotheses:

$$z = \frac{\text{sample mean statistic} - \text{hypothesized parameter mean}}{\text{estimate of the standard error of the mean}}$$

$$z = \frac{\overline{X} - \mu}{\hat{\sigma}_{\overline{x}}} = \frac{150 - 175}{2.5} = -10 \tag{8.6}$$

Figure 8.2 shows that a sample mean of 150 milliseconds, when equal to a z deviate value of -10, is far out at the lower end of the hypothesized sampling distribution of means when the parameter mean is 175 and the

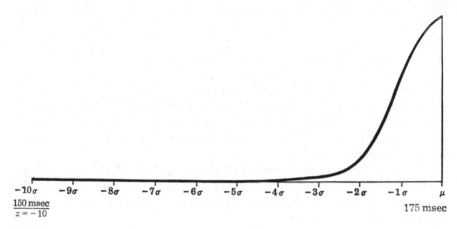

Fig. 8.2. **Location of a Sample Result of 150 Milliseconds, a z Deviate Distance of -10 Units from a Hypothesized Parameter Mean of 175 Milliseconds on the Left Half of the Normal Probability Model**

(In random sampling, for the hypothesis of 175 milliseconds, the odds are less than 1 in 50 billion for a sample mean $\leq$ 150 milliseconds to occur simply in consequence of random variation.)

standard error is 2.5. Only a very, very small fraction of the total area is subtended beyond that point. Hence the probabilities of such a result for a subject whose parameter mean is 175 are very slight. Pearson (1914) gives the area between the mean and a z deviate of -6 as equal to .499999999. Hence the probability of results $-10z$ deviations from the mean is *less than* 1 in 50 billion.

Consequently, if a sample mean result of 150 milliseconds for a person whose parameter mean is taken to be 175 milliseconds should actually occur under conditions of random sampling, sample size, and controlled observations and measurements, with the variation indicated ($s = 15$), then either a very, very rare result has occurred or the probability model is not applicable. Because of the *assumed* conditions, the latter alternative is rejected; so is the idea of the very rare result for a parameter mean of 175. Hence 175 is itself rejected as a likely parameter mean possibility. This value was hypothesized to begin with and now it is seen to be clearly untenable as a realistic value. It is rejected with the confidence of practical certainty.

The *3-Sigma* Confidence Criterion

If the researcher wishes to be practically certain that the confidence interval will include the subject's parameter mean reaction time, it has been indicated that he may broaden the confidence interval by choosing a smaller value for *alpha*. An *alpha* level of significance of .001 is sometimes used. In interval estimation, the z deviate value for an alpha of .001 will need to be such that .0005 of the area of each tail of the normal probability distributed is subtended. From Table A, the z deviate values that will include .999 of the area (or probabilities) about the mean are ± 3.3. Rounded off to an integer value of 3, this is often used as the confidence criterion to establish confidence limits of "practical certainty," i.e., a confidence interval that should include the value of the parameter sought. Since a z deviate of ± 3 is three standard deviation units from the mean of the normal probability distribution, this criterion is often referred to as the 3σ confidence criterion.

By this criterion, the confidence interval of the subject's reaction time is as follows:

$$150 \text{ msec} \pm 3(2.5) = 150 - 7.5 \quad \text{and} \quad 150 + 7.5$$

$$= 142.5 \quad \text{and} \quad 157.5 \text{ msec}$$

This is a spread of only 15 milliseconds. In view of the unit of measurement, this might be interpreted as a fairly reliable result as an estimate of the subject's parameter mean reaction time.

To Increase Precision of Estimates

It is doubtless evident that the likelihood of including the parameter mean in the confidence interval is increased with increases in the value of the confidence criterion. However, this is not the preferred way to increase the usefulness to research statistics of the techniques for the estimation of parameters. In fact their usefulness will decrease if the confidence interval is extended to such extremes as to include practically everything. The way to increase the usefulness of a parameter estimate is to increase its precision or reliability. This is perhaps best done by replicating the randomized samples and thus increasing the volume of information. The interval estimates of parameters will decrease, other things equal, and hence the precision of the estimates increase because the margin of the difference between sample results and the population parameters will be less with replication as against a single sample result.

An examination of the estimation procedure for a parameter mean shows that as n (the size of the sample) increases in size, other things equal, the estimate of the sampling variation decreases. But as indicated in Formula 8.4, the standard error of the mean decreases in proportion to the square root of the size of the sample. Hence, to *double* the precision of a sample result, its size needs to be *quadrupled*.

The precision of parameter estimates can be increased even more effectively by the method of replicated interpenetrating subsamples when the sampling units are persons, or dwelling units, families, etc., rather than behavioral units of a particular person, as in the reaction time test. The technique will be described shortly. First, however, it will be seen that precision is also related to the size of the sampling fraction when *finite* populations are sampled.

Estimation of μ of Finite Populations

In most survey research, as well as in some experimental research, the populations to be studied are finite in size. In psychological research, the sampling units are usually persons whose behavior or attitudes or opinions are to be sampled and studied. Sampling is usually without replacement.

The single value or point estimate of μ will be the same for finite populations as for populations infinitely large. However, other things equal, the interval estimate of μ will be a narrower band of possible values when the sampling fraction n/N is large enough noticeably to restrict the variance of a sampling distribution of means. The adjustment for this effect, called the *finite multiplier*, is as follows:

Finite Multiplier: $$\sqrt{\frac{N-n}{N}} = \sqrt{1 - \frac{n}{N}} \tag{8.7}$$

where N is the number of sampling units in the parent population or frame and n is the number in the sample. The estimate of the standard error of the mean for finite populations thus becomes

Estimate of $\hat{\sigma}_{\bar{x}}$: $$\hat{\sigma}_{\bar{x}} = \frac{s}{\sqrt{n}} \cdot \sqrt{1 - \frac{n}{N}} \tag{8.8}$$

Usually the finite population multiplier can be ignored in the computation of the standard error of the mean when the sampling fraction n/N is $1/20$ (5%) or less.

A finite multiplier is not used with a finite population, regardless of its size, if the sampling is done *with replacement*. This method of sampling has the effect of converting a finite population to an indefinitely large one.

The effect of not using the finite multiplier, when it is proper to use it, is to increase the value of the estimate of the standard error. Hence, without it, the confidence limits of an interval estimate of a parameter mean are overstated rather than understated for a given *alpha* significance level. The error would thus be on the side of safety rather than tending toward increased risk.

Estimation of μ from Replicated Samples

Earlier in the chapter three methods for the estimation of the standard error of the mean were mentioned. Only one has so far been presented, that of Formulas 8.4 and 8.8, for use with sample data treated as a single randomized sample. The additional two methods will be presented in this section and the one that follows.

If two or more independent, randomized samples have been drawn from a population, then the best single value estimate of the parameter mean will be the mean of the means of the subsample results. If the n's of the subsamples are unequal, then the overall mean has to be obtained by the weighted method described on p. 63. However, in planning to use replicated samples, one should include equal size samples in the design. All computations will be facilitated when n_j's are equal.

The estimate of the standard error of the mean is in effect based on a small sampling distribution of means, consisting of a mean for each subsample. When n_j's are equal, the estimate is as follows:

Estimate of $\hat{\sigma}_{\bar{x}}$ for Replicated Samples:

$$\hat{\sigma}_{\bar{x}}^2 = \frac{1}{k(k-1)} \sum_1^k (\overline{X}_j - \overline{X})^2; \quad \hat{\sigma}_{\bar{x}} = \sqrt{\hat{\sigma}_{\bar{x}}^2} \qquad (8.9)$$

where k is equal to the number of subsamples, $\overline{X}_j$ is the mean of any subsample, and $\overline{X}$ is the mean of all subsample results combined.

When sampling *without replacement* the finite multiplier of Eq. 8.7 is used with the preceding formula as well as with the one that follows (Eq. 8.10) unless the sampling fraction is less than 1/20 or 5%.

Estimation of μ from Range of Means of Replicated Samples

A *replicated sample* is one drawn in the same way, of the same size, and from the same population as a sample already made. When there are three to ten replicated samples of a population, with each n_j equal in size, a satisfactory estimate of the standard error of the mean may be obtained from the range of subsample means, as follows (Mantel)*:

Estimate of $\hat{\sigma}_{\bar{x}}$ from Range of Means:

$$\hat{\sigma}_{\bar{x}} = \frac{\overline{X}_{\max} - \overline{X}_{\min}}{k} \qquad (8.10)$$

where $\overline{X}_{\max}$ is the largest subsample mean, $\overline{X}_{\min}$ is the smallest subsample mean, and k is the number of subsamples (and hence the number of means).

The use of this estimate of the standard error of the mean is not to be preferred over that given by Formula 8.9, but it does yield a quick, ordinarily satisfactory estimate of sampling error when there are available the mean results of replicated samples. Such replication may come about with the method of randomized groups: A series of subsamples, each equal in size, of a given population would be drawn *independently* of each other, with or without replacement, depending on the nature of the sampling units, objective of the inquiry, etc.

---

*Mantel (1951) shows this estimate to be unsatisfactory when $k = 2$ or more than 10.

Perhaps the most useful replicated sample design is the zonal method of interpenetrating subsamples developed by Mahalanobis (1946a) and used extensively by him in India (1946b). The method is also described and applied to problems of business research by Deming (1960). One great advantage of the method is the simplicity of the arithmetic for the estimation of sampling error (Formula 8.10 is ordinarily employed). At the same time the overall benefits of stratification are in effect obtained.

Replicated Sampling by Zonal Method of Interpenetrating Subsamples

This method yields k replicated subsamples each of which is a randomly drawn *network* of sampling units from a series of *subframes* of a population. That is to say, each subsample consists of sampling units drawn from each of m *zones* into which the frame of a population is divided. The procedure for the identification of sampling units for each sample is summarized in Table 8.1.

The method not only has the advantage of the quickness with which parameter means can be estimated by Formula 8.10 from the *range* of mean results, but it also readily permits the detection of bias in such estimates (see Deming, 1960, p. 425 ff.). Furthermore, when the zones are established so that they are stratifications of one or more factors significant to the inquiry, the result should be more efficient than unrestricted randomized replications of the frame as a whole. The zonal method should be more efficient in the sense that it can yield smaller estimates of sampling variation and hence more precise estimations of parameters.

The greater efficiency of the zonal method may be achieved by *arraying all sampling units* (S.U.'s) of the frame of a population in the order of one or more factors known or thought to be significant to the research inquiry.* In psychological research, for example, I.Q., amount of schooling, as well as sex and socio-economic status are usually significant factors. Each research study also may have some additional relevant factors for stratification. Thus a college population whose knowledge of current events is to be studied by this zonal method of interpenetrating subsamples might be arrayed or ordered on the following factors and hence "stratified":

1. The population would first be divided into two broad strata of all males together and then all females.
2. Within each sex group, the sampling units (males and females) would be arrayed into substrata according to their college degree objectives (engineering, science, social studies, etc.).
3. Finally, within each of these substrata, students would be arrayed in order of the number of credits so far earned for the degree.

---

*Mahalanobis recommends that each zone of S.U.'s be as homogeneous as possible; zones should also be equal in size (number of S.U.'s).

If the third factor, number of earned credits, were thought to be more relevant to the aim of the inquiry (the measurement of knowledge of current events) than was the second factor, then their order would be reversed,

The frame of the population of students would then be set up for sampling by assigning each person a *serial number* from 1 to N, according to his position in the arrays established by the preceding three steps.

If N were 10,000, 10 replicated samples of 10 students each should yield a more efficient result than a single, unrestricted random sample of 100 students.

The procedure for the zonal method may be summarized as follows:

1. The sampling units of the frame are divided into m zones, each equal in size (except possibly for the last one if N/m isn't an even number). The number of zones should not exceed the size of a subsample, and it may be less. In Table 8.1, 10 zones, each with 1000 sampling units (S.U.'s), and 5 subsamples of 20 each, are used.

2. The number of sampling units per zone is equal to N/m. When N is 10,000 and m is 10, each zone will have 1000 S.U.'s. Thus $N_z = 1000$.

3. Subsamples of size n_j are drawn by a random method from the 10 zones. Five subsamples, each with 20 S.U.'s have been identified by their serial numbers in Table 8.1. Subsamples B, C, D, and E are replicated, interpenetrating networks of 2 S.U.'s each from each of the 10 zones, drawn in the same way as sample A. To recapitulate:

N = 10,000 (the number of S.U.'s in the frame).
m = 10 (the number of zones).
N_z = 1000 (the number of S.U.'s in each zone).
k = 5 (the number of subsamples).
n_j = 20 (the number of S.U.'s per subsample).

4. The serial number of the first sampling unit for the first zone of the first subsample is identified by use of a table of random numbers. A number between 1 and 1000 is needed. By the use of Table L of the Appendix, a random start was made in row 5, columns 24–25–26, with the number 539. This is the first entry in Table 8.1. The second sampling unit for the first zone of the first subsample was then selected by proceeding to the next number *down* columns 24–25–26 of Table L. The number is 226.

This randomization procedure may be continued through the successive zones, 2 S.U.'s per zone until 20 serial numbers for the first subsample are obtained. However, *systematic sampling after the two random starts* is just as satisfactory and much easier to apply. Thus the random start of number 539 is systematically used to identify the serial number of the first S.U. of the remaining 9 zones of the first subsample: 1539, 2539, 3539 $\cdots$ 9539. The second random start of number 226 is similarly used to identify the remaining 9 S.U.'s needed for each zone of the first subsample: 1226, 2226, 3226 $\cdots$ 9226.

5. The above procedure of randomized starts and systematic sampling is used for the selection of the serial numbers of each of the remaining subsamples, with the result presented in Table 8.1. The sampling is *without replacement* inasmuch as the S.U.'s are persons. Their knowledge of current events could, of course, be measured two or more times on different occasions, but the purpose of the inquiry would be to ascertain the population's knowledge at a given time, with each S.U. being a different person.

Stratifying Possibilities of Zonal Method

1. Were the college population of 10,000 students composed of 60% males and 40% females, then the S.U.'s drawn from zones 1 through 6 would always be males, and those drawn from zones 7 through 10 would always be females.

2. If 20% of the student population were male engineers, and they were arrayed at the head of the list of male degree groups, then the S.U.'s drawn from zones 1 and 2 would be male engineers.

Table 8.1. Layout of Serial Numbers of Sampling Units for Replications by Zonal Method of Interpenetrating Subsamples

($N = 10,000; N_z = 1000; k = 5; n_j = 20; n = 100$)

ZONE	Serial Numbers of Sampling Units	FIVE SUBSAMPLES*				
		A	B	C	D	E
1	0001–1000	0539	0129	0243	0810	0999
		0226	0637	0648	0247	0188
2	1001–2000	1539	1129	1243	1810	1999
		1226	1637	1648	1247	1188
3	2001–3000	2539	2129	2243	2810	2999
		2226	2637	2648	2247	2188
4	3001–4000	3539	3129	3243	3810	3999
		3226	3637	3648	3247	3188
5	4001–5000	....	....	....	....	....
6	5001–6000	....	....	....	....	....
7	6001–7000	....	....	....	....	....
8	7001–8000	....	....	....	....	....
9	8001–9000	....	....	....	....	....
10	9001–10000	9539	9129	9243	9810	9999
		9226	9637	9648	9247	9188
	$N = 10,000$	$n_j = 20$	20	20	20	20

*Selected by random starts and systematic sampling. Sampling is without replacement.

3. If 50% of the male engineers were upper-classmen and they were originally arrayed in order of most to least degree credits, then the S.U.'s drawn from zone 1 would be male engineers who are upper-classmen.

In practice, zones are difficult to make as homogeneous as the one just described. Real life situations—states of nature—ordinarily do not come tied together in such even counts. But the significant point about zonal sampling remains. Each subsample is a network of S.U.'s that systematically penetrate into each zone. Each subsample will always include characteristics of each zone. After the first subsample is drawn, all remaining subsamples are thus replications.

The requirement that zones be equal in number of S.U.'s permits a considerable simplification of the arithmetic for the estimate of error variance and hence the estimate of the parameter mean. When $k > 2$ or <11 either Formula 8.9 or 8.10 can be used, the latter being, of course, somewhat easier to apply; otherwise Formula 8.9 is used.

The number of zones may be few or many: The more homogeneous population characteristics possibly related to the variable being studied or measured, the less the need for many. On the other hand, since the importance of possible stratifying factors is often unknown, it may be better to have many zones with S.U.'s arrayed through the frame with respect to characteristics that may well be correlated with that one to be investigated. Thus, in Table 8.1, it would have been better to have used 20 zones with 1 S.U. per zone per subsample. In this way an array of characteristics found among only 500 students would be sure to have representation in the sample if all 500 were within one zone. Even if the 500 S.U.'s were distributed, part in one zone and part in an adjacent zone, the odds that such S.U.'s would appear in the subsamples when N_z is 500 would be greater than when N_z is 1000.

Summary of Advantages of Zonal Method for Parameter Estimation

The advantages of the zonal method with interpenetrating subsamples over usual methods of stratification, described in the preceding chapter, are the greater ease with which replications can be made and the greater simplicity of the arithmetic for the estimation of the standard error of the mean. The main objective is, of course, the estimation of parameter means of a population. However, the use of the method does not preclude the study of results between and within any strata or substrata. Having set up the various arrays through the zones, the researcher will know where the cutting-off points are, i.e., where a particular stratum or substratum begins and ends. Hence he can pull out of the subsamples all S.U.'s identified with a particular stratum or substratum. The chief problem in such extractions of S.U.'s from a series of subsamples would be the question of margin of error. When the size of a sub-subsample of a particular sub-substratum is very small, the margin of error for the estimate of a parameter may be too great to be useful.

Comparison of Error Estimates

A fictional set of results for the sampling units of Table 8.1 is presented in Table 8.2. The range of the means of the subsamples is 47.9 to 56.4.

Table 8.2.   Fictional Measurements for the Sampling Units
(in part) of the Replicated Samples of Table 8.1

			SUBSAMPLES				
ZONES	A	B	C	D	E		
1	64	60	71	76	62		
	54	58	42	74	67		
2	34	59	37	48	59		
	52	33	49	54	26		
..	..	..	..	..	..		
10	41	37	39	39	49		
	52	33	49	54	26		
$\sum$'s	958	1020	960	1128	1024		5090
n_j's	20	20	20	20	20	$n =$	100
$\overline{X}_j$'s	47.9	51.0	48.0	56.4	51.2	$\overline{X} =$	50.9

$$\hat{\sigma}_{\bar{x}} = \frac{\overline{X}_{max} - \overline{X}_{min}}{k} = \frac{56.4 - 47.9}{5} = 1.7$$

The overall mean for the 100 measurements is 50.9. The estimate of the standard error of the mean by the range method (Formula 8.10) is as follows:

$$\hat{\sigma}_{\bar{x}} = \frac{\overline{X}_{max} - \overline{X}_{min}}{k} = \frac{56.4 - 47.9}{5} = 1.7$$

The interval estimate of the parameter mean, by the *3-sigma* confidence criterion of "practical certainty," is therefore as follows:

Interval Estimate of μ:

$$50.9 - 3(1.7) < \mu < 50.9 + 3(1.7)$$
$$45.8 < \mu < 56.0; \quad 46 < \mu < 56$$

On the other hand, the estimate of the standard error of the mean based on the sampling distribution of the five subsample means is as follows (Formula 8.9):

$$\hat{\sigma}_{\bar{x}}^2 = \frac{1}{5(5-1)} [(47.9 - 50.9)^2 + (51.0 - 50.9)^2 + \cdots + (51.2 - 50.9)^2]$$

$$= \frac{1}{20} (9.0 + 0.01 + 8.41 + 30.25 + 0.09) = \frac{47.76}{20} = 2.388$$

$$\hat{\sigma}_{\bar{x}} = \sqrt{2.388} = 1.55$$

The interval estimate by the *3-sigma* confidence criterion, as before, is therefore as follows:

Interval Estimate of μ:

$$50.9 - 3(1.55) < \mu < 50.9 + 3(1.55)$$

$$46.3 < \mu < 55.6; \quad 46 < \mu < 56$$

There is thus no difference in this particular example when the two sets of confidence limits are rounded off to the nearest integer values.

Finite Multiplier

The use of the finite multiplier with the preceding estimates would not appreciably affect the result, since $(1 - 100/10,000)^{1/2} = .995$. A total sample of 100 cases is only 1% of $N = 10,000$.

Small Samples and Estimates of μ

When replicated samples can be used, the estimates of the sampling variation of means can be made, even for small samples, by Formulas 8.9 and 8.10. However, when it is not feasible to replicate samples and a single randomized sample consists of fewer than 25 or 30 measurements, the confidence criterion, c.c., will have to be obtained in terms of t rather than by the normal z deviate. Thus, the estimation of sampling variation is related to a family of distributions that are approximately normal when $n \geq 30$ but which become increasingly leptokurtic as n approaches only 2. Thus, in the latter instance, only 50% (instead of 68%) of the sampling variation of means is expected within the range of $\mu \pm 1\hat{\sigma}_{\bar{x}}$.

This family of distributions is known as that of the t *statistic*, where t is equal to the following:

The t Statistic: $\qquad t = \dfrac{\overline{X} - \mu}{\hat{\sigma}_{\bar{x}}} = \dfrac{\sqrt{n}(\overline{X} - \mu)}{s}$ $\qquad\qquad$ (8.11)

since $\hat{\sigma}_{\bar{x}} = s/\sqrt{n}$.

The t statistic is more relevant to significance testing of means and mean differences than to the estimation of parameter means. At this point, it is relevant to accurate estimates of parameter means from the data of small samples. Such estimates are more likely to be important in showing up the *unreliability*, or lack of precision, of a small sample result than in giving satisfactory interval estimates of μ.

The theory of sampling variation characteristic of t was developed by W. S. Gossett, writing under the pseudonym of "Student" (1908; 1942, pp. 11–34). Gossett (1876–1937) was an Oxford scholar in mathematics and natural science. His work with small samples at the Guiness Brewery in Dublin led to his discovery that as n decreases, the standard deviation, s, of small samples is **increasingly biased** for estimates of $\sigma_{\bar{x}}$. The t statistic is thus to the sampling distributions of means of small samples as the normal z deviate is to large samples.

Critical values of t are given in Table B of the Appendix. The t statistics are in the body of the table. The *alpha* level of significance for various t values is indicated at the top of each column. Two interpretations are indicated: "one-tailed" and "two-tailed." Since both tails of sampling distributions are involved in the setting up of the confidence intervals of parameter estimation, the critical values of t are located by reference to the *alpha* values under the two-tailed heading.

An inspection of Table B shows that for a given level of significance (say, $\alpha = .01$), there are considerable differences in the size of t in that particular column. These differences are related to differences in sample size but are measured in terms of *degrees of freedom* rather than in n. Degrees of freedom (d.f.) range from 1 to infinity in the left-hand column of Table B. At infinity the distribution of t is the same as the normal distribution of z deviates.

Degrees of Freedom

The number of d.f.'s for any t statistic depends on how many measures entering into the computation of s, the standard deviation, were "free" to take any possible values. The number with such freedom for variation is equal to $n - 1$, where n is the total number of measures in the sample. One degree of freedom is lost in that one measure of a sample result has to be such that when its x deviation from the mean is added in algebraically with all other x deviations, their sum will be zero.

The critical values of t (those in the columns of Table B headed by *alpha* values to be used in the estimation of parameter means as well as in significance testing) vary considerably for very small samples but hardly at all for samples with more than 30 d.f.'s. Hence this contrast is the rationale for the earlier statement that the implications of the normal probability model can ordinarily be used when n is 30 or more. The differences between t values for 30 d.f.'s and z deviate values may be seen by examining the t values of the row for 30 d.f. and the bottom row of Table B for infinitely large samples. The confidence criterion for $\alpha = .01$ is 2.75 for 30 d.f.'s and 2.58 for the normal probability model. For $\alpha = .001$, the critical values are 3.65 and 3.29

Unreliability of Estimates of μ from a Small Sample

Should a subject's reaction time measurements be based on a small sample of only nine observations, the unreliability of an estimate of his parameter mean reaction time is rather marked. Thus, if as before the standard deviation of his sample result is 15 milliseconds (with 8 d.f.'s), and his mean is 150 milliseconds, then by the *alpha* confidence level of .001, the confidence criterion in terms of t is equal to 5.0 (Table B). Hence the estimate is as follows:

Interval Estimate of μ:

$$150 - 5.0 \left(\frac{15}{\sqrt{9}}\right) < \mu < 150 + 5.0 \left(\frac{15}{\sqrt{9}}\right)$$

$$150 - 25 < \mu < 150 + 25$$

$$125 < \mu < 175 \text{ msec}$$

As already indicated, estimates of parameter means based on the results of a single, small sample are ordinarily not very satisfactory. However, when replication is feasible, the results of several small samples may provide efficiently satisfactory estimates by means of Formulas 8.9 or 8.10.

ESTIMATION OF PARAMETER VARIANCES

The reliability or precision of a variance or a standard deviation can be judged from the interval estimate of these parameters. When samples are fairly large (say, 100 or more measurements), the z deviates of the normal probability model can be employed to establish the confidence limits for an interval estimate of σ^2 or of σ. But when samples are much smaller than 100 (note that the "dividing line" here is not "around 30 cases," as for means), the normal z deviate does not provide a satisfactory estimate.

Interval Estimation of σ^2 and σ with Small Samples

If the standard deviation of a randomized sample of I.Q. measures is equal to 15 I.Q. units, the best single value estimate of the parameter standard deviation of the parent population is 15 I.Q. units. How reliable or precise is this estimate when the size of the sample is only 30 such measurements, say, obtained randomly from the fourth grade population of a large city? The sampling fraction will be assumed to be less than 5%, and hence the finite multiplier will not enter into the estimate.

The interval estimate of the parameter standard deviation will be set up first for the parameter variance with the aid of the chi-square sampling distributions of Table C in the Appendix. Then the confidence limits for variances will be converted to limits for the parameter standard deviation.

The sampling distributions of the statistic $\sum x^2 / \sigma^2$ are chi-square distributions with $n - 1$ d.f.'s (Walker & Lev, pp. 180–181). This statistic is the ratio of the sum of the squared deviations of the sample result to the population variance (see Eq. 9.10, p. 245):

Variance and Chi-Square: $\qquad \chi^2 = \dfrac{\sum x^2}{\sigma^2}$ $\hfill$ (8.12)

Hence,

$$\sigma^2 = \frac{\sum x^2}{\chi^2} \qquad\qquad (8.12a)$$

When the sum of the squared deviations is not directly available, it can be obtained from the sample variance:

$$\Sigma x^2 = (n - 1)s^2$$

inasmuch as

$$s^2 = \frac{\Sigma x^2}{n - 1}.$$

The statistic

$$\frac{\Sigma x^2}{\sigma^2}$$

may thus take the form of

$$\frac{(n - 1)s^2}{\sigma^2},$$

and by Formula 8.12a an estimate of σ^2 is therefore:

$$\hat{\sigma}^2 = \frac{(n - 1)s^2}{\chi^2} \qquad (8.12b)$$

An inspection of Table C for chi-square shows that the *alpha* values of significance are the headings of the columns, the number of d.f.'s are given in the column at the left of the table, and the body of the table consists of chi-square statistics. If an *alpha* level of significance of .01 is employed in setting up confidence limits for σ^2, then for 29 d.f.'s (30 − 1), the two values of chi-square needed will be found in the columns headed .005 and .995. This is the case because the *alpha* value of .01 for two-tailed probability is divided in half. Therefore one-half of 1%, or .005, is subtended at the lower end of the sampling distribution of chi-square, and the other one-half of 1%, is subtended at the upper end of the distribution, viz., at .995. The respective chi-square values at these points for 29 d.f.'s are 13.1 and 52.3.

The interval estimate of the parameter variance is therefore as follows:

Interval Estimate of σ^2 (when $\alpha = .01$):

$$\frac{(n - 1)s^2}{\chi^2_{.995}} < \hat{\sigma}^2 < \frac{(n - 1)s^2}{\chi^2_{.005}} \qquad (8.13)$$

Since the sample variance was 225, the estimate is equal to

$$\frac{29(225)}{52.4} < \hat{\sigma}^2 < \frac{29(225)}{13.1}; \quad 124.5 < \hat{\sigma}^2 < 498.1$$

and therefore the interval estimate of the parameter standard deviation is:

Interval Estimate of σ:

$$\sqrt{124.5} < \hat{\sigma} < \sqrt{498.1}; \quad 11.2 < \hat{\sigma} < 22.3$$

The single value estimate of the parameter standard deviation of 15.0 I.Q. units thus lies nearer to the lower confidence limit of 11.2 than to the higher one of 22.3. This is the case because the sampling distribution of chi-square for 29 d.f.'s is skewed. These distributions are increasingly skewed with fewer d.f.'s. Thus the limits of the confidence interval are asymmetrical with respect to the single value estimate of σ. As the d.f.'s increase, the skewness decreases and the sampling distributions increasingly approximate the form of the normal probability model.

The interval estimate of the parameter standard deviation is rather large, being a range of more than 11 I.Q. points. The estimate is thus not very precise. This is to be expected with such a small sample. Were the size of the sample quadrupled to n of 120, the confidence limits would be reduced by approximately half and the precision of the estimate would therefore be doubled.

Since the sampling distributions of s for large samples ($n \geq 100$) are approximately normal, the z deviate procedure may be employed for the estimation of parameter σ when $n = 120$.

Interval Estimation of σ^2 and σ with Large Samples

For large samples, the estimate of the standard error of the sampling distributions of s is as follows:

Standard Error of s: $\qquad \hat{\sigma}_s = \dfrac{s}{\sqrt{2n}}$ $\qquad\qquad$ (8.14)

When n is only 30, as in the preceding example, the estimation of the parameter standard deviation with this measure of sampling variation would be noticeably in error. Thus the interval estimate for $\alpha = .01$ would be as follows:

Interval Estimate of σ **(incorrect procedure when $n < 100$):**

$$s - z_{.005}\hat{\sigma}_s < \sigma < s + z_{.995}\hat{\sigma}_s$$

$$15 - 2.58 \frac{15}{\sqrt{2(30)}} < \sigma < 15 + 2.58 \frac{15}{\sqrt{2(30)}} \qquad (8.15)$$

$$15 - 5.0 < \sigma < 15 + 5.0$$

$$10.0 < \sigma < 20.0$$

By the correct method of the preceding section, these confidence limits should be 11.2 and 22.3 I.Q. units.

When the sample size is quadrupled to 120, the estimate of σ is as follows:

Interval Estimate of σ:

$$15 - 2.58 \frac{15}{\sqrt{2(120)}} < \sigma < 15 + 2.58 \frac{15}{\sqrt{2(120)}}$$

$$15 - 2.5 < \sigma < 15 + 2.5$$

$$12.5 < \sigma < 17.5 \quad \text{I.Q. units}$$

These confidence limits have a range of 5 I.Q. units and are approximately half as large as those of 11.2 and 22.3 for $n = 30$. The confidence limits of 12.5 and 17.5 mark off a relatively narrow band of possible values for σ of the I.Q. distribution of the fourth grade population. The result is thus fairly precise. How *accurate* it may be for this population depends also on the extent to which nonsampling errors entered into the results. Even though the I.Q. measures may have been obtained by the best available testing procedures, I.Q. measures in themselves are subject to nonrandomized errors of measurement.

ESTIMATION OF PARAMETER PRODUCT-MOMENT CORRELATION COEFFICIENT

When an r correlation is obtained for a bivariate distribution of measurables, a pertinent question is always asked about the reliability of the result. Thus, in the development of a proficiency test for an area of semi-professional work, a correlation of .55 is obtained between the test results and an independent measure of proficiency. The parent population (frame) consists of all persons in the occupation that can be identified with a serial number and who can be reached for testing and measurement. The results are based on, say, 300 sampling units (persons) drawn randomly (by means of a table of random numbers) from a parent population of between 9000 and 10,000 persons in the occupation.

The estimation of the parameter correlation coefficient will describe the reliability of the r of .55 in the sense that the confidence interval measures the margin of difference between the sample r and the parameter, reasonably to be expected as the result of sampling variations.

The sampling distributions of r become increasingly skewed as parameter rho (ρ) approaches 1.00 or -1.00 as limits. Only when the parameter product-moment coefficient ρ is zero and n' is 30 or more, or when ρ is not more than $\pm.25$ and n' is large, is the sampling distribution of r statistics normal or approximately so. (Note that n' is used to signify the number of *pairs* of measurements on which the correlation coefficient is computed.)

Fisher's Transformation Function for r and ρ

Fortunately the problem of the estimation of ρ is simplified by the following transformation function developed by R. A. Fisher (1938, pp. 202 ff.). It is related to r as follows:

Fisher's Z Function:

$$Z = \tfrac{1}{2}[\log_e(1 + r) - \log_e(1 - r)] \qquad (8.16)$$

Values of Z for various values of r from zero to 1.00 are given in Table E of the Appendix, p. 405.

This variable, Z, is satisfactory for the estimation of parameter r correlations because its sampling distributions are approximately normal. The sampling variations of Z are thus measurable by normal z deviates. This is the case even though n' may be small and the parameter is a value equal to ρ of 1.0 (or -1.0). The parameter of the sampling distributions of Z will be designated as *zeta* and symbolized accordingly, ζ.

Since Z statistics are normally distributed, at least approximately so, the confidence limits for the parameter estimate of ζ may be set up in terms of the normal z deviate. (Note that the two *zed's* here are distinguished by lower case type for the normal z deviate and upper case type for Fisher's transformation function.)

The standard error of the sampling distributions of the Z statistics depends only on the number of d.f.'s in the bivariate distribution, viz., $n' - 3$.

The Standard Error of Z:

$$\sigma_Z = \frac{1}{\sqrt{n' - 3}} \qquad (8.17)$$

With an r of .55 for the bivariate distribution of 300 pairs of observations, the interval estimate of ρ is obtained from the interval estimate of ζ, as follows:

Interval Estimate of Zeta:

$$Z - \text{c.c.}\,\sigma_Z < \zeta < Z + \text{c.c.}\,\sigma_Z \qquad (8.18)$$

When $r = .55$, $Z = .62$ (Table E); when $n' = 300$, $\sigma_Z = 1/\sqrt{300 - 3} = .058$. If the *3-sigma* confidence criterion is used, then the interval estimate is as follows:

$$.62 - 3(.058) < \zeta < .62 + 3(.058)$$

$$.62 - .17 < \zeta < .62 + .17$$

$$.45 < \zeta < .79$$

By reference to Table E, these confidence limits for *zeta* are transformed to *rho*, as follows:

Interval Estimate of Rho:

$$.42 < \rho < .66$$

This interval estimate of ρ is a rather broad band of values. If non-sampling errors are at a minimum, it is reasonable to conclude that the parameter correlation of test performance with proficiency on the job is at least .42 but not more than .66. This is not a very precise result. The lack of precision is more a function of the single value estimate of ρ, viz., $\rho = .55$, than it is of the size of the bivariate sample ($n' = 300$).

For very high values of ρ, the band of possibilities bounded by the confidence limits of an interval estimate is not only narrower for a given n' but is more asymmetrical with respect to the single value estimate of ρ. Thus, if the r statistic were .85 instead of .55, the confidence limits for ρ, when $n' = 300$ and c.c. is again taken at 3σ, would be as follows: When $r = .85, Z = 1.256$.

Interval Estimate of ζ:

$$1.256 - 3(.058) < \zeta < 1.256 + 3(.058)$$
$$1.08 < \zeta < 1.43$$

Therefore the

Interval Estimate of ρ:

$$.79 < \rho < .89 \qquad \text{(From Table D)}$$

Thus, although n' remains the same at 300, and the confidence criterion is unchanged, the band of values within the confidence interval is much less when $r = .85$ than when $r = .55$. This is in accord with the meaning of high values of ρ, compared with low values. When the scatter or variation of bivariates around the regression line is not very great, as for values of .85, the expected sampling variation is correspondingly restricted. When the scatter increases, as it does with values of .55, the expected sampling variation increases also.

It will be observed that the confidence limits of the preceding estimate are not symmetrical with respect to the single value estimate of ρ, viz., .85. This is the case because, as indicated earlier, sampling distributions of r statistics for high values of ρ are considerably skewed. It was for this reason that Fisher's transformation function was used to obtain the interval estimate.

ESTIMATION OF PARAMETER PROPORTIONS

Estimates of parameter proportions (or percentages, when p is multiplied by 100) are most commonly needed in survey research where the research data are more likely to be *countables* rather than measureables. The populations surveyed are therefore usually finite and are sampled without replacement. The technique of sampling requisite to the estimation of parameters proportions is, of course, that of probability sampling. The measures of sampling variation, viz., standard errors of proportions, describe the expected margin of difference between the sample result and the parameter proportions of two-class populations.

One class, P, of a two-class population usually signifies a characteristic for which the research is designed to study, such as the proportion of a population preferring community fall-out shelters to single family shelters. The other class, Q, which always equals $1 - P$, signifies the remainder of the population—those who prefer family fall-out shelters, those who have no preference, those who prefer none at all, those who don't know, as well as those who refuse to answer questions about fall-out shelters. Any one of these different subclasses of Q may become the P class if the researcher wishes to focus attention on it.

The probability models for the estimate of parameter proportions are either those of the discrete Bernoulli distributions (described in the preceding chapter) or the Laplace-Gaussian normal curve. The latter model is more frequently employed in survey research inasmuch as samples are usually very large.

The sampling distributions of proportion (p) statistics for small samples are increasingly skewed as P differs from Q. However, when $P = Q$, even if n is only 10, the normal distribution satisfactorily approximates the expected sampling variation, as was illustrated in the preceding chapter.

When $P \neq Q$, the appropriate probability models of the sampling variation of p in small sample results are the Bernoulli distributions, especially so when P is less than .25 or more than .75. On the other hand, even when P is less than .25 or more than .75, the normal probability distribution will give a satisfactory approximation of expected sampling variation if the samples are very large, as they are in much survey research.

Standard Error of Proportions

The sampling variation of proportions obtained from single random samples is measured by Formula 8.19 when P is known or hypothesized, as in significance testing (Chapter 9). It is estimated by Formula 8.20 when the expectation of p is P, as in the estimation of parameters.

The finite multiplier is used whenever sampling from a finite population is without replacement and the sampling fraction is 5% or more. Otherwise, it may be ignored.

Standard Error of p:

$$\sigma_p = \sqrt{\frac{PQ}{n}} \cdot \sqrt{1 - \frac{n}{N}} \tag{8.19}$$

$$\hat{\sigma}_p = \sqrt{\frac{pq}{n}} \cdot \sqrt{1 - \frac{n}{N}} \tag{8.20}$$

If, instead of single samples, a method of replicated sampling is employed, then an estimate of sampling variation may also be made from the range of sample results, provided the n_j's (sizes of the subsamples) are equal and there are from three to ten subsamples:

Range Estimate of Standard Error of p:

$$\hat{\sigma}_p = \frac{p_{max} - p_{min}}{k} \tag{8.21}$$

where k is, as before, the number of subsamples. The finite multiplier of Formulas 8.19 and 8.20 is used with Formula 8.21 when the sampling fraction n/N is 5% or more. Formula 8.21 is most satisfactory when k, the number of independent subsamples, equals 10.

Estimation of P When n Is Large

If p, a sample proportion, is .45 and n is 100, the estimation of the parameter proportion P may be made with the normal probability model as the assumed mode of sampling variation. This is the case even though some of the sampling distributions involved in the confidence interval may be somewhat skewed.

The single value estimate of P will of course be .45, since

$$E(p) = P \tag{8.22}$$

The precision or reliability of this single value estimate may be indicated by the confidence interval with the confidence criterion in terms of a normal z deviate. If the "practically certain" limits are desired, then c.c. will be the *3-sigma* criterion.

Interval Estimate of P:

$$p - \text{c.c.} \, \hat{\sigma}_p < P < p + \text{c.c.} \, \hat{\sigma}_p \tag{8.23}$$

By Formula 8.20,

$$\hat{\sigma}_p{}^2 = \frac{(.45)(.55)}{100} = .002475; \qquad \hat{\sigma}_p = .0497$$

The sampling fraction n/N is less than 5%, and therefore the interval estimate of P is as follows:

$$.45 - 3(.0497) < P < .45 + 3(.0497)$$
$$.45 - .149 < P < .45 + .149$$
$$.30 < P < .60$$

When stated as a percentage, the interval limits are 30% and 60%, a spread of 30 percentage points. Whether or not such a range of value possibilities for the parameter percentage may be considered a satisfactory estimate is relative to the nature of the data. If the sample result of .45 represents those persons of a random sample of 100 (from a parent population or frame of 3000) who have received summons for traffic violations and who have ignored them, the parameter estimate is meaningful but not very precise, since in the parent population such "scofflaws" may be as few as 3 in 10 or as many as 6 in 10. On the other hand, if the sample result of .45 represents the proportion of a random sample of a community's taxpayers who oppose tax reform and the q of .55 represents the proportion in the sample who favor such reform, the result is inconclusive. This is the case because it cannot be inferred that either side has a majority of followers in the parent population. The interval estimate of P includes values both above and below .50. The same can be said for Q. Either parameter, P or Q, may be more than .50, equal to .50, or less than .50. Certainly, for a result like this, additional sampling would be needed in order that *majority opinion* might be ascertained.

Estimation of P When n Is Small and $p \neq .50$

When n is small, the sampling distributions of p are increasingly skewed as the value of P approaches zero or 1.0. Hence the z deviate method of parameter estimation on the normal probability model of Formula 8.23 won't give satisfactory estimates unless n is sufficiently large or the value of P is not too different from .50. How large an n is needed for a given $P \neq .50$? The answer, of course, varies with different values of $P \neq .50$. Some insight into the course the answers take may be obtained by a comparison of z deviate estimates with approximately exact interval estimates. The latter can be obtained for sample sizes of 10, 15, 20, 30, 50, 100, 250, and 1000 for any value of p from the Pearson-Hartley (1958) charts of Appendix I. Thus, if a small sample of 10 observations yields a p statistic of .30, the normal z deviate estimate of P, with c.c. of 1.96 for $\alpha = .05$, would be:

z Deviate Estimate of P ($n = 10$; $p = .30$):

$$.30 - 1.96\sqrt{\frac{(.30)(.70)}{10}} < P < .30 + 1.96\sqrt{\frac{(.30)(.70)}{10}}$$

$$.30 - .284 < P < .30 + .284$$

$$.016 < P < .584$$

Estimate by Pearson-Hartley Chart:

$$.07 < P < .65$$

The error of the z deviate estimate is seen to be very sizable. There is still a discrepancy when $n = 20$ because of the skewness of the sampling distributions involved in the estimate:

***z* Deviate Estimate of *P* (*n* = *20*; *p* = *.30*):**

$$.30 - 1.96(.102) < P < .30 + 1.96(.102)$$
$$.30 - .20 < P < .30 + .20$$
$$.10 < P < .50$$

Estimate by Pearson-Hartley Chart:

$(\alpha = .05, \text{p. } 418)$ $.12 < P < .54$

Rule of Thumb for *z* Deviate Interval Estimates of *P*

The normal probability model for z deviate interval estimates of parameter proportions ordinarily will be satisfactory when both np and nq are at least equal to or greater than 10. Where p was .30 and n is only 20, as in the preceding example, the product of np is only 6; hence the z deviate procedure would be unsatisfactory (as was demonstrated to be the case). When p is .30, n needs to be at least 34 for the use of the normal probability model, since $10/p = 10/.30 = 33.3$.

Possibly the best procedure, whenever n is small and the rule of TEN is barely or not quite satisfied, is to use the Pearson-Hartley charts of Table I for the interval estimate. Although they do not yield a mathematically exact result, they will give confidence limits that are often satisfactory, in the case of samples as small as 8 or as large as 1000.

Estimation of *P* from Replicated Samples

When the method of replicated, independent sampling of a population is employed, the standard error of p can be estimated by Formula 8.21 when k, the number of subsamples, is at least 3 but not more than 10.

As an example, a survey of student opinion at University C might be made by means of the method of interpenetrating subsamples. Especially would a series of such subsamples increase the representativeness of the result if student's identification numbers were assigned in some meaningful order, such as number of credits earned toward a degree. Ten such independent subsamples of 20 each would be preferred to a single random sample of 200. If the student population to be surveyed consisted of 6000 sampling units (students), this population frame of 6000 would be divided into 10 zones of 600 sampling units each. The samples would then be drawn as described in Table 8.1, viz., by systematic sampling down each column for each subsample after a randomized start at the beginning of each column. Or the subsamples could be drawn from each zone by randomized determinations throughout.

Were each student to answer a question of fact YES or NO, the results would form a two-class variate. If the proportion of YES answers in the subsamples ranged from .30 to .55, then the estimate of the standard error of p would be as follows:

Range Estimate: $\qquad \hat{\sigma}_p = \dfrac{.55 - .30}{10} = .025$ $\qquad\qquad$ [8.21]

If the mean of the proportions of YES's over the 10 subsamples were .40, then the interval estimate of the proportion of YES's in the parent population would be as follows, using the *3-sigma* confidence criterion of "practical certainty":

Interval Estimate of P ($n_j = 20$; $k = 10$; $p = .40$):

$$.40 - 3(.025) < P < .40 + 3(.025)$$

$$.325 < P < .475$$

Thus one could be quite confident that at least 32%, but not more than 48%, of the student population would answer YES to the question of fact.

Had a *single* random sample of 200 students been drawn from the population of 6000, and had the proportion of YES's been .40, the error variance would have been greater and the interval estimate of P consequently less precise than that obtained with the 10 small, replicated samples of 20 cases each. Thus

$$\sigma_p = \sqrt{\frac{(.40)(.60)}{200}} \cdot \sqrt{1 - \frac{200}{6000}} = .035(.98) = .034 \qquad [8.20]$$

Interval Estimate of P ($n = 200$; $p = .40$):

$$.40 - 3(.034) < P < .40 + 3(.034)$$

$$.298 < P < .502$$

ESTIMATION OF A PARAMETER MEDIAN

In the preceding sections, methods have been developed for estimating the parameter values of several different measures whose variables are *measurables* (the mean, standard deviation, Pearson's r) as well as parameter proportions, whose data are essentially *countables,* classifiable into dichotomies. In this section, a measure of a *rankable* series will be considered, viz., the median. In a series of ranks, the median is the *midrank;* when n of the series is even, it is the average of the two midranks. The median is also defined as the 50th point centile, C_{50}, of a continuous distribution of measures. Methods for the parameter estimation of both kinds of medians will be developed: first, the median as C_{50} in a continuous distribution of measures, and secondly, the median as the midrank in a series of ranks. The first estimate will be based on a *parametric method;* the second, on a distribution-free (or *nonparametric — sic*) method. In either case the estimate of the parameter median will be subject to the basic condition or requirement of all parameter estimates, viz., *randomization* of observations from the population whose parameter median is to be estimated.

Estimate of a Median by Parametric Method

The *classical* approach to the estimation of a parameter median is based on the assumption of normally distributed populations of measures. The standard error of the median, on such an assumption, is equal to:

Standard Error of the Median for Normal Populations:

$$\hat{\sigma}_{mdn} = 1.253 \frac{s}{\sqrt{n}} \tag{8.24}$$

This estimate is thus $1\frac{1}{4}$ times larger than the standard error of a mean (Formula 8.4).

When all computations are by centile ranks and the standard deviation s is not readily available, a point value estimate of σ is provided by approximately three-fourths of the interquartile range, $Q_3 - Q_1$:

Estimate of σ from Quartiles:

$$\sigma = .74(Q_3 - Q_1) \tag{8.25}$$

The standard error of the median, based on centile information, is therefore:

Standard Error of the Median for Normal Populations
(based on centiles):

$$\hat{\sigma}_{mdn} = 1.253 \frac{.74(Q_3 - Q_1)}{\sqrt{n}} = \frac{.93(Q_3 - Q_1)}{\sqrt{n}} \tag{8.26}$$

Interval Estimate of MDN (μ_{mdn}):

$$mdn - c.c. \; \hat{\sigma}_{mdn} < MDN < mdn + c.c. \; \hat{\sigma}_{mdn} \tag{8.27}$$

where mdn is the statistic; MDN, the parameter, could also be symbolized as μ_{mdn}, or as μ, inasmuch as MDN is the *mean* of a sampling distribution of medians on a normally distributed probability model.

Applied to the data of Chapter 3, Table 3.1, the median endomorphy value was found there to be equal to 3.05; Q_3 was 4.0 and Q_1 was 2.2; and n was 36. Therefore, on the assumption of a normal population (a very dubious one for these data), the interval estimate of the median is as follows when c.c. is taken at *3-sigma:*

Interval Estimate of MDN (Data of Table 3.1):

$$3.05 - 3\left[.93\,\frac{(4.0 - 2.2)}{\sqrt{36}}\right] < \text{MDN} < 3.05 + 3\left[.93\,\frac{(4.0 - 2.2)}{\sqrt{36}}\right]$$

$$3.05 - 3(.279) < \text{MDN} < 3.05 + 3(.279)$$

$$2.2 < \text{MDN} < 3.9$$

Estimate of Median by Distribution-Free Method

Since distribution-free methods are also characterized as nonparametric methods, it may come as a surprise that such methods can be used for the estimation of parameters. But this was what was done in the preceding section in the estimation of parameter proportions. The methods for this are distribution-free in the sense that they do not depend on the condition that the randomized samples are drawn from normally distributed populations. They are free of this assumption.

Lincoln Moses (1952, 1953) presents various methods for inferential statistics that are free of the assumption of normally distributed populations. Included is a method for an interval estimate of a median when no assumption whatever need be made about the nature of the parent population. Such a method would certainly be safer to use with the data of the extremely skewed distribution of Table 3.1 than would the parametric method just described.

The median parameter estimate is based on the probability concept of the equiprobability of random observations *exceeding* the population median *and being less* than the population median. Measures fall into either one of two classes: above the median or not-above the median. The assumption is made that these two classes of events are equiprobable and therefore $\mathbf{P} = .50$ for each class. Thus, if samples consisted of only *two* independent measures, X_1 and X_2, the probability that both are *below* the population median is the product of their respective probabilities (product theorem, p. 155):

$$\mathbf{P}[(X_1 \text{ and } X_2) < \text{MDN}] = \tfrac{1}{2} \cdot \tfrac{1}{2} = \tfrac{1}{4}$$

and the probability that both are *above* the population median is also $\tfrac{1}{4}$:

$$\mathbf{P}[(X_1 \text{ and } X_2) > \text{MDN}] = \tfrac{1}{2} \cdot \tfrac{1}{2} = \tfrac{1}{4}$$

Only one other alternative remains, viz., that one measure will exceed and the other will be less than the population MDN. This can happen in either one of two ways, and therefore the probability is the *sum* of their respective probabilities (addition theorem, p. 154):

$$\mathbf{P}[(X_1 < \text{MDN} < X_2) \quad \text{or} \quad (X_2 < \text{MDN} < X_1)] = \tfrac{1}{4} + \tfrac{1}{4} = \tfrac{1}{2}$$

Hence the binomial can be used as the appropriate probability model for small samples. When $n \geq 25$, the normal probability distribution is a satisfactory approximation, with $\mu = nP$ and $\sigma_f = \sqrt{nPQ}$.

The Interval Estimate of MDN (μ_{mdn}) by a Distribution-Free Method:

$$\text{mdn} - \text{c.c.}\,\sigma_f < \text{MDN} < \text{mdn} + \text{c.c.}\,\sigma_f \qquad (8.28)$$

where mdn is the *midrank position*.

If α of .01 is used for the parameter estimate, c.c. is 1.96; and with $n = 36$, the value of the standard error of a sampling distribution of *frequencies*, $\sigma_f = \sqrt{(.5)(.5)(36)}$, is 3.0. Hence

$$\text{mdn} - 1.96(3.0) < \text{MDN} < \text{mdn} + 1.96(3.0)$$

$$\text{mdn} - 5.88 < \text{MDN} < \text{mdn} + 5.88$$

When $n = 36$, as for the data of Table 3.1, the *median as the midrank* of the sample lies between X_{18} and X_{19} (the 18th and 19th measures arrayed in order of size into a rank series). The confidence interval is now obtained by counting off 5.88 frequencies from the midrank position of 18.5,

$$18.5 - 5.88 < \text{MDN} < 18.5 + 5.88$$

$$12.62 < \text{MDN} < 24.38$$

and by rounding off to the nearest integer rank values, the interval estimate for the parameter median of the endomorphy measures is

$$X_{13} < \text{MDN} < X_{24}; \ 2 < \text{MDN} < 4$$

For the data of Table 3.1, the 13th measure is an endomorphic value of 2, and the 24th is a value of 4. This result is thus similar to that obtained by the parametric method, where the limits were 2.2 and 3.88. Here, however, the sample data are treated as constituting a rankable rather than a measurable, and hence all values are integers of a *discrete* series of measures rather than of a continuous one.

Efficiency of Median

When a given parameter can be estimated by more than one method, that estimate which has *the smallest standard error* is called *efficient*. Other estimates are called *inefficient* even though such inefficiency is *relative* and alternative methods may be used for computational convenience but with a loss in efficiency. Just how efficient is an alternative method?

An efficient statistic has an efficiency of 1.0. If there is only one method available for estimating a particular kind of parameter, then the efficiency of the estimate is 1.0 even though it may be based on a "nonparametric," or distribution-free, method. When there is an alternative, less efficient method available, its efficiency is measured by the ratio of the error variance of the efficient statistic to the error variance of the alternative:

Efficiency of a Statistic:

$$\frac{\text{Error variance of the efficient statistic}}{\text{Error variance of the inefficient statistic}} \qquad (8.29)$$

Thus the efficiency of the median, an inefficient statistic for estimating a parameter mean, as compared to the mean, which is an efficient statistic, is as follows:

*Efficiency of the Median:**

[where E(mdn) and $E(\overline{X}) = \mu$]
$$\frac{\dfrac{\sigma^2}{n}}{\dfrac{(1.57\sigma^2)}{n}} = \frac{\sigma^2}{1.57\sigma^2} = 0.64 \qquad (8.30)$$

The median is thus only about two-thirds as efficient as the mean in the estimation of parameter means of normally distributed populations. Since this measure of efficiency is in effect *a loss in number of cases*, an efficiency of .64 for the median is equivalent to a result with a mean based on only 64% as many cases or measures in the sample.

CONFIDENCE LIMITS AS SIGNIFICANCE CRITERIA

The limits of a confidence interval can be used as criteria to indicate what a sample result needs to be like in order to be considered significantly different from only a chance result, i.e., a random variation for a chance hypothesis. This is illustrated by the following example, which serves also to introduce the subject matter of the remaining chapters of this book, viz., *significance testing*.

How many *correct* answers on a true-false examination does one need to obtain in order to demonstrate a result not reasonably explainable as the result of guessing (chance)? If the true-false examination consists of 100 items, the limits of an appropriate confidence interval will be the criteria of significance, i.e., *the critical values*, and hence provide an answer to the question.

Since sheer guessing would average out in the long run as a P of .50, the interval estimate will be set up with respect to .50 and with the *3-sigma* confidence criterion:

---

*The error variance of the median is the square of its standard error (Formula 8.24).

Critical Values by an Interval Estimate of P:

$$.50 - 3\sqrt{\frac{(.50)(.50)}{100}} < P < .50 + 3\sqrt{\frac{(.50)(.50)}{100}}$$

$$.50 - 3(.05) < P < .50 + 3(.05)$$

$$.35 < P < .65$$

Multiplied by the number of the items, 100, the critical values are .35(100) = 35 items and .65(100) = 65 items respectively.

Thus at least 65 items answered correctly would be needed to indicate with reasonable "certainty" that a result is not entirely a matter of luck. Should a person's score be less than 35 correct items, it is also likely that such a result would not be entirely a matter of chance. It could well be a mixture of bad luck and a constant error, i.e., a nonsampling error, arising from a persistent negative response to minor exceptions conjured mentally for otherwise "true" statements.

REITERATION AND SUMMARY

By way of summary, emphasis is again directed toward the fact that the estimation of parameters from the data of samples of populations has to be based on the use of probability sampling. This means that the technique of randomization, the randomized selection of the sampling units, has to enter into the sampling procedure. The simplest and surest method of randomization is accomplished by the use of a table of random numbers, each sampling unit in the population, or frame of a population, having its own serial number; at least each sampling unit needs to be accessible for such identification by a number.

When a large population can't be reached and identified, then the randomized sample is drawn from that part of the population that can be. Such subpopulations have been designated as the *parent populations* of randomized samples. They are the *frames* of sampling units.

Estimates of parameters are statistical inferences from the data of probability samples to the parent populations. Their generality is necessarily restricted to the members of the parent population. The greater the difference between the number of sampling units in the frame of the parent population and the number of sampling units in whole population, the greater the *gap* between statistical inferences about parameters and generalized conclusions about the whole population.

Survey Research

1. Therefore the first task in survey research as well as in experimental research is to define the population whose characteristics are to be counted or measured.

2. The second task is to work out a method for the identification with a serial number of the sampling units of the population, whether they be dwelling units, families, persons, or such things as "teaching machines" coming off a production line.

3. The sampling units are drawn from the frame of the parent population by the technique of randomization, with or without stratification, and with or without subsampling.

To be avoided is the use of probability statistics for the estimation of parameters of populations that have not been sampled by probability methods. Nonprobability samples such as *judgment* samples or *stratified-quota* samples may be useful in many phases of research. But results based on nonprobability samples, such as many of the so-called representative samples of market research as well as those of public opinion research, cannot be legitimately employed for the statistical estimation of parameters. They may be used as "evidence" for a judgment about the whole, but this kind of judgment is not statistical inference. Rather, at its best it is reasonable inference made in the light of the "evidence." The "evidence" from nonprobability samples is analogous to the kind of nonstatistical evidence that a lawyer produces for his case in court. Whether or not it is reasonable to accept it is the decision a judge has to make.

4. Finally, the fourth task in the estimation of parameters is the calculation of the margin of difference to be expected between sample results and population characteristics in consequence of sampling variation. This *margin of difference* is measured by the standard error of the statistic.

SIGNIFICANCE TESTS FOR ENUMERATION STATISTICS AND PROPORTIONS

The seed which ripens into vision may be a gift of the gods but the labour of cultivating it so that it may bear nourishing fruit is the indispensable function of arduous scientific technique.

Morris Raphael Cohen

SIGNIFICANCE testing is to experimental research as parameter estimation is to survey research. Although both methods of inferential statistics are employed in both research areas, there is the distinction of emphasis in applied research. It exists primarily because survey research so often has as its objective the estimation of population values—of parameters—whereas experimental research more often requires the testing of a hypothesis in order to ascertain whether experimental variables have had *effects*, or consequences, according to design. In a later section of this chapter, *the joint usefulness* of both techniques for statistical inference will be described.

SIGNIFICANCE TESTS FOR TWO-CLASS UNIVARIATES

Enumeration statistics are countables. The data are frequencies, usually symbolized by f but sometimes by n. In practice, the statistics of f are transformed into p statistics, proportions.

The simplest kinds of enumeration statistics are those obtained from univariate populations whose data are of two classes, P and Q, where $Q = 1 - P$. As indicated in Chapter 7, classes of events symbolized by P may include successful results (vs. Q as not-successful), or the presence of a characteristic (vs. Q as its absence), or preferences for A (vs. Q as preferences for *not-A*), or opinions favoring A (vs. Q as opinions favoring *not-A*), etc.

Questions of the following kind can be answered by significance tests when the requirements of probability sampling and scientific (reliable and repeatable) measurement are satisfied. Do a *majority* of citizens living in city X favor the establishment of a community college in their city? The population of persons to be sampled consists of all citizens of city X. They are the primary sampling units. The population to be counted consists of their *replies* to the question. If all have an opinion, YES or NO, then the population to be sampled is a two-class univariate.

Can a cigarette smoker pass the "blind-fold test" in favor of brand X? Now the population consists of responses of identification which are classifiable as SUCCESSFUL (when the brand presented is correctly identified) and NOT-SUCCESSFUL (when a brand is not correctly identified). The subpopulation for brand X consists of successful and unsuccessful identifications of X, which is randomly alternated with other brands under the controlled conditions of the experimentally designed test situation. Theoretically the population is indefinitely large. It is sampled by the extraction of one or more temporal segments of behavior for observation under the conditions of the experiment. The samples drawn are probability samples of the person's behavior-in-the-situation of the experiment. The difficulty of maintaining a probability sample of the SAME population often arises out of changes in these person-situation transactions that are irreversible. Under repeated testing, for example, a person may lose some of his taste discrimination for cigarettes, or his discriminations may become sharpened. In either event, the population of successes and nonsuccesses will have changed, and consequently the character of the samples of observations will also have changed.

Can a cat discriminate a circle from a square? Red from green? Again, as in the foregoing, the population to be sampled consists of a two-class univariate: CORRECT or successful responses as P, and INCORRECT or unsuccessful responses as Q. But since the animal cannot talk, "correctness" or "successfulness" of a response will have to be defined in terms of an *extra-chance* consistency of a sequence of responses to a circle-associated-with-an-award, such as food, or with an electric-shock-associated-with-the-square. Significance testing can give the answer to the possible extra-chance, hence discriminatory character of the cat's behavior in the experimental situation. However, a significance test will hardly be needed if the cat LEARNS to do what the experimenter has designed for him, i.e., practically always goes to the circle for food or always avoids the square. In effect the cat will have met the requirement of the *3-sigma confidence criterion*.

The data for questions such as the foregoing are enumeration statistics obtained by counting the preferences, anticipations, discriminations, etc., in the sample of observations made. Questions of fact will ordinarily yield replies that are dichotomous, and when this is so, the sample data are in two classes. Other questions, especially those concerning preferences, attitudes, and opinions, usually yield at least three classes of replies, one of which may be a DK (don't know, or no opinion) class. In this section, significance tests will be developed for countables whose populations are treated as two-class populations, even though they may be classifiable into more than two classes. A hypothetical population of REPLIES is classifiable into P and Q classes, where P consists of all replies of a specified kind and Q consists of *all the remaining replies:* $Q = 1 - P$, where P and Q are proportions rather than frequencies.

For example: A randomized sample of 100 students from a college population of 8000 is asked a question of fact, "Did you attend a religious service last week end?" If 68 reply YES and 32 reply NO, then the question of whether or not a *majority* of the entire population attended a religious service can be reasonably determined. Furthermore, if it appears likely that a majority did attend, it may be relevant and desirable by interval estimation to indicate the parameter proportion of attenders.

Null Hypothesis, H_0

In significance testing, statistical hypotheses are formulated. Many of these hypotheses have a value of zero; some take on a value other than zero. Whichever may be the case for a particular problem, they are referred to as *null hypotheses* in that they are hypotheses of *no effect* or *no difference*. "Null" in German means zero. In English it means "amounts to nothing."

When null hypotheses are tested, the facts obtained from counting or from measurement are given the opportunity to *nullify* the null hypothesis. Such nullification, however, is but rarely if ever absolute. Rather, null hypotheses are *rejected* with varying levels of confidence. When they can be rejected with "practical certainty," as by the *3-sigma* criterion of confidence, then in effect they have been *practically nullified*. The rejection of a null hypothesis signifies that an experimental result cannot be reasonably attributed simply to the random variations of chance effects: Effects other than chance ones have contributed to the result. In a properly designed experiment, such *extra-chance* effects are those by DESIGN. Thus, in significance testing, the attempt is made oftentimes to determine whether it is reasonable to draw inferences in favor of DESIGN as against CHANCE. This is especially characteristic of experimental research.

Design does not enter into a question of *fact* about a population's preferences or behavior. Rather, it is a question of a *chance division* of replies YES or NO versus an *extra-chance* division. By definition, a chance division of a two-class population is an equal division—a 50–50 dichotomy.

Thus the null hypothesis relevant to a significance test to determine whether a majority of a population did something, or preferred something, etc., is $P = .50$, where P is the hypothesized parameter proportion of a population. Since $Q = 1 - P$, Q also $= .50$. Therefore $P = Q = .50$, and the *difference* between P and Q equals zero. This null hypothesis asserts that there is no difference between the parameter frequency or proportion of YES's and the parameter frequency or proportion of NO's.

If this null hypothesis of $P = .50$ can be rejected, it follows logically that a majority (more than .50) of the population would reply YES or NO, as the case may be, depending on which way a majority of the sampled replies answered the question. Thus, in the example of 68 YES's from the 100 students sampled randomly from the population of 8000, if the null hypothesis can be confidently rejected, it is therefore *likely* that a *majority* of the 8000 students attended a religious service on the last week end. Although there is no certainty that this is correct, the researcher may very reasonably infer it to be substantially correct, provided the sample is a probability sample of the student population.

Significance Test for Proportions

The null hypothesis to be tested in the preceding example is statable thus:

Null Hypothesis, H_0:

$$P = .50$$

$$(\text{or, } P - Q = 0) \tag{9.1}$$

This is the hypothesis of an equal division of YES's and NO's in the population. The parameter value of the proportion of YES's (or NO's, for that matter) is hypothesized at .50.

The significance test takes the following form:

$$z = \frac{\text{Sample statistic} - \text{hypothesized value of parameter}}{\text{Standard error of the sampling distribution of the statistic}} \tag{9.2}$$

Not all significance tests take exactly this form, but this one of Formula 9.2 may be generalized for frequencies of two-class populations as well as proportions; also, for means and correlation coefficients.

In the case of proportion statistics, with the null hypothesis of $P = .50$, Formula 9.2 is a measure of the distance that p, the proportion statistic, is from P, the parameter proportion, in units of the standard deviation of the hypothesized sampling distribution of p statistics, when $n = 100$. The model for this is the normal probability distribution. Hence the ratio of the significance test of Formula 9.2 is a normal z deviate:

***z* Test of Significance:** $$z = \frac{p - P}{\sigma_p} \qquad (9.3)$$

where p is the statistic proportion, P is the parameter proportion of the null hypothesis, and σ_p is the standard error of the hypothesized sampling distribution of proportions (normal probability model in this case). In the preceding chapter, the standard error of p was given as equal to:

Standard Error of *p*: $$\sigma_p = \sqrt{\frac{PQ}{n}} \cdot \sqrt{1 - \frac{n}{N}} \qquad (9.4)$$

where P is the value of the hypothesized value of the parameter proportion, $Q = 1 - P$, and the second term, based on the sampling fraction n/N, is the finite multiplier that may be ignored when less than 5%, as it always is for infinitely large populations as well as for finite populations *sampled with replacement*.

That the significance test measures the z deviate distance of the sample result (proportion) from the parameter mean proportion is illustrated in Fig. 9.1. The z deviate is as follows:

For H_0, $P = .50$:

$$z = \frac{.68 - .50}{\sqrt{\frac{(.50)(.50)}{100}}} = \frac{.18}{.05} = 3.6$$

Since the z deviate is positive (meaning that the sample statistic is *larger* than the parameter value), the sample result of .68 is located 3.6 standard error units beyond the parameter mean value of .50. Irrespective of the criterion chosen in advance of the significance test, it is apparent that the odds are very small that a result of .68 would occur in random sampling of a population whose $P = .50$ when the size of the samples is 100. That is to say, if random samples of 100 observations each were drawn (with replacement) from a population whose parameter proportion of YES's was exactly .50, only once in 5000 times on the average would sample results $\geq .68$ be expected to occur. From the point of view of deductive probability, therefore, the odds for such results are about 1 in 5000. The "$64.00 question" for the actual research result with the student population is one of deciding whether the statistic of .68 should be associated with a population whose parameter is .50, or whether such an association is too fantastic or unreasonable to be acceptable.

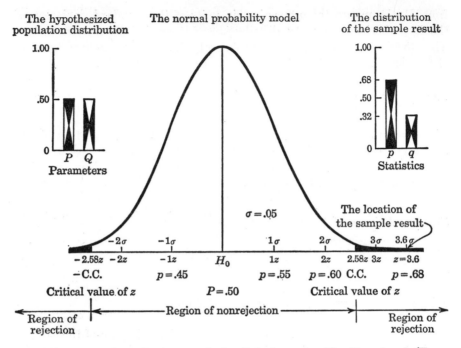

Fig. 9.1. Three Distributions and the Relation of a Nondirectional (Two-Tailed) Significance Test to a Probability Model (the Normal Distribution)

In view of considerations in the preceding chapter about significance levels and confidence criteria, the student should have little doubt in this particular case about the direction of the decision. Such an association of $p = .68$, with $P = .50$, is unreasonable and therefore untenable. Thus the null hypothesis is rejected. This leads logically to the conclusion that the p of .68 is a random sample result from a population whose parameter P is greater than .50. *Ergo*, it is reasonable to conclude that a majority of the student population attended a religious service on the past week end.

z Test of Significance When n Is Small or $P \neq .50$

The normal probability model is appropriate for any significance tests about proportions when $P = .50$ and n is at least 20. When n is < 20 or > 9, the normal model still may be used if the correction for the discontinuity of the Bernoulli binomial probability distribution is made. (See p. 167.) And as was indicated in the preceding chapter, the normal probability model will be satisfactory *when n is large*. Generally, n may be considered sufficiently large if both nP and nQ are at least equal to or greater than 10. Thus, if $P = .25$, random samples of 40 cases or more would satisfy this rule of thumb, since

$$n = \frac{10}{P} = \frac{10}{.25} = 40 \tag{9.5}$$

The applicability of this rule of thumb to a particular sample result can be checked against the Pearson-Hartley Chart I of the Appendix.

Decision About Significance

In order to relate empirical information from sample results to a hypothesized probability model, a decision about the *alpha* level of significance needs to be made in the planning of the research and therefore before the results are in. Generally the first two steps in significance testing are similar to those described in the preceding chapter for parameter estimation, viz.:

1. A decision about the *alpha* significance level to be employed, which is in effect a *coefficient of risk* and which determines the *critical value* of the *criterion* to be used for the rejection or nonrejection of the null hypothesis.

2. The postulation of a mathematical probability distribution appropriate to the parameter value of the null hypothesis to be tested (as in Fig. 9.1).

In significance testing, the additional steps are as follows:

3. A decision as to whether a particular significance test is directional or nondirectional, i.e., whether it involves only one or both tails of the hypothesized probability distribution. (Very often it involves both, depending on what the reasonable alternative hypotheses may be.)

4. The calculation of the appropriate statistic for the test of significance: In the case of proportion statistics this means the determination of the value of the z deviate of the significance test for $P = .50$. (In other significance tests, the appropriate statistic may be x^2, t, or F.)

5. *The decision of significance*, viz., the decision to reject or not-to-reject the null hypothesis that is tested. This decision is made in the light of the results of step 4 as related to earlier decisions in steps 1, 2, and 3.

Some researchers *accept* null hypotheses when they are not rejectable by the significance criterion used. Logically this is analogous to the acceptance of the proposition that a man is innocent of violating a traffic law because he hasn't been proved to be guilty. Insufficient evidence against a proposition is not proof of its correctness. In other words, a null hypothesis cannot be proved to be true. It may gain a certain acceptance as a result of repeated failures of research results to "disprove" it. But, logically, this is the kind of decision made on the basis of *absence of evidence* rather than evidence.

Generally it is recommended that the researcher be guided toward the following alternatives in his decisions of significance; either:

1. Reject the null hypothesis, or
2. Do not reject it, and hence suspend a definitive inference or judgment until more evidence is collected.

Strategy of Choice of *Alpha* Significance Level

When an *alpha* significance level of .05 is used in a significance test, the risk of rejecting a null hypothesis that is true is in the long run greater than when $\alpha = .01$ is used. Contrariwise, the risk of failing to reject a false null hypothesis is less in the long run with $\alpha = .05$ than with $\alpha = .01$.

The strategy of what is done depends on the circumstances of the research and is discussed at some length at the end of the next chapter. For the present, the following general rule is suggested for hypotheses about proportions of two-class populations, when the null hypothesis is $P = .50$ and the attempt is being made to *infer a fact about a majority* of a population: A fairly strict *alpha* significance level should be used, such as .01 or .001, in order to protect the researcher from the error of rejecting the null hypothesis when true.

In research on *experimental effects*, as in the effects of drugs on behavior, a different strategy is usually employed. In such research an *alpha* of 0.02 or .05 may be used in order to give such effects a greater opportunity to manifest themselves as possibly significant, than would be the case if *alpha* of .01 or .001 were used. The *definitive significance* of possible effects, thus isolated, can then be explored further with additional samplings and research.

For the problem of trying to ascertain a fact about a population of people, a coefficient of risk equal to *alpha* of .01 may be used. The value of the confidence criterion (c.c.) in terms of a normal z deviate, when $\alpha = .01$, will depend on whether the test is *nondirectional* or *directional*. In other words, the value of c.c. will depend on whether both tails of the distribution of the probability model are to be considered or whether the probabilities subtended in only one tail are to be taken into account.

Nondirectional (Two-Tailed) vs. Directional (One-Tailed) Significance Tests

The decision about *directionality* of a significance test is not a matter of free choice. Rather, the decision will depend on a consideration of what *alternative hypotheses* are reasonable or predictable in the light of information or theory. There are two classes of alternatives to the null hypothesis, which will be stated at this point in relation to the null hypothesis of $P - Q = 0$:

1. $P \neq Q$ (that P is not equal to Q).
2. $P > Q$ or $P < Q$ (that P is greater than Q or that P is less than Q).

The first alternative, viz., $P \neq Q$, is the implication of a significant nondirectional test. This is the case because a nondirectional test is employed when (1) one is chiefly concerned with the possible existence of a difference between two parameters (in this case P and Q) irrespective of the direction of the difference; and (2) one is in doubt about the directionality of a test. The nondirectional hypothesis asserts only that there is no difference between P and Q, since $P - Q = 0$; hence the subscript 0 with H for this null hypothesis H_0: $P - Q = 0$; $P = .50$.

Delta Hypothesis and a Directional Significance Test

The hypothesis for a directional test is symbolized as H_Δ, with the subscript *delta* signifying *directional*. Both alternatives of the second class of alternative hypotheses to the null hypothesis are implications of directional significance tests. A directional hypothesis is thus statable in two ways:

1. In a positive direction from the hypothesized parameter of the null hypothesis such that $H_\Delta(\geq)$ (equal to, or more than).
2. In a negative direction such that $H_\Delta(\leq)$, (equal to, or less than).

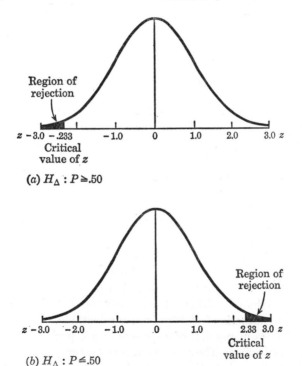

(a) $H_\Delta : P \geqslant .50$

(b) $H_\Delta : P \leqslant .50$

Fig. 9.2. **Directional (or *Delta*) Significance Tests and Normal Probability Models**
(*Alpha* = .01; Critical Value of z = ±2.33)

Used with proportions, the first of these alternative *delta* hypotheses asserts that $P \geq .50$ and would be used whenever one's theory or information predicts a parameter *less than* $P = .50$. The significance test would be one-tailed, and its *critical region* for the rejection of the hypothesis would be subtended at the *negative tail* of the probability model, as illustrated in Fig. 9.2a.

The other *delta* hypothesis asserts that $P \leq .50$ and would be used when one's theory or information predicts a parameter greater than $P = .50$. The critical region for the rejection of this hypothesis is subtended at the *positive tail* of the probability model, as illustrated in Fig. 9.2b.

When the first *delta* hypothesis (viz., $H_\Delta: P \geq .50$) can be rejected in consequence of the significance test, the inference follows quite logically that the value of the parameter is most likely *less than .50*. When the second *delta* hypothesis (viz., $H_\Delta: P \leq .50$) can be rejected, the inference follows logically that the value of the parameter proportion is most likely *greater than .50*.

Most survey research in search of *facts*, such as the question of whether a majority of a student population did or did not do something, is *nondirectional in conception* but hopes to be *directional in its conclusion*. The significance test is therefore set up nondirectionally as a two-tailed test. If it turns out that the null hypothesis is rejectable, then it is quite logical to make an inference either about a majority or a minority, depending on which direction the p statistic was from .50. If it were .68, as in the foregoing example, and the z deviate significance test is 3.6, then not only is the null hypothesis of $P = .50$ rejectable but the *delta* hypothesis of $P \leq .50$ is also. The reason may be apparent: For a given coefficient of risk, the c.c. for a nondirectional test is always larger (without regard to sign) than for the directional test.

With the normal probability model, for example, and $\alpha = .01$, the critical criterion is a z deviate of 2.33 for a directional test and ± 2.58 for a nondirectional test. For the latter to be rejectable, the z of the significance test needs to be larger than ± 2.58. If z is equal to or more than $+2.58$, and the c.c. for the directional test is $+2.33$, then the *delta* hypothesis of $H_\Delta(\leq)$ is also rejectable. If the z of the significance test is equal to or more than -2.58 and the c.c. for the directional test is -2.33, then the *delta* hypothesis of $H_\Delta(\geq)$ is also rejectable.

Directional tests in psychological research are perhaps not so common as nondirectional ones. They are common to certain areas of research, however. Thus, if one is testing a drug that is supposed to have a positive or stimulating effect on psychological output, then the appropriate hypothesis to test is $H_\Delta(\leq)$, which asserts that the drug has either no effect or a negative effect. The rejection of the hypothesis would support the contention. On the other hand, if a drug is supposed to be a sedative that will depress psychological output, the appropriate directional hypothesis to test is $H_\Delta(\geq)$, which asserts that the drug has either no effect or a positive effect.

If it should happen that a *delta* hypothesis is tested and the z deviate result is in the same direction and sufficiently large to be "significant," then either the prediction was ill-conceived or the result has the significance of *serendipity*, which is defined as the accidental discovery of something significant while searching for something else; in this case, searching in the opposite direction.

Critical Regions of Rejection and Nonrejection

A z deviate value for the critical criterion when *alpha* is taken at .01 and when the test is *nondirectional* or two-tailed will be a magnitude on the scale that subtends .005 of the area at each end of the normal probability curve. Hence, for $\alpha = .01$, $z_{.005}$ and $z_{.995}$ are the locations of the critical points. Their respective values can be readily determined by reference to columns 3 and 4 of Table A. The entry of column 3 is .9951, and that of column 4 (the same row) is .0049. As already indicated, the value of z at these points is -2.58 and 2.58. They are marked off on the normal probability model of Fig. 9.1. They are the *critical values for the decision of significance*. They divide the scale of expected sampling variation into a broad *region of nonrejection* and subtend *regions of rejection* at each tail of the probability distribution. Theoretically these tails are asymptotic to the abscissa; in the case of the random variations of proportions, they extend to the limits of zero and 1.0.

The z deviate value for the critical criterion of a directional test for an *alpha* coefficient of risk of .01 is also found from Table A. It will be a value that subtends 1% of the area at either end of the distribution and therefore at points $z_{.01}$ or $z_{.99}$, depending on the direction of the test. As already indicated and illustrated in Fig. 9.2a and b, the *critical value* is 2.33.

Rejection of the Null Hypothesis

Since the value of the z test for the nondirectional null hypothesis with the statistic of .68 was found to be 3.6, the hypothesis was rejected with confidence, i.e., 3.6 is well within the region of rejection which begins at 2.58. And since the critical value for the directional hypothesis $H_\Delta : P \leq .50$ is 2.33, this is also rejected with confidence. The decision is therefore made that the evidence supports the conclusion that a majority of the college population attended a religious service on the past week end: $P > .50$.

Inconclusiveness of Nonrejection

Had the sample result been .58 instead of .68, then z would have been 1.6, as follows:

For H_0, $P = .50$: $z = \dfrac{.58 - .50}{.05} = 1.6$

No positive decision would have been permissible, since a normal z deviate of 1.6 is well within the range of nonrejection of Fig. 9.1. Not only could it not have been concluded that a majority attended, but neither could it have been concluded that less than a majority attended or that exactly 50% attended.

The student may well ask why a more definite conclusion cannot be reached when $z = 1.6$. The answer to this question lies in the fact that available information is insufficient to permit a decision of significance.

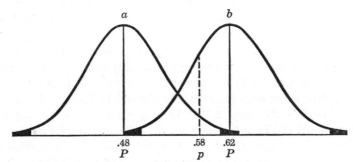

Critical areas of $H_0 : P = .48$ and $H_0 : P = .62$ are shaded at the tails of their respective hypothesized probability models

Fig. 9.3. Location of p Statistic with Respect to Critical Areas of Two Nondirectional Hypotheses
(Normal Probability Model; *Alpha* $= .01$)

As indicated in Fig. 9.3, a sample result of .58 is quite plausible in random variation for a parent population whose parameter proportion is .48; it is also quite plausible in random variation for a parent population whose parameter proportion is .62. In fact there is a fairly broad continuum of parameter possibilities, each of which can be reasonably expected to yield by chance a sample proportion of .58 more frequently than once in 100 times (the *alpha* level of .01) when random samples of 100 cases are drawn from any of these populations.

From Significance Testing to Parameter Estimation

The full range of nonrejectable hypotheses can be established as indicated in the preceding chapter (p. 225), in which confidence limits of an interval estimate were employed as significance criteria. In other words, the range of nonrejectable hypotheses is the range of the confidence interval.

An approximation of the interval, and hence the range of nonrejectable hypotheses, can be obtained for proportions as follows, when c.c. is 2.58, and

$$\hat{\sigma}_p = \sqrt{\frac{pq}{n}} = \sqrt{\frac{(.58)(.42)}{100}} = .049$$

Interval Estimate of P: *

$$.58 - 2.58(.049) < P < .58 + 2.58(.049)$$

$$.45 < P < .71$$

Although it is not possible with such a statistic as .58 and $n = 100$ to reject the null hypothesis, it should now be clear that it is possible to make an inference, broad as it may be, about the possible value of the parameter of the parent population. It will be most likely a value somewhere on the scale of parameter possibilities between .45 and .71. In other words, it may be .50 (the null hypothesis), or it may be as low as .45 or as high as .71.

The confidence interval thus describes the range of parameter possibilities, a continuum of hypothetical values, any one of which is conceivably (and reasonably so) the value of the parent population whose random sample yielded a p of .58. However, all are not equally likely. Those nearest the value of the statistic (.58) presumably are more likely than those that differ most (.45 and .71). This is the presumption, and in the long run it *probably* works out, but with a single sample result the validity of the distinction is doubtful. Recall the variations in sample means of Fig. 7.6, p. 178.

How Large a Probability Sample for Significance

When a researcher plans an investigation, he has to make a decision about sample size. If he thinks the result for a two-class population will be close, he can draw a randomized sample large enough to give the facts an opportunity to nullify the null hypothesis at a given significance level. If he surmises the result may be as close as 55% YES's and 45% NO's, he can solve the following equation for n and thereby determine the minimum sample size (in simple random sampling) needed for significance when $p \geq .55$:

Sample Size: $\quad e = z_\alpha \sqrt{\dfrac{PQ}{n}}$; $\quad$ therefore $\quad n = \dfrac{z_\alpha{}^2 PQ}{e^2}$ $\qquad$ (9.6)

where e denotes the chosen maximum error of sampling variation (in proportions) to be tolerated for the nonrejection of the null hypothesis; z_α equals the critical criterion (c.c.) in terms of a normal z deviate for significance level *alpha*, and P is the parameter proportion of .50 for the null hypothesis.

When $\alpha = .01$, the critical criterion is a z value of 2.58 for a two-tailed significance test. If e is taken as $\pm.05$, this signifies the maximum variation

---

*This interval estimate of P can also be made with the aid of the Pearson-Hartley charts in the Appendix (I). As was pointed out in the preceding chapter (p. 219), these charts will give a more accurate interval estimate than the above procedure as the value of P approaches zero or 1.0. For the above data, the estimate is $.455 < P < .70$.

in sampling error to be tolerated for the null hypothesis of $P = .50$. For these criteria, n is as follows:

$$n = \frac{(2.58)^2(.50)(.50)}{(.05)^2} = \frac{1.6641}{.0025} = 666$$

Thus a randomized sample of at least 666 observations would be needed when the p statistic $= .55$, in order to give *information* (the facts) the opportunity to "nullify" the chance hypothesis at the predetermined level of significance of .01:

For H_0, $P = .50$: $z = \dfrac{.55 - .50}{\sqrt{\dfrac{(.50)(.50)}{666}}} = 2.58$

Adjustment for Sampling Fraction

If the sampling fraction of a finite population is greater than 5%, its effect on the reduction in sampling error variance should be taken into account. Thus, if in the preceding example the parent population had consisted of a frame of 6000 sampling units, n would be reduced to 592, since the square of the finite multiplier is

$$1 - \frac{n}{N}, \quad \text{and} \quad 666\left(1 - \frac{666}{6000}\right) = 592$$

A randomized sample of 600 would thus be sufficient.

Sample Size for a Close Result

Should a result considerably closer to $P = .50$ (than a $p = .55$) be anticipated, then a much larger sample than 600 or 666 would be needed for significance, even for $\alpha = .05$, for which the z deviate critical criterion would be 1.96. Thus, if the sample result were a p of .51, n would need to be at least 10,000:

$$n = \frac{(1.96)^2(.50)(.50)}{(.01)^2} = \frac{1}{.0001} = 10,000$$

Should a junior researcher jump to the conclusion that all a pollster of opinion needs to do in order to be sure of an election outcome in an apparently close race is to take a sample of at least 10,000 eligible voters, he needs to be reminded, first, that the problem of obtaining a *probability* sample of millions of potential voters is very complicated and cannot be done cheaply and at the same time adequately; secondly, that not all eligible voters will vote on election day; and thirdly, that even if a properly designed probability sample of 10,000 eligible voters "guaranteed" to vote on election day were attainable, only *intent* can be sampled and inferred.

Actual voting behavior on election day constitutes an unsampled population of behavior which may or may not correlate highly enough with pre-election polls to permit a successful forecast of the outcome.

Statistical Significance vs. Practical Significance vs. Significance for Theory

It is perhaps apparent that it may be possible to obtain statistical significance by the use of very large random samples. But is statistical significance really sufficient? The researcher is not interested in statistics per se but in the aid statistical techniques can give him in the search for significance. He is interested in *practical* significance and (or) *theoretical* significance, i.e., significant results relevant to psychological theory, for example. Savage (1957) has emphasized that "exclusive reliance on tests of significance obscures the fact that statistical significance does not imply substantive significance." How much statistical significance it takes to have substantive significance is relative to the nature of the variables and the problems under consideration. It is here that methods for the estimation of parameters are often invaluable in that they give the likely *magnitude* (within the range of the confidence interval) of parameter differences.

Two statistically significant statistics that may have very little practical significance are the percentages of males and females in the 1960 population of the United States: 49.3% males and 50.7% females.* Random samples of persons could be drawn of sufficient size to warrant the rejection of the null hypothesis of $P = Q = .50$, known to be false. The sample difference could be statistically significant, but does this slight population difference of one percentage point have any practical significance? It could, psychologically, if knowledge of the fact should alert unmarried members of the "major" sex group to great urgency in the "capture" of marriageable mates. But for most social problems and interpersonal relations the overall difference may have little or no practical significance; differences at various age levels are likely to be more pertinent.

There are some areas of research in which a statistically significant difference, although not duplicated, has been interpreted as significant for psychological theory. Hudgins' (1933) widely publicized (in psychological texts) experiment in which he reported "conditioning" of the pupillary reflex (presumably an involuntary response) to voluntary control of some subjects' voluntary processes (subvocal thinking, "contract") is perhaps a case in point. So far this has evidently been a nonrepeatable result. Several have tried and have failed. The field of parapsychological research is pertinent here: Although no results of any *practical* significance have ever been scientifically demonstrated insofar as the writer is aware, pro-

---

*U.S. Bureau of the Census, 1960 figures: Population all ages: 179,323,175; males = 88,331,494, females = 90,991,681. (Statistical Abstract of U.S., 1962, p. 25.)

ponents of research in this area, such as Gardner Murphy (1961), place confidence in the statistical significance of some research results, with ESP as an acceptable alternative hypothesis to the rejected null hypothesis of purely chance effects. An inference of *statistical significance* may thus have tremendous implications for theorists in a particular area.

CHI-SQUARE SIGNIFICANCE TESTS FOR UNIVARIATES

Chi-Square as a Test of Significance

Chi-square tests of significance are for *hypotheses about frequencies.* They have greater usefulness than z deviate tests for frequencies because the latter are restricted in their application to two-class populations whereas chi-square is not. Thus chi-square has a much broader range of applicability than a z deviate test of significance for frequencies or proportions.

Generally, chi-square is useful to test the following classes of hypotheses:

1. The division of frequencies of a univariate into two or more classes, such as successes and failures (two classes), yes's, no's, and don't knows (three classes), boys, girls, and men, and women (four classes).

The data themselves may be countables per se (as in the foregoing examples) or they may be *measurables reduced to countables;* for example, the division of a population of I.Q.'s into a trichotomy of those below the average range, those in the average range (90 to 110), and those above the average range.

As was pointed out in the first chapter, several distribution-free methods have been developed by the reduction of measurables to countables and the use of chi-square for the consequent significance test (see the median test by chi-square, p. 365).

Goodness of Fit for Distributions of Frequencies. A general subclass of hypotheses about the division of frequencies of a univariate tested by chi-square consists of *distributions of frequencies*, in contrast to unordered divisions of frequencies characteristic of nominal variates. The trichotomy of I.Q.'s, just cited, is a case in point but not a typical example. More typical is the use of chi-square to test the significance of *discrepancies* between the distribution of the frequencies of a sample and the distribution of the frequencies of an hypothesized parent population; for example, a Gaussian normal distribution or a Bernoulli binomial distribution. Such tests by chi-square have long been referred to as tests of *goodness of fit.*

2. Chi-square is also used to test a second broad class of hypotheses about frequencies, viz., the independence of bivariates whose data take the form of countables. They are sometimes referred to as *contingency tests* and will be developed in a later section.

z Test of Significance for Frequencies

Before the chi-square test is presented, a z test for *frequencies* will be illustrated. The null hypothesis for **F**, the expected frequency, is equated to the number of frequencies in the sample result in order that the particular value of F will be on the same scale as the statistic f. This is done so that the *differences* between them can be directly compared with the expectations of random variation. It is *as if* a small population, with $N = n$, were sampled indefinitely by the method of replacement after each observation.

When $n = 100$ and there are but two classes, F for either class may equal $n/k = 100/2 = 50$. Thus the hypothesized population for purposes of the significance test, consists of an equal division of frequencies into two classes:

Null Hypothesis, H_0: $F_1 = F_0$ $\qquad\qquad\qquad\qquad\qquad$ (9.7)

where the numerical subscript 1 denotes one class (as, for example, YES's) and the subscript zero denotes the remainder (*not* YES's).

The measure of expected sampling variation in random sampling for a two-class population of frequencies is given by the standard error as follows:

Standard Error of f: $\qquad\qquad \sigma_f = \sqrt{nPQ}$ $\qquad\qquad\qquad$ (9.8)

where n, as usual, is the size of the sample and P is the proportion of hypothesized expected frequencies F_1 to all expected frequencies F, and $Q = 1 - P$.

Hence for H_0: $F_1 = 50$:

$$z = \frac{f_1 - F_1}{\sigma_f} = \frac{68 - 50}{\sqrt{100(.50)(.50)}} = \frac{18}{5} = 3.6 \qquad (9.9)$$

This z deviate value of 3.6 is the same as that obtained in the earlier test of significance with proportions. This is, of course, as it should be, since the same probability model, viz., the normal distribution, is employed here with the same set of sample information. The only difference is that this time the random variations of sample results are measured in terms of frequencies rather than in terms of proportions.

Development of Chi-Square Test of Significance

The chi-square test of significance was developed by Karl Pearson (1901) for hypotheses about the divisions of frequencies into classes (univariates) or into cells (bivariates). On the assumption of normally distributed population variables, chi-square is equal to the following:

$$\chi^2 = \sum \frac{(x - \mu)^2}{\sigma^2} \qquad (9.10)$$

Pearson showed that if the condition is imposed that parameter N shall always be the same for a given universe, then chi-square for the comparison of f statistics with expected $\mathbf{F}$'s, as hypothesized, is as follows:

Chi-Square:
$$\chi^2 = \sum^{k} \frac{(f_i - \mathbf{F}_i)^2}{\mathbf{F}_i} \tag{9.11}$$

where the summation is taken over all the classes (or cells), k; f_i is the sample frequency of the ith class, $\mathbf{F}_i$ is the hypothesized expected frequency of the corresponding ith class, and k is the number of classes (or cells).

This formulation (9.11) of chi-square for frequencies is *not* based on the assumption of normally distributed population variables; hence it is *a distribution-free method* for significance testing.

Degrees of Freedom with Chi-Square

When there are only two classes of sample results, as in the preceding example, there is but one degree of freedom inasmuch as the number of hypothesized frequencies can be varied in only one class. Their number added to the frequencies of the other class have to give a total N equal to n. In general the number of d.f.'s for a chi-square test for hypotheses about single variates is the number of classes or divisions less one: d.f. $= k - 1$.

Probability Models for Chi-Square

A remarkable fact about the sampling distributions of chi-square is that they are dependent not on n but on the number of d.f.'s, which in turn is dependent only on the number of classes (or cells) to which hypothesized $\mathbf{F}_i$ values may be assigned without restriction. The sampling distributions themselves are *discrete;* they are analogous in this respect to the Bernoulli probability models. The discrete distributions of chi-square describe the expected patterns of variation to be expected in random sampling. The patterns change as the number of degrees of freedom change; however, when $k - 1$ for univariates is around 30 or more, the patterns approximate that of the normal probability curve.

The probability models generally used for chi-square tests of significance are, however, *approximations* consisting of a family of *curves*, rather than the exact, discrete distributions. The situation here is analogous to the use of the normal probability model, when proper to do so, for discrete binomial models: A great deal of time is saved.

Critical values of chi-square for the probability *curves* are given in Table C of the Appendix. Several of the models for distributions with only one or a few degrees of freedom are illustrated in Fig. 9.4.

The use of the approximation probability models of chi-square, as in Table C, for significance testing is based on the assumption that the mini-

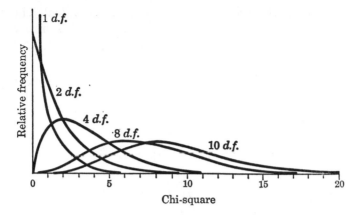

Fig. 9.4.   Some Probability Models of the Chi-Square Statistic
(For Various Degrees of Freedom as Indicated: 1, 2, 4, 8, and 10)

Statistical Inference, Helen M. Walker and Joseph Lev, Copyright © 1953, Holt, Rinehart and Winston, Inc. By Permission.

mum number of hypothesized **F**'s for any class k is five. If the number is less than five, then the continuous sampling distributions of chi-square statistics will not be satisfactory approximations of the exact, discrete distributions. In such cases *the exact test* should be made. That is to say, the test of significance should be made against the discrete probability model rather than against the curved approximation.

Walker and Lev (1953, p. 107) point out, however, that when there are more than 2 d.f.'s and the hypothesized frequencies in all classes (or cells) but one satisfy the minimum-of-five-F_i's rule, then even only one frequency in the remaining class (or cell) is sufficient to give a satisfactory approximation of the exact probabilities.

When there are many classes or divisions of frequencies, two or more may be combined if it is logically permissible to do so. By this device, the necessary minimum number of hypothesized F_i's of five may be set up. Lest there be confusion about this question, the student should note that the rule about the minimum number of frequencies for a class (or cell) applies *not* to sample f_i's but to the hypothesized F_i's.

Computation of Chi-Square

When the sample results are in two classes and the frequencies are 68 and 32, as in the earlier example, chi-square for the null hypothesis of $F_1 = F_0 = N/2 = 50$ is equal to 13.0, as follows:

For H_0: $F_1 = F_0$:

$$\chi^2 = \frac{(68 - 50)^2}{50} + \frac{(32 - 50)^2}{50} = 6.5 + 6.5 = 13.0$$

The significance of this chi-square statistic of 13.0 is evaluated in relation to the critical value of chi-square in Table C for one d.f. The values of chi-square statistics are in the body of the table, as are the t statistics in Table B. Centile point values for the sampling distributions of chi-square are given at the top of the columns. Degrees of freedom are indicated in the left-hand column of the table. *Critical values* of chi-square can thus be determined for (1) the desired *alpha* significance level and (2) the appropriate d.f. Significance level of 0.01 is defined in Table C by the column headed $\chi^2_{.99}$.

Table C indicates that a chi-square statistic of 13.0 for one d.f. occurs in random sampling less than once in a thousand times, on the average. This is the case inasmuch as the critical value of chi-square at the 99th centile is 10.8. Thus the null hypothesis is rejected with a great deal of confidence.

Chi-Square When d.f. > 30

The sampling distributions of chi-square statistics tend toward the form of the normal probability distribution as the number of d.f.'s increases. When there are more than 30 d.f.'s, the approximation is sufficiently close to permit the use of a normal z deviate significance test of the result, provided the following z transformation for chi-square is used:

When d.f. > 30: $\qquad z = \sqrt{2\chi^2} - \sqrt{2(\text{d.f.}) - 1}$ $\qquad$ (9.12)

For an *alpha* significance level of .01 and 30 d.f.'s, the critical value of chi-square by Table C is 50.9; hence the value of χ^2 by Formula 9.11 would need to be larger than 50.9 for the rejection of the null hypothesis. Whenever the number of d.f.'s > 30, then the z deviate test of Eq. 9.12 is made.

A Rule of Thumb

A labor-saving feature of Table C may be noted. The *median* value of chi-square for any d.f. is approximately equal to the d.f. The difference is less than an integer. Consequently, in any significance test by chi-square, the null hypothesis won't be rejectable when the calculated value of chi-square is less than the number of d.f.'s. Median values are at $\chi^2_{.50}$.

Relation of χ^2 to z When d.f. = 1

In practice, a researcher would not use both a z test of significance for frequencies (or proportions) and a chi-square test with the same set of data. When d.f. = 1, one of the two tests is sufficient, since the implications of their results for significance testing are identical. This is the case because *chi*, the square root of χ^2, is distributed as a normal z deviate. Thus

When d.f. = 1: $\qquad\qquad \sqrt{\chi^2} = \chi = z$ $\qquad\qquad$ (9.13)

and therefore, for the preceding example:

$$\sqrt{\chi^2} = \sqrt{13.0} = 3.6$$

which is the same value obtained in the z test with Formula 9.8.

Chi-Square as a Nondirectional Test

Although only the upper tail of the chi-square probability distributions of Table C are referred to in significance testing and hence it may appear that chi-square is a directional or one-tailed test, this is not the case. Chi-square is a nondirectional test. The statistic itself is a squared value which thus eliminates the direction of differences between f and $\mathbf{F}$. Perhaps the point can be clarified by an example. The critical value of χ^2 for one d.f. and alpha of .01 is found in Table C under the column headed $\chi^2_{.99}$. The area of the probability distribution of χ^2 is subtended 1% beyond this point, and so the critical values are always at the upper tail. But the test itself is nondirectional, as will be seen when compared with the z deviate nondirectional test:

With one d.f. and $\alpha = .01$:

Critical value of $\chi^2_{.99} = 6.6$ (Table C)

$$\sqrt{\chi^2} = \pm z = \sqrt{6.6} = \pm 2.57$$

An inspection of Table A will show that $-z$ of 2.57 is $z_{.005}$ and $+z$ of 2.57 is $z_{.995}$. These are the critical values of z for a nondirectional or two-tailed test when $\alpha = .01$.

Exact Tests for Two-Class Results When $n < 10$

Sampling distributions of chi-square were seen to be discrete, but the probability models ordinarily used as satisfactory approximations are continuous (Table C). They are unsatisfactory approximations when $n < 10$ and d.f. ≥ 1. Significance tests for samples of less than ten observations can be made by an exact test. However, whenever possible it is better to design an experiment with larger samples so as not to have to rely on so little information.

The null hypothesis of $\mathbf{F}_1 = \mathbf{F}_2 = n/k$ can be tested by means of the probability implications of the Bernoulli binomial sampling distributions. This was illustrated in the context of probability theory, rather than of significance testing, on p. 168 by the *sign test*.

When there are two classes or divisions of frequencies for a single variate, f_1 and f_2, the exact probability of the various kinds of results, from zero YES's to n YES's, can be obtained by the algebra of permutations for sets and subsets. Thus, when samples of eight observations are drawn, the null hypothesis asserts $\mathbf{F}_1 = \mathbf{F}_2 = n/k = 8/2 = 4$. The discrete distribution of the sampling variations of f_1 (YES's, for example) can be determined from the number of different ways, irrespective of order, that the nine subsets can be obtained. (The number of subsets equals $n + 1$.)

For a particular significance test, however, only those subsets at one or the other end of the distribution need be considered for the determination of the desired probability values. For example, if f_1 (YES's) $= 7$, then the difference between an f of 7 and an $\mathbf{F}$ of 4 is 3. The question for significance testing is one of ascertaining whether, for a given value of *alpha*, this difference of three frequencies is great enough to warrant the rejection of the null hypothesis. If such a difference occurs but rarely as a random variation, the decision to be made is either one of identifying the sample result f_1 with such a random variation and thus not rejecting the null hypothesis, or of rejecting such an identification and thereby rejecting the null hypothesis.

When $n = 8$, the total number of ways the nine different subsets of a two-class population may occur is equal to $2^n = 2^8 = 256$. A subset consisting of eight f's (YES's) may be obtained only in one way, since $r = n$:

$$\binom{n}{r} = \binom{n}{n} = \binom{8}{8} = 1$$

Hence $\mathbf{P}$ (8 f's) $= 1/256 = .0039$.

A subset consisting of seven f's may be obtained in eight ways, since

$$\binom{n}{r} = \binom{8!}{7!} = \frac{8 \times 7!}{7!} = 8$$

Hence $\mathbf{P}$ (7 f's) $= 8/256 = .0312$.

The odds in random sampling of seven or more f's (YES's) in samples of eight are therefore as follows:

$$\mathbf{P} \text{ (at least 7 } f\text{'s)} = \mathbf{P} \text{ (7 } f\text{'s)} + \mathbf{P} \text{ (8 } f\text{'s)} = \frac{1+8}{256} = .035$$

If the significance test were directional and *alpha* were taken at .05, the null hypothesis would be rejected, since .035 is less than .05. If, however, the test were nondirectional and *alpha* remained at .05, the hypothesis would not be rejected. This would be the case because the probability of at least seven f's is greater than the critical probability of .025 at one tail of the distribution.

Whether or not a test is directional or nondirectional is not a matter of choice. As already indicated, chi-square is a nondirectional test.

Exact Test vs. Chi-Square When $n = 8$ and d.f. $= 1$

Had this test for eight observations been made against the continuous probability model of chi-square for 1 d.f., the result would have been as follows:

$$\chi^2 = \frac{(7 - 4)^2}{4} + \frac{(1 - 4)^2}{4} = 4.50$$

Chi-square is calculated to be 4.50. By Table C, for one d.f., $\chi^2_{.95} = 3.8$, and $\chi^2_{.975} = 5.0$. Hence the probability for a chi-square value of 4.50 is between .05 and .025. It can be computed exactly from a normal z deviate, since there is but one d.f.

For one d.f., $\sqrt{\chi^2} = \chi = z$, and therefore $\sqrt{4.50} = 2.121$. A normal z deviate of 2.121, by Table A, is slightly above the 98.3 centile. Hence the probability of sample results equal to chi-square values of at least 4.50 is .017. The continuous sampling distribution of chi-square thus underestimates the probability of the discrete sampling distribution of .035 by .018, since $.035 - .017 = .018$.

Chi-square for one d.f. by the approximations of the continuous sampling distribution used for the various point values of Table C is thus unsatisfactory when n is 8. It becomes increasingly unsatisfactory when n is less than 8. Generally when $n < 10$, the exact test should be made.

SIGNIFICANCE TESTS FOR UNIVARIATES OF MORE THAN TWO CLASSES

z Test for Proportions

On occasion it may make sense to combine all alternatives *but one* of a sample result into a single class so that there will then be but two classes, and the null hypothesis $P = .50$, can be tested. Thus a random sample of 50 chairmen of departments of physics, drawn randomly from a population frame of 1400 United States senior colleges, might show the distribution of preferences for five current introductory texts in general physics presented in Table 9.1. The proportionate results for text A could be taken as one class (P) and the alternatives B, C, D, and E would be combined into a single class (Q), where $Q = 1 - P$.

Table 9.1. Distribution of
Preference Among
Five Categories

Text	f	$\dfrac{f/n}{p}$
A	35	.70
B	10	.20
C	3	.06
D	1	.02
E	1	.02
$k = 5$ $\quad n = 50$		1.00

The significance test for the null hypothesis, $P = .50$, with the sampling fraction not taken into account because the finite multiplier would be .996, is as follows:

$$\textbf{\textit{For } } H_0, \textbf{\textit{ P}} = \textbf{\textit{.50:}} \qquad z = \frac{.70 - .50}{\sqrt{\dfrac{(.50)(.50)}{50}}} = 2.8 \qquad\qquad [9.3]$$

This significance test is a nondirectional test, since P_A could conceivably be equal to or less than .50 as well as greater than .50. For an *alpha* significance level of .01, the critical value of z is 2.58. Hence the null hypothesis is rejected with confidence. The result is not only *statistically significant* but also of considerable *practical significance* for the publisher of text A. Inasmuch as he can confidently infer that at least a majority of the chairmen of the parent population prefer his book, his sales should profit accordingly.

Chi-Square for Multiclass Samples of Multiclass Populations

When a sample result consists of more than two classes of frequency information, the preceding procedure oftentimes cannot be employed for a meaningful z test of significance for $P = .50$. Unless one class has a sample result of more than half the total number of frequencies, it would make no sense to test the hypothesis of $P_A \leq .50$. It might, however, make sense to set up an interval estimate of a parameter proportion of less than .50 so that a particular publisher, as in the preceding example, would have an idea of the "outside limits" of preferences for his text. It would also make sense to use chi-square to test the null hypothesis for an equal division of hypothesized frequencies among the several categories.

Table 9.2.   Distribution of
Preference Among
Five Categories

Text	f	f/n p
A	23	.46
B	10	.20
C	8	.16
D	5	.10
E	4	.08
$k = 5$	$n = 50$	1.00

If, for example, in the preceding fictional study, the poll of departmental chairmen had yielded the distribution of results of Table 9.2, there would be no point in testing the hypothesis that $P = .50$, since no category has a result of more than half the sample frequencies. It wouldn't make sense to combine any of these results if each text were published by different firms. Chi-square would therefore be used to test the hypothesis that the expected F_k's are equally divided among the k categories. For this test, the null hypothesis is therefore as follows:

Null Hypothesis, H_0 of Equal F_k's

$$H_0: F_1 = F_2 = \cdots = F_k = \frac{n}{k} \tag{9.14}$$

Since there are five categories or classes and n is 50, $F_k = 10$. The significance test by chi-square is therefore as follows:

$$\chi^2 = \frac{(23 - 10)^2}{10} + \frac{(10 - 10)^2}{10} + \frac{(8 - 10)^2}{10} + \frac{(5 - 10)^2}{10} + \frac{(4 - 10)^2}{10}$$

$$= 16.9 + \text{zero} + 0.4 + 2.5 + 3.6 = 23.4$$

With $k - 1$ d.f.'s $= 4$, Table C shows the critical values of chi-square to be 13.3 for $\chi^2_{.99}$ and 18.5 for $\chi^2_{.999}$. Chi-square is larger than either of these criterion values and sufficiently greater than the larger of the two to warrant the rejection of the null hypothesis with great confidence.

What is the practical significance of such a statistically significant result? The publisher of text A should be pleased because this text not only ranks first in the sample but in all likelihood rates a plurality in the population, since its ratio of 16.9 in the computation of chi-square contributes the major portion of the discrepancy between the sample f's and the hypothesized F's. With such information it might be desirable, as already suggested, to make an interval estimate of the parameter proportion for text A; the other texts would be combined into a single Q class. The point estimate of F_A would be $(f_A/n)(N) = (23/50)(1400) = 644$ senior colleges. (See p. 191.) The interval estimate with $\alpha = .01$ would be $.28 > P > .65$ (p. 419).

Trichotomies

One of the most common classifications that occur in field studies of attitudes and opinions, as well as in research for information, is the trichotomy that includes DON'T KNOW (DK), or "no opinion," or "refuse to answer." When this kind of result occurs and the data are treated as a trichotomy of three classes or categories, two dimensions are really mixed into one:

1. First dimension: Having an opinion vs. not having an opinion.
2. Second dimension (for those with an opinion): Agree or not agree.

Thus the mixed trichotomy is

Agree, not agree (or disagree), and $\begin{cases} \text{Don't know} \\ \text{No opinion} \\ \text{Refusal to answer} \end{cases}$

If the attempt is made to convert a two-dimensional trichotomy into a one-dimensional dichotomy, one runs the risk of considerable error. How should the third mixed category be treated? If it should be ignored, it will be *not really ignored* because the frequencies of this category would *in effect* be distributed to the other two categories, proportionate to their relative frequencies. Thus when $n = 100$:

$$\text{Agree} = 40 \qquad \text{Disagree} = 40 \qquad \text{No Opinion} = 20$$

and therefore

$$p_A = .40 \qquad\qquad p_B = .40 \qquad\qquad p_C = .20$$

With the third category presumably "ignored," the result is as follows:

$$\text{Agree} = \frac{40}{80} = .50 \qquad \text{Disagree} = \frac{40}{80} = .50$$

With the frequencies of the third category distributed among the other two in their respective proportions, the result for the *relative frequencies* (proportions) is the same:

$$f \text{ of "Agree"} + \tfrac{1}{2} \text{ of } f_C = 40 + 10 = 50; \quad p = \frac{50}{100} = .50$$

$$f \text{ of "Disagree"} + \tfrac{1}{2} \text{ of } f_C = 40 + 10 = 50; \quad p = \frac{50}{100} = .50$$

There is ordinarily no empirical basis for assuming a division of DK's, "no opinions," refusals, etc., in proportion to the division of replies among those with opinions. In fact the preelection presidential polls of 1948 revealed the danger of forecasting on such an assumption. (Cf., Peatman, 1948–1949.) The major pollsters distributed a high proportion of DK's (including no opinion, refusals, etc.) to Dewey and Truman in proportions similar to what they were polling from those eligible voters with opinions. This, among other errors of procedure, as well as errors of sampling, led to an early prediction that Dewey would be elected. One pollster stopped polling several months in advance of the election because he made the decision that Dewey was so far ahead of Truman it wasn't necessary to obtain another sample of opinions.

An Inadequate Analysis of a Trichotomy. A sample of 1470 persons was asked whether they possessed horoscopes; 919 said they did. These were divided according to the amount of schooling they had had into the three groups of Table 9.3. The null hypothesis of $\mathbf{F} = n/k$ is tested and chi-square is found to be equal to 97.4. The probability of a chi-square result of this magnitude when there are but two d.f.'s is considerably less than .001. Thus it is very unlikely that the differences among these three educational groups in the possession of horoscopes is just a matter of chance.

Table 9.3.   An Inadequate Analysis of Differences by Chi-Square

Educational Groups	Number Having Horoscopes f	Null Hypothesis $\mathbf{F} = n/k$ $\mathbf{F}$	$(f - \mathbf{F})$ d	$\dfrac{(f - \mathbf{F})^2}{\mathbf{F}}$
Graduates	287	306.3	19.3	1.2
Undergraduates	437	306.3	−130.7	55.8
Nonmatriculates	195	306.3	111.3	40.4
	919	919	0 (Check)	$\chi^2 = 97.4$

$$\mathbf{P}(\chi^2 = 97.4) < .001, \text{ when d.f.} = 2$$

The correct analysis of this information is made in Table 9.11 with a chi-square significance test. The above analysis is incorrect in that it does not take into account the fact that the three educational groups of the original sample differed in size irrespective of the number having horoscopes.

The result, however, does not make clear whether the differences in the numbers possessing horoscopes may not be simply a consequence of differences in the sizes of the groups themselves. The undergraduate group, for example, may have more horoscopes simply because there are more undergraduates than graduates or nonmatriculates.

The correct analysis of these data is made in Table 9.11. There the significance test by chi-square takes into account the *relationship* between the respective sizes of the educational groups (a trichotomy) and the *having* or *not-having* a horoscope (a dichotomy). Thus both the size of the groups and the *proportions* of each having horoscopes are taken into account.

CHI-SQUARE TESTS FOR GOODNESS OF FIT

Hypotheses about multiclass univariates testable by chi-square include a category known as *goodness of fit*. One of the most common examples of this class of hypothesis is the determination of the possible significance of the difference between the distribution of the frequencies of a sample result and their distribution in a hypothesized probability model. This is illustrated for the data of Table 9.6.

A goodness of fit test by chi-square is also used to check upon the possible presence of bias in samples on known characteristics of a population. Thus a sample of 100 students might be drawn from a college population of 6000 students by an untested method of sampling intended to satisfy the requirements of randomization. If the known proportions of the four college class years in the population frame of 6000 students were as indicated in Table 9.4, a goodness-of-fit test could be made for the sample discrepancies. In other words, is the fit on this known characteristic "good" except for the role of random variation in sampling? Or are the discrepancies too great to permit the interpretation that this sample is a random sample of the known population characteristic, viz., the proportions of students in each of the four college class years?

Table 9.4. Goodness of Fit Test by Chi-Square for a Sample Result Against a Known Population Characteristic

College Class k	SAMPLE f	POPULATION P	F	$(f - F)$	Chi-Square $(f - F)^2/F$
Senior	25	0.15	15	10	6.67
Junior	30	0.20	20	10	5.00
Sophomore	20	0.30	30	−10	3.33
Freshman	25	0.35	35	−10	2.86
$k = 4$	$n = 100$	1.00	100	0	$\chi^2 = 17.86$

$$P(\chi^2 = 17.86) < .001 \text{ when d.f.} = 3$$

The establishment of the hypothesized frequencies, F_k's, for each of the four classes in Table 9.4 is relatively simple, since the population proportions are known. Each proportion is related to a finite *universe* taken as equal to the size of the sample, viz., $N = 100$. (The student is reminded that a finite universe, even though small, can be sampled indefinitely when the method of sampling is that of *replacement* after each observation.

The discrepancies in Table 9.4 between the sample results and the known facts about the population are apparently too large to be reasonably attributed to random variation. With three d.f.'s, chi-square can be expected to be equal to or greater than 16.3 only once in a thousand times, on the average. The obtained chi-square value of 17.86 would therefore be *a very long shot* for the hypothesis. It is therefore more reasonable to interpret the sample as a biased sample for the known characteristic of the population than to judge it to be a *long-shot* random sample.

If there were no correlation between the known characteristic(s) and the to-be-studied characteristic, then the possible sample bias of Table 9.4 would *not* necessarily carry over to the sample results of observation or measurement. But since the researcher would not know whether or not there were any correlation, the wisest course would be either to discard the sample or to enlarge it and stratify for college class so that the sample would reflect the population proportions of college class membership. Additional safeguards in order *to insure randomization* would also be needed. In fact this would be a more important consideration than stratification. The effectiveness of stratification in probability sampling is predicated on randomization within each stratum or substratum.

Fit of a Sample Distribution with a Probability Model

Goodness of fit of a sample result with a statistical probability model can be tested by chi-square. Two of the most common distributions in psychological statistics and the behavioral sciences are the binomial of Bernoulli and the normal of Laplace and Gauss. Sampling distributions of countables based on only a few elements per sample are best described by

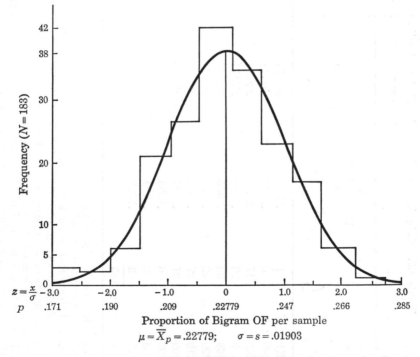

Fig. 9.5. Comparison of an Empirical Sampling Distribution of a Statistic with the Normal Probability Model

(Bigram Data of Table 9.5)

Table 9.5. **Calculation of F_k's of a Finite Distribution for a Chi-Square Test of Goodness of Fit[a]**

(Bigram Samples from *The New York Times*)[b]

Sample Proportions of Bigram OF (1)	f (2)	X Upper Limit of Interval (3)	$(X - \mu)$ x (4)	x/σ z (5)	Cumulated Proportions of Area (TABLE A) (6)	Proportions of Area per Interval P (7)	(PN) Hypothesized Frequencies F_k (8)
.270–.279	1	.2795	.05171	2.717	1.0000	.0142	9 {2.6
.260–.269	6	.2695[c]	.04171	2.192	.9858[d]	.0336	{6.1
.250–.259	17	.2595	.03171	1.666	.9522	.0792	15
.240–.249	23	.2495	.02171	1.141	.8730	.1422	26
.230–.239	35	.2395	.01171	.615	.7308	.1949	36
.220–.229	42	.2295	.00171	.090	.5359	.2045	37
.210–.219	27	.2195	−.00829	−.436	.3314	.1632	30
.200–.209	21	.2095	−.01829	−.961	.1682	.0997	18
.190–.199	6	.1995	−.02829	−1.487	.0685	.0464	8
.180–.189	2	.1895	−.03829	−2.012	.0221	.0166	4 {3.0
.170–.179	3	.1795	−.04829	−2.538	.0055	.0055	{1.0
	$n = 183$					1.0000	$N = 183$

[a] With the point estimate of $\mu = \overline{X}_p = .22779$, and the point estimate of $\sigma = .01903$.

[b] These data were obtained by students in the author's introductory course in applied statistics from a random sampling (over a two-year period) of bigrams (two-letter words) used in headings and text of *The New York Times*. The proportions of column 1 for the bigram OF are the ratios of the frequencies of OF's to all bigrams on the front page and the editorial page for each of 183 different issues of this daily newspaper.

[c] The original proportions of the bigram OF to all bigrams per sample were rounded off to three decimal places from the nearest fractions beyond three places; hence the limits of these intervals are as indicated, rather than .2699, etc.

[d] The values of column 6 may be interpolated from columns 3 and 4 of Table A of the Appendix where entries are given for z deviates to two decimal places rather than three places as in column 5 above.

the discrete binomial. Sampling distributions of countables based on more than 10 or 20 elements, with dichotomies of YES and NOT-YES, or PRESENT and NOT-PRESENT, etc., are often similar to the Laplace-Gaussian curve.

An empirical sampling distribution of the proportions of the *bigram* OF to all bigrams for 183 samples from *The New York Times* is given in Table 9.5 and illustrated in Fig. 9.5. The distribution "looks" similar to the normal Gaussian type. Is it? Obviously it is not exactly normal; no discrete distribution can be. The question to be asked is not, "Is it normal?"; rather, "Are the differences between the frequencies per interval of the empirical distribution and the corresponding intervals of a normal distribution significantly greater than might reasonably be expected in random variation?" The use of a significance test by chi-square will provide the basis for a decision on this question. Chi-square will measure the discrepancies between the obtained frequencies f, and the frequencies $\mathbf{F}$, for the distribution of the hypothesized normal model. The test is for goodness of fit.

In this test of goodness of fit, as in the preceding one, the null hypothesis is not expressible as a single ratio of frequencies such as $\mathbf{F}_k = n/k$, where k is the number of class, because the hypothesized frequencies per class have to be distributed as they should be for a normal curve. Moreover, since the distribution of the sample results is by class intervals, rather than actually continuous from point value to point value, the normal distribution is set up with intervals corresponding to those of the empirical distribution.

The computations of Table 9.5 are necessary in order to determine those $\mathbf{F}_k$'s that will follow the pattern of the normal curve and at the same time be a function of *three constants* derived from the empirical distribution, viz.,

$$n \text{ of } 183 \qquad \overline{X}_p \text{ of } .22779 \qquad s_p \text{ of } .01903$$

N is therefore taken as a finite universe equal to the n of 183, and point estimates of μ and σ are .22779 and .01903, respectively. With these three constants (and hence a loss of three d.f.'s for the chi-square test), a normal curve can be developed by Formula 7.5.

More than the general curve is needed in order that the significance test can be made. As indicated, the frequency distribution has to be set up into class intervals, each of whose limits will match those of the empirical distribution. Hence the following computations are made in Table 9.5 in order to obtain the hypothetical frequencies, $\mathbf{F}_k$'s, of column 8, needed for the null hypothesis.

1. The limits of the class intervals are entered in column 1.
2. The empirical f_k's of the sampling distribution are entered in column 2.
3. The upper mathematical limit (the exact limit) of each interval is entered in column 3.

4. The x deviate value of these upper limits are calculated and entered in column 4: $x = (X_{\text{upper limit}} - \mu)$.
5. The z deviate value of each upper limit is calculated and entered in column 5: $z = x/\sigma$.
6. The proportions of the area of the normal curve are cumulated through each successive class interval, beginning at the lower end of the distribution, and entered in column 6. The area data for z values of the normal probability integral of Table A are used for these determinations.
7. The proportions of the total area *within* each class interval are determined by successive subtractions from the cumulated values of column 6, and entered in column 7.
8. The hypothesized F_k's for the frequency distribution of the bigram OF are thus equal to PN, the products of the proportions of column 7 and N, the size of the sampling distribution. These are the values of column 8 and are used in Table 9.6 with the sample f_k's for the computation of chi-square. As indicated, these are the F_k's for the null hypothesis, i.e., H_0: the F_k distribution of column 8, Table 9.5.

Table 9.6.   Calculation of Chi-Square for the Goodness of Fit of an Empirical Sampling Distribution with Its Hypothesized Normal Distribution*

Class Interval	f	F	$f - F$	$(f - F)^2/F$
.260–.269	7	9	−2	.44
.250–.259	17	15	+2	.27
.240–.249	23	26	−3	.35
.230–.239	35	36	−1	.03
.220–.229	42	37	+5	.68
.210–.219	27	30	−3	.30
.200–.209	21	18	+3	.50
.190–.199	6	8	−2	.50
.180–.189	5	4	+1	.25
	183	183	$\Sigma = 0$	$\chi^2 = 3.32$

*Data from Table 9.5.

The Question of "Fit"

The closer the fit of any empirical distribution of frequencies to a hypothesized distribution of frequencies, the smaller will be the value of chi-square. The computations of Table 9.6 show that the discrepancies for this particular sampling distribution are indeed very small. Chi-square is calculated to be equal to 3.32.

How many degrees of freedom are there for this chi-square test of significance? Table 9.4 was set up with 11 class intervals. However, in column 8 the intervals at both ends of the frequency distribution were found to have so few hypothesized F_k's that each was combined with the F_k's of the adjacent intervals. Thus the chi-square computation of Table 9.6 is based on nine classes. The number of degrees of freedom is therefore nine less the number of restrictions imposed on the hypothesized distribution. These restrictions were three, viz., N, μ, and σ. Hence, there are six d.f.'s.

The *rule of thumb* for chi-square clearly indicates the *significance* of the result. That is to say, the calculated value of chi-square is *less* than the number of degrees of freedom. Hence the null hypothesis is *not* rejected.

Exploration and Discovery

This result points up the role of sampling-inferential statistics in the exploration and possible discovery of relations and patterns of variation in behavioral phenomena. The relative frequency to all bigrams with which at least one bigram, viz., OF, is used on the front and editorial pages of *The New York Times* distributed itself over a two-year period in a form that so closely approximates the Laplace-Gaussian distribution that the difference between the latter and the empirical distribution could very well be just a matter of chance. Notice the interpretation **could be:** *The null hypothesis cannot be proved to be the correct one*, but it may be at least tentatively accepted in the absence of evidence to the contrary.

Such a result as this raises a number of questions for further analysis and research, such as:

1. How many other bigrams, such as TO, ON, AT, HE, etc., are similarly distributed over the same 183 samples? What is the form of their distributions of relative frequencies (proportions)?
2. Can the result for the bigram OF be generalized to other text material such as other newspapers, or to periodicals, or to various types of literature?
3. In general, to what extent is the proportionate usage of particular words in a language possibly distributed in Laplace-Gaussian fashion? Or in some other predictable fashion?

SIGNIFICANCE TESTS FOR
DIFFERENCES BETWEEN PROPORTIONS

When the problem is one of determining the significance of sample differences, the null hypothesis tested is that there is *no difference* between the parameter proportions of the parent populations. This null hypothesis can be stated in three ways:

For H_0:

$$(1) \quad P_1 = P_2 = P; \quad (2) \quad P_1 - P_2 = 0; \quad (3) \quad \frac{P_1}{P_2} = 1.0 \quad (9.15)$$

The second mode of statement, viz., $P_1 - P_2 = 0$, is used here because it relates directly to the sampling distribution of the significance test. The value *zero is the mean* of the hypothesized probability model of a sampling distribution of differences between proportions. This is illustrated in Fig.

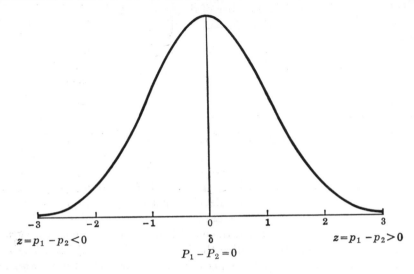

Fig. 9.6. **Hypothesized Sampling Distribution of Differences Between Proportions, with Parameter Difference, *Delta*, Taken as Zero**

9.6. The Greek letter *delta*, δ, is used to symbolize the parameter zero difference. Therefore the hypothesis tested may be written:

$$H_0: \quad \delta = 0 \tag{9.16}$$

The model of Fig. 9.6 is the normal probability curve. It gives the pattern of expected sampling variation of differences between sample proportions when (1) the respective samples are not too small, and (2) sample p is neither very small nor very large. This model can be expected to be a satisfactory approximation of the exact sampling distribution of differences when the product of the smaller proportion and the smaller n is equal to or more than 5. Thus, if the smaller sample had 15 cases and the smaller proportion were .10, the product of 15 and .10 is 1.5; hence either the sample is too small or p is too small to warrant the development of a significance test on the normal probability model.

As has been previously emphasized, the greater value to research of larger samples is obvious. If n were 60, for example, then with a p of .10, the product would be 6, and by the rule of FIVE,* the normal curve model should be a satisfactory approximation of the exact sampling distribution; hence a z deviate could be computed for the significance test.

---

*Note that this rule was taken at TEN for sampling distributions of single proportions (p. 220). With *differences* between proportions, FIVE in each sample works out to 10 when both are considered separately.

Significance of Differences When Samples Are Independent

Sample proportions may be derived from the same set of sampling units (persons, for example) or from different sets of sampling units that are independent of each other. The method of calculation of the z deviate for the sample differences between proportions will depend on which of these two situations prevails. The case for independent samples will be considered first.

Independence of samples is represented by the Sindlinger* samples of radio audiences, on the one hand, and television viewers on the other. To the question of who won the "Great Debates" of 1960 in the contest for the Presidency, which was asked the respondents the day following the fourth debate:

1. 22.2% of the sample of the *radio audience* said *Kennedy*.
2. 37.4% of the sample of the *television audience* thought *Kennedy* won.

Is this difference between 22.2% and 37.4% just a matter of random variation in sampling, or is it significantly greater than may be expected by chance. The answer will depend on the size of the respective samples, assuming them for the argument to have been probability samples. Since the respective populations were estimated at 9 million radio listeners and 63 million television viewers, the sampling fractions would be very small and the finite multiplier unnecessary. The significance test for the null hypothesis is therefore as follows:

$$\textit{For } H_0, \delta = 0: \qquad z = \frac{(p_1 - p_2) - 0}{\hat{\sigma}_{(p_1-p_2)}} = \frac{\delta}{\hat{\sigma}_d} \qquad (9.17)$$

where the standard error of the difference between proportions of independent samples is equal to the square root of the sum of point estimates of their population variances:

Standard Error of Sampling Differences Between Proportions:

$$\hat{\sigma}_{(p_1-p_2)} = \hat{\sigma}_d = \sqrt{\hat{\sigma}_{p_1}^2 + \hat{\sigma}_{p_2}^2} = \sqrt{\frac{p_1 q_1 + p_2 q_2}{n_1 + n_2}} \qquad (9.18)$$

The null hypothesis asserts that the parameter values of P_1 and P_2 are equal; hence their difference is zero, and the point values of p and q for Formula 9.18 are therefore calculated from the information of both samples combined:

---

*Reported in *Broadcasting Magazine*, 1960, Nov. 7, pp. 27–29.

Standard Error of Difference
for Combined Sample Results:

$$\hat{\sigma}_{(p_1 - p_2)} = \sqrt{pq \left(\frac{1}{n_1} + \frac{1}{n_2} \right)} \qquad (9.19)$$

where

$$p = \frac{f_1 + f_2}{n_1 + n_2} \text{ and } q = 1 - p \qquad (9.20)$$

If the original frequencies are not available for Formula 9.20, they can readily be determined as follows:

$$f_1 = n_1 p_1 \qquad \text{and} \qquad f_2 = n_2 p_2$$

And thus,

$$p = \frac{n_1 p_1 + n_2 p_2}{n_1 + n_2} \qquad (9.20a)$$

When two samples have equal n's, the two proportions can then be directly averaged and Formula 9.20 is not needed. When $n_1 = n_2$:

$$p = \frac{p_1 + p_2}{2} \qquad (9.20b)$$

The finite multiplier is used with Formula 9.19 whenever the sampling fraction of the two samples averages 5% or more:

Finite Multiplier: $\quad \sqrt{1 - \frac{n}{N}} : \quad \sqrt{1 - \frac{n_1 + n_2}{N_1 + N_2}} \qquad (9.21)$

Directionality of a Significance Test for Differences

Is the preceding test for differences between proportions directional or nondirectional? The answer may very well depend in this case on who gives it. Thus a directional test of a delta hypothesis might be set up by the proponents of the view that television messages generally have significantly greater impact in influencing attitudes and behavior than do radio messages. If P_r represents the parameter proportion for radio and P_{tv} represents television, then the relevant delta hypothesis to test and nullify, if possible, would be:

$$H_{\Delta}: (P_{tv} - P_r) \leq 0$$

where *less than* is a negative difference that would arise from $P_r > P_{tv}$. The rejection of this hypothesis leads logically to the inference that most likely $(P_{tv} - P_r) > 0$; in other words, $P_{tv} > P_r$.

On the other hand, a wait-and-see attitude toward the effectiveness of a candidate's words and personality over the two media of communication would lead to a nondirectional test. If the null hypothesis that $P_{tv} - P_r = 0$ could be rejected, then, as already indicated, the implications of a directional test could also be inferred. Thus, if H_0: $(P_{tv} - P_r) = 0$ is rejectable, then H_Δ: $(P_{tv} - P_r) \leq 0$ is also rejectable, *provided* p_{tv} is larger than p_r, as it was in the example. An inference could therefore be made with confidence to the effect that most likely $P_{tv} - P_r > 0$; i.e., $P_{tv} > P_r$. Furthermore, an estimate of the likely magnitude of the difference could be made, as described in the next section.

The respective sizes of the Sindlinger radio and television samples were not reported. If each consisted of a minimum of 1000 persons, then on the assumption of probability sampling, the null hypothesis could be rejected with considerable confidence, since $z = 7.6$, as follows:

For H_0, $\delta = 0$:

$$z = \frac{\delta}{\hat{\sigma}_\delta} = \frac{(.374 - .222) - 0}{\sqrt{(.298)(.702)\left(\frac{1}{1000}\right)\left(\frac{1}{1000}\right)}} = \frac{.152}{.020} = 7.6$$

where the value of $p = .298$ is the average of .374 and .222 (Formula 9.20a).

The conclusion that Kennedy did better with the television audience as a whole than with the radio audience is thus indicated. It is again emphasized, however, that the statistical inference to reject the null hypothesis is conditional on probability sampling with each sample sufficiently large to give a z result in the significance test of more than 2.58.

Estimation of a Parameter Difference Between Proportions

How substantive may the parameter difference be? The actual difference for the sample result is approximately 15 percentage points, since the difference between the television and radio proportions was found to be .152. What is the likely minimum difference between the television and radio audiences as a whole? What is the likely maximum difference? The possible magnitude of the parameter difference between the two proportions, when n is large, can be estimated by means of the confidence interval (on the assumption of probability sampling):

Estimation of δ: $d - \text{c.c. } \hat{\sigma}_d < \delta < d + \text{c.c. } \hat{\sigma}_d$ (9.22)

where d symbolizes the sample difference and *delta* is the parameter difference.

For the radio and television audiences the estimate would be as follows, with c.c. taken at *3 sigma*:

$$.152 - 3(.020) < \delta < .152 + 3(.020)$$
$$.09 < \delta < .21$$

the estimate of the standard error of the sampling distribution of differences having been found in the significance test to be .020.

An estimated minimum difference of .09 (or nine percentage points) is fairly substantial, especially when considered in relation to the magnitude of the proportions involved in the comparison.

A Psychologically Significant Null Hypothesis

Some null hypotheses that cannot be rejected, even with very large samples, may have significant consequences in the psychological dimension. The failure to attain statistical significance does not prove, of course, the null hypothesis to be correct. However, when large samples have in effect given psychological "facts" a good opportunity to nullify the hypothesis of no difference between two groups, and have failed to do so, the theorist is tempted to generalize about the psychological significance of such results. Evidence sometimes cited for the contention that there are no sex differences, or no race differences, etc., in a trait such as I.Q. intelligence may be in this category.

Thus R. L. Thorndike and G. H. Gallup (1944) through the offices of the American Institute of Public Opinion attempted to measure the *verbal intelligence of the voting population* in the United States. At the time, this population was estimated to be about 60 million. A stratified-quota sample of nearly 3000 adults was given a 20-word, steeply graded, multiple-choice vocabulary test. The 1236 women respondents averaged 56% correct responses on the test. The 1738 men respondents averaged 54%. This difference of two percentage points amounted to less than one word difference, since each word of the 20-word list counted 5% of the total.

Even though the samples were thus very large, the difference was not statistically significant, since $z = 1.1$, as follows:

$$z = \frac{(56\% - 54\%) - 0}{100 \sqrt{(.55)(.45)\left[\dfrac{1}{1236} + \dfrac{1}{1738}\right]}} = \frac{2\%}{1.8\%} = 1.1$$

where the estimate of the standard error of a difference between percentages of independent samples is 100 times the estimate of the standard error of a difference between proportions:

Standard Error of a Difference Between Percentages:

$$\hat{\sigma}_{(\%_1 - \%_2)} = 100 \sqrt{pq\left(\frac{1}{n_1} + \frac{1}{n_2}\right)} \cdot \sqrt{1 - \frac{n}{N}} \qquad (9.23)$$

(In the preceding example, the finite multiplier is practically 1.0 and hence not used. Note that for stratified-randomized samplings, Formula 9.23 is an approximation.)

The psychological significance of this null hypothesis is obvious: It asserts no sex difference, i.e., that there is no difference in the verbal intelligence of adult male voters and adult female voters. Furthermore, even if the difference of two percentage points were found to be statistically significant with the use of much larger samples, the substantive significance of the difference might remain questionable. This could be the case even if the 20-word test were projected as a random sample of, say, 5000-word vocabularies, and thus a difference of two percentage points would equal an estimated difference in vocabulary knowledge of 100 words.

Significance of Difference When Samples Are Not Independent

When the sampling units of a second sample are obtained in a way conditional on the selection of those in a first sample, the two samples are not independent. They are dependent or related samples. The repetition of observations or measurements on the same persons (sampling units) is the most common example of related samples in psychology and the behavioral sciences. In effect, the same set of sampling units is employed twice for a series of separate measurements. The use of *matched pairs* for the establishment of two experimental groups is also an example of two related samples, i.e., samples not independent of each other. If pairs are matched on I.Q., then each of the samples has a series of pairs of persons (or *blocks* of persons, when there are more than two samples) with the I.Q.'s *within* each pair (or block) approximately the same.

Such dependency as just described will reduce the variance of the sampling differences between proportions when the characteristic being studied shows a significant degree of correlation between sample results. In other words, if the observed characteristic for the one sample is correlated with that of another, the standard error of the sampling distribution of differences between percentages (or proportions) will be less, the higher the correlation. The possible relationship existing between the results of a duplicated set of observations on the same group, or duplicated observations on matched groups, one of which has been subjected to one experimental treatment or condition and the other to a different condition should be taken into account for a significant test of their differences.

The effect of dependent samples on the variance of a sampling distribution of differences between proportions can be taken into account by the use of chi-square with the *frequencies* of a 2 by 2 contingency table (Cochran, 1950). The hypothesis *in effect* tested is that the parameter proportions of the observed characteristic do not differ: $H_0: P_1 = P_2 = P$.

As an example, a sample of 100 family units, each with at least one child in public school, might be drawn randomly from all such family units in city X. The head of each family unit would be interviewed twice. In the first interview each respondent would be asked whether the public school authorities should make available the school's psychological test records to any parent requesting such information about his child, or children. Following an educational campaign by the school authorities to keep such information restricted, the heads of each of the 100 families would again be interviewed. Each would be asked the same question as before.

**Table 9.7. Significance of Difference Between
Proportions of Dependent Samples**

(By Chi-Square for Difference Between Frequencies)

		FIRST INTERVIEW		
		"Should Not"	"Should"	
SECOND	"Should":	$f_a = 5$	$f_b = 45$	50
INTERVIEW	"Should Not":	$f_c = 20$	$f_d = 30$	50
		25	75	100

$$\chi^2 = \frac{(f_a - f_d)^2}{f_a + f_d} = \frac{(5 - 30)^2}{5 + 30} = 17.9 \quad (1 \text{ d.f.})$$

$$\sqrt{\chi^2} = \chi = z = \sqrt{17.9} = 4.23$$

Fictional results for such a study are summarized in the contingency table of Table 9.7. Chi-square is 17.9 and *chi* for one d.f. is equal to a z deviate value of 4.23, since the square root of 17.9 is 4.23. Hence the null hypothesis can be rejected with considerable confidence (*alpha* of .001 $= 3.3$ for a two-tailed z significance test; for a chi-square test, $\chi^2_{.999} = 10.8$). The change from 25% SHOULD NOT's of the first interview to 50% "SHOULD NOT's" of the second interview is significant, presumably (but not necessarily) the consequence, at least in part, of the educational campaign.

The significance test for the data of Table 9.7 can thus be made in terms of chi-square or in terms of a normal z deviate inasmuch as there is but one d.f. and *chi* is equal to z:

$$\chi^2 = \frac{(f_a - f_d)^2}{f_a + f_d} \tag{9.24}$$

or

$$\chi = z = \frac{(f_a - f_d)}{\sqrt{f_a + f_d}} \tag{9.24a}$$

The null hypothesis here asserts that the difference between the expected frequencies of cells a and d is zero. Since the n's of the two samples are equal, the difference between their proportions can be stated simply as the difference between the frequencies of cell a and those of cell d:

The proportion of SHOULD's, second interview:

$$p_2 = \frac{f_a + f_b}{n}$$

The proportion of SHOULD's, first interview:

$$p_1 = \frac{f_b + f_d}{n}$$

The difference between these proportions:

$$(p_2 - p_1) = \frac{f_a + f_b}{n} - \frac{f_b + f_d}{n} = \frac{f_a - f_d}{n}$$

Hence the difference between the sample results can be simply stated as the difference between the frequencies of cell a and cell d taken as a ratio to n.

SIGNIFICANCE TESTS FOR CONTINGENT RELATIONS OF BIVARIATES OF ENUMERATION STATISTICS

The simplest type of bivariate distribution was described in Chapter 5 as the 2 by 2 crosstabulation of frequencies into four cells. This crosstabulation of two dichotomized variates is often referred to as a *contingency table*, since the significance test is made to discover whether the dichotomized distribution of f's of the one variate is in any way *contingent upon* the division of f's of the other dichotomized distribution. Either *phi* or chi-square can be computed to measure the correlation present in such 2 by 2 crosstabulations. For more than two classes or categories in either variable, however, chi-square needs to be employed inasmuch as *phi* is a technique for a 2 by 2 bivariate (p. 135).

Significance Test for *Phi*

The significance of a sample result in a 2 by 2 correlation table is determined by testing the hypothesis of *no contingency*, i.e., zero correlation. This can be done for *phi* in any one of three ways, depending on the circumstances indicated:

1. By the calculation of exact probabilities for 2 by 2 contingency tables, where the probability of any arrangement of cell frequencies for a given set of marginal frequencies is as follows (Fisher, 1925):

Probability of Any 2 by 2
Combination of Sample Result:

$$\mathbf{P} = \frac{(A + B)!(C + D)!(A + C)!(B + D)!}{N!A!B!C!D!} \tag{9.25}$$

where the letters represent the number of frequencies in each of the cells and the marginal totals:

A	B	$A + B$
C	D	$C + D$

$$A + C \quad\quad B + D \quad\quad N$$

2. By the use of the continuous sampling distributions of chi-square, critical values of which are given in Table C. The *phi* coefficient is related to chi-square as follows:

$$\chi^2 = n'(\phi^2), \quad \text{since} \quad \phi = \sqrt{\frac{\chi^2}{n'}} \tag{9.26}$$

where n' is the number of pairs of correlational frequencies.

3. By the use of the normal z deviate when $n' \geq 30$. The normal probability distribution will approximately describe the sampling variation of *phi* for the null hypothesis of parameter $\Phi = 0$ when $n' \geq 30$.

The first method is used only for small samples when the hypothesized frequencies for any cell for the null hypothesis of parameter $\Phi = 0$ is less than 5.

The second method is used when n' is less than 30 and the minimum F_k (expected frequency for a cell) is at least 5.

The third method is used when n' is equal to or greater than 30.

Of these three methods, the third is most frequently used, since samples usually consists of at least 30 observations. It is the method to be used to test the significance of the *phi* coefficient found on p. 83 for the data of Table 5.1, a 2 by 2 crosstabulation of sex with attitude toward baseball. *Phi* was found to be equal to .60.

The standard error of a sampling distribution of *phi* statistics for the null hypothesis of parameter $\Phi = 0$ is approximated by the following:

Standard Error of ϕ:

$$\hat{\sigma}_\phi = \frac{1}{\sqrt{n'}} \tag{9.27}$$

The significance test for the null hypothesis is therefore:

For H_0, $\Phi = 0$:

$$z = \frac{\phi - 0}{\frac{1}{\sqrt{n'}}} - \phi\sqrt{n'} = .60(\sqrt{100}) = 6.0 \tag{9.28}$$

Inasmuch as a z deviate value of 6.0 is an extremely unlikely result in random variation from a *phi* coefficient of zero, the null hypothesis is rejected with considerable confidence. It is therefore reasonable to conclude from these fictional data that people's attitudes toward baseball is contingent on their sex. (Note that the organismic characteristic of sex is taken as the independent variable in this relationship. It would not make sense to interpret sex as contingent upon attitude toward baseball.)

Chi-Square vs. an Exact Test

The exact probabilities for the possible variations in the division of frequencies of a bivariate in a 2 by 2 contingency table is determined by the algebra of permutations of Formula 9.25. This method is used when it is difficult or impossible to have at least five hypothesized F_k's in each cell.

Table 9.8 presents fictional data for a small sample of ten cases. A rather definite relationship between type of therapy and response to treatment is indicated. All five cases having G therapy respond satisfactorily: four of the five cases under H therapy do not respond satisfactorily. Is this difference in the effects of the therapies just a matter of random variation? *Alpha* of .05 will be used for the decision.

Table 9.8.   Response to Treatment:
Therapy G vs. Therapy H

	RESPONSE TO TREATMENT		
THERAPY	*Satisfactory*	*Unsatisfactory*	
Therapy G:	a 5	b 0	5
Therapy H:	c 1	d 4	5
	6	4	10

The null hypothesis is that of *no difference* in the results of the two therapies; that the satisfactory results are divided evenly between G and H, as are the unsatisfactory results. Therefore, with the subscripts a, b, c, d of the four cells, the null hypothesis is statable as follows:*

$$H_0: F_a = 3, F_b = 2, F_c = 3, F_d = 2$$

Chi-square for the data of Table 9.8 is equal to 6.67:

$$\chi^2 = \frac{(5-3)^2}{3} + \frac{(0-2)^2}{2} + \frac{(1-3)^2}{3} + \frac{(4-2)^2}{2} = 6.67^{**}$$

By Table C, for 1 d.f., $\chi^2_{.95} = 3.8$. *Presumably* the result is significant at an *alpha* significance level of .05; also at $\alpha = .01$, since for 1 d.f.

*See Formula 6.17, p. 138: $F_a = 5(6)/10 = 3$, etc.

**Chi-square for a 2 by 2 distribution may also be computed by a reshuffling of the arithmetic as in Formula 12.8, p. 366.

$\chi^2_{.99} = 6.6$. However, the case for the rejection of the null hypothesis may be overstated because the hypothesized F_k's of the data of Table 9.8 are less than 5 for each cell.

Yates' Correction for Continuity

A correction for the continuous approximation of the sampling distribution of chi-square may be made for a 2 by 2 bivariate distribution by means of a procedure developed by Yates. It consists in the *subtraction* of a half-frequency from each of the diagonal cells whose sum of frequencies is the greater. These are cells a and d of the bivariate distribution of Table 9.8. The subtracted frequency is *added* to the cells of the other diagonal, one-half a frequency to each cell.

Chi-square corrected for continuity is therefore as follows:

$$\chi^2 = \frac{(4.5 - 3)^2}{3} + \frac{(0.5 - 2)^2}{2} + \frac{(1.5 - 3)^2}{3} + \frac{(3.5 - 2)^2}{2} = 3.75$$

The critical value of chi-square for a coefficient of risk of .05 is 3.8. When the calculation was not corrected for the fact that chi-square distributions are really discontinuous, the result was a chi-square statistic of 6.67, and hence the null hypothesis was rejected. However, when corrected for continuity by Yates' method, the value of the chi-square statistic is less than the critical value of 3.8, and hence the null hypothesis would *not* be rejected.

Where there is thus a contradiction in the character of the results, the best procedure for testing the null hypothesis is the exact test. For these data, it shows that Yates' correction *understates* the *evidence* for the rejection of the null hypothesis. Generally in such small samples, it is better to employ the exact test than to rely on Yates' correction.

Exact Test (Fisher, 1925)

The exact test is based on the calculation of the number of permutations for each subset of a 2 by 2 result within the restrictions of the marginal totals of Table 9.8. The generalized *set* for Formula 9.25 is given in Table 9.9. With the marginal restrictions of Table 9.8, there are only five different subsets. The probability of each is given in Table 9.10.

Table 9.9.   Generalized Set and Restrictions
Imposed for Exact Test

SET			IMPOSED RESTRICTIONS		
A	B	$A + B$			5
C	D	$C + D$			5
$A + C$	$B + D$	N	6	4	10

Subset A is that one which corresponds with the result of Table 9.8. By chi-square, uncorrected for continuity, its probability was estimated to be slightly less than .01. By the exact test it is seen to be .0238. Hence the null hypothesis is rejected with confidence since **P** of .0238 $<$ α = .05.

Table 9.10.   Exact Test for 2 by 2 Bivariate Distribution
(Probability of Each Possible Subset by Eq. 9.25)

	Subset			Permutations	Probability
A.	5 0 / 1 4 ; 5 5 ; 6 4 10			$\dfrac{6!5!5!4!}{10!5!4!1!0!} = \dfrac{120}{5040} =$	.0238
B.	4 1 / 2 3 ; 5 5 ; 6 4 10			$\dfrac{6!5!5!4!}{10!4!3!2!1!} = \dfrac{1200}{5040} =$	.2381
C.	3 2 / 3 2 ; 5 5 ; 6 4 10			$\dfrac{6!5!5!4!}{10!3!3!2!2!} = \dfrac{2400}{5040} =$	.4762
D.	2 3 / 4 1 ; 5 5 ; 6 4 10			$\dfrac{6!5!5!4!}{10!4!3!2!1!} = \dfrac{1200}{5040} =$	.2381
E.	1 4 / 5 0 ; 5 5 ; 6 4 10			$\dfrac{6!5!5!4!}{10!5!4!1!0!} = \dfrac{120}{5040} =$	.0238

$$\Sigma\text{'s} = \frac{5040}{5040} = 1.0000$$

Significance of a Contingency Coefficient *C*

The contingency coefficient described in Chapter 6 was based on chi-square. It was developed to provide a measure of correlation of multiclass relations of enumeration statistics, such as the crosstabulated trichotomies of Table 6.4. Chi-square for the frequencies of that 3 by 3 crosstabulation was found to be 45.0, p. 139. Since n' and the ratios of frequencies of the marginal totals n_r (rows) and n_c (columns) impose three sets of restrictions upon the variations of f's within the cells of a contingency table, the number of d.f.'s is the product of the number of classes less one of the first variate, $k_c - 1$, and the number of classes less one of the other variate, $k_r - 1$. This product is often written simply as d.f. $= (c - 1)(r - 1)$.

Thus for a 3 by 3 table, d.f. $= 2 \times 2 = 4$; the hypothesized frequencies may take any values within two cells of any row and within two cells of a second row. Thus:

a	b	c	$a + b + c$
d	e	f	$d + e + f$
g	h	i	$g + h + i$
$a + d + g$	$b + e + h$	$c + f + i$	n'

Once frequencies are assigned to the cells whose letters are in boldface type, the number of frequencies for each of the remaining cells is restricted by the marginal sums of frequencies.

By Table C, the critical value of chi-square at the 99.9th centile for four d.f.'s is 18.5. Hence the probabilities in random sampling of a sample result as large as a chi-square statistic of 45 are very slight. The null hypothesis is thus rejected with considerable confidence, and it is concluded for the data of Table 6.4 that either body weight is contingent on personality status as classified there or that personality status is contingent on weight, or that they are contingent on each other or on some x factor(s) not readily identified.

SIGNIFICANCE OF SUBGROUP DIFFERENCES BY CHI-SQUARE

Chi-square is frequently used to test the significance of differences in two-class results on a characteristic among subgroups of a population. Thus Mahalanobis (1946b) surveyed "certain sections of Calcutta's middle-class families" and found that .625 of the persons in a sample of 1470 had horoscopes. The data are presented at the top of Table 9.11 for each of three educational subgroups. The "graduates" had had the most education; the "nonmatriculates" had had the least. The chi-square test for "half" of these data in Table 9.3 was shown to be inadequate. More information needed to be taken into account, viz., the sizes of the three subgroups and the proportions of each having horoscopes. All this information has been taken into consideration in the *contingency analysis* of Table 9.11.

Table 9.11. Significance of Differences Among Subgroups with Respect to the Having of Horoscopes

OBTAINED FREQUENCIES

EDUCATIONAL SUBGROUPS	Have Horoscopes	Do Not Have Horoscopes	n_j
Graduates:	287 a	147 b	434
Undergraduates:	437 c	219 d	656
Nonmatriculates:	195 e	185 f	380
	919 (n_p)	551 (n_q)	$n' = 1470$

$$\text{d.f.} = (r - 1)(c - 1) = 2; \quad p = 919/1470 = .625;$$
$$q = 1 - p = .375$$

EXPECTED FREQUENCIES
UNDER THE HYPOTHESIS

$$P = .625 \text{ and } Q = .375$$

	Have Horoscopes	Do Not Have Horoscopes	N_j
Graduates:	271.3 a	162.7 b	434
Undergraduates:	410.0 c	246.0 d	656
Nonmatriculates:	237.5 e	142.5 f	380
	919.	551.	$N' = 1470$

$$\chi^2 = \frac{(287 - 271.3)^2}{271.3} + \frac{(147 - 162.7)^2}{162.7} + \cdots + \frac{(185 - 142.5)^2}{142.4} = 27$$

$$P(\chi^2 \text{ of } 27) < .001, \quad \text{when d.f.} = 2$$

Mahalanobis obtained the chi-square result of 27, as indicated in Table 9.11. This is a value considerably larger than would be expected by chance for the hypothesis tested. The null hypothesis here is a division of frequencies within each subclass that is proportionate to their division in the total sample. The latter division was 919 (.625) for those having horoscopes and 551 (.375) for those not having horoscopes.

The hypothesized number of graduates having horoscopes is entered in cell a of the lower bivariate distribution of Table 9.11 as 271.3, since

$$\mathbf{F}_a = N_p N_j / N' = P N_j = .625(434) = 271.3$$

and the hypothesized number of undergraduates having horoscopes is 410.0, since

$$\mathbf{F}_c = PN_j = .625(656) = 410.0$$

Inasmuch as there are only two d.f.'s in a 2 by 3 bivariate distribution, the hypothesized number of frequencies for the remaining four cells in the bottom bivariate distribution of Table 9.11 can be obtained by subtraction. One more cell value, however, is calculated in order to check the accuracy of the other **F** values:

$$\mathbf{F}_f = QN_j = .375(380) = 142.5$$

The hypothesized bivariate distribution is for the null hypothesis, viz., there are no differences between the proportionate division of frequencies of the HAVE's and HAVE NOT's of each subgroup and the sample as a whole: They are exactly the same throughout. The greater the divergence of the obtained frequencies from the hypothesized frequencies, the greater the likelihood that the differences among the educational subgroups are not just a matter of chance. Since a chi-square value of 27 will occur by chance considerably less than once in a thousand times for such a *set* of differences between the obtained and hypothesized frequencies, presumably some of divergence from the null hypothesis is a function of factors other than chance. In other words, there are significant differences among the educational groups in the proportions having horoscopes: the graduates and undergraduates have *more* than would be expected, and the nonmatriculates have fewer (195 as against the expectancy of 237.5).

CHAPTER 10

SIGNIFICANCE TESTS FOR MEANS, VARIANCES, r CORRELATIONS, AND THEIR DIFFERENCES

*To wonder why the universe should be as it is
presupposes the notion of its being different.*

William James

TESTS OF SIGNIFICANCE FOR A MEAN

A SAMPLE of I.Q.'s of 100 children, drawn randomly from the third
grade population of a large city, is found to have the following
statistics:

$$\overline{X} = 97 \qquad s^2 = 196 \qquad s = 14$$

The problem is to determine whether or not it is reasonable to infer that
this sample of 100 I.Q.'s can be interpreted as possibly derived from a third
grade population with an assumed average I.Q. of 100. Statistically the
question is asked: Does this sample mean of 97 differ from a hypothesized
parameter mean of 100 by an amount that can be reasonably explained in
terms of a random variation?

The facts will be given the opportunity to nullify the null hypothesis.
The facts consist of the statistical information derived from the sample

result. They include not only the information already cited, viz., n of 100, a mean of 97, and a variance of 196, but also knowledge of the form of the distribution of the sample result. If this distribution appears to be a satisfactory approximation of the normal bell-shaped type, then the procedure now to be described can be used to assist in arriving at a decision in the form of a statistical inference, viz., whether the difference between a parameter of 100 and the statistic of 97 can be reasonably explained as a random variation from 100.

Null Hypothesis

A test will be made of the hypothesis that the parameter mean of the parent population of the sample, and a parameter mean I.Q. of 100, are one and the same value. Put in another way, a test will be made of the null hypothesis that the difference between these two parameter values is zero:

$$H_0: \mu \text{ of } 100 \quad \text{or} \quad \mu - 100 = 0 \tag{10.1}$$

In two senses the *null hypothesis* is being tested. Not only can the hypothesis be set in terms of zero; the facts also are given the opportunity to *nullify* the hypothesis.

Test of Significance

A test of significance for means takes the following form:

For $H_0: \mu = 100$:
$$t = \frac{\overline{X} - \mu}{\hat{\sigma}_{\overline{x}}} \tag{10.2}$$

For infinite or very large populations, the standard error of a sampling distribution of means was seen in Formula 8.4 to be estimated by:

Standard Error of the Mean:
$$\hat{\sigma}_{\overline{x}} = \frac{s}{\sqrt{n}} \tag{8.4}$$

where the circumflex signifies the measure is an estimate and s is an unbiased estimate of the parameter standard deviation of the parent population:

$$s = \sqrt{\frac{\sum x^2}{n - 1}} \tag{4.6}$$

For a finite population, the standard error of the sampling distribution of means will be reduced in value somewhat by the *finite multiplier* if the *sampling fraction* n/N is as large as 1/20 (or 5%) and the sampling is without replacement. Thus:

$$\hat{\sigma}_{\overline{x}} = \frac{s}{\sqrt{n}} \cdot \sqrt{\frac{N - n}{N - 1}} \tag{10.3}$$

When N is large, this can be written as follows:

With the Finite Multiplier:

$$\hat{\sigma}_{\bar{x}} = \frac{s}{\sqrt{n}} \sqrt{1 - \frac{n}{N}}$$ [8.8]

If the third grade population consists of 5000 pupils, then the standard error of the mean is:

$$\hat{\sigma}_{\bar{x}} = \frac{14}{\sqrt{100}} \cdot \sqrt{1 - \frac{100}{5000}} = 1.4(.99) = 1.39$$

and therefore

For $H_0: \mu = 100$: $t = \dfrac{97 - 100}{1.39} = -2.16$

Although t loses its formal character as $t = (\bar{X} - \mu)/(\hat{\sigma}_{\bar{x}})$, it is nevertheless often written in the following form when the population is infinitely large or large enough that in effect the finite multiplier $\sqrt{1 - (n/N)} = 1.0$:

For $H_0: \mu = 100$:

$$t = \frac{\sqrt{n}\,(\bar{X} - \mu)}{s}$$ (10.4)

$$= \frac{\sqrt{100}\,(97 - 100)}{14} = \frac{-30}{14} = -2.14$$

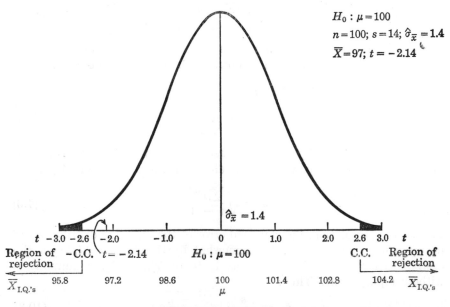

$H_0 : \mu = 100$

$n = 100; \ s = 14; \ \hat{\sigma}_{\bar{x}} = 1.4$

$\bar{X} = 97; \ t = -2.14$

$\hat{\sigma}_{\bar{x}} = 1.4$

t -3.0 -2.6 -2.0 -1.0 0 1.0 2.0 2.6 3.0 t

Region of $-$C.C. $t = -2.14$ $H_0 : \mu = 100$ C.C.   Region of
rejection   rejection

$\bar{X}_{\text{I.Q.'s}}$ 95.8   97.2   98.6   100   101.4   102.8   104.2 $\bar{X}_{\text{I.Q.'s}}$

μ

Fig. 10.1.   Approximately Normal Probability Model for a Nondirectional (Two-Tailed) Significance Test of a Parameter Mean I.Q. of 100

When $n = 100$, this value of -2.14 for t is a statistic whose sampling distribution is hypothesized as approximately equal in form to that of the normal probability model, as indicated in Fig. 10.1. An examination of the five rows at the bottom of Table B (Appendix) shows that for any desired level of significance there is very little difference between the values of the t statistic when the number of degrees of freedom is 30, 40, 60, 120, or infinity; hence the *forms* of their respective sampling distributions are similar. That for infinity is the normal probability distribution. In practice, therefore, z deviates are often used instead of t when $n > 30$.

Significance Level and the t Test

If a significance level of .01 is employed for the test of significance, then by Table B, t is 2.6 whether n is 100 or whether n is infinitely large. For 60 degrees of freedom (n of 61), t is 2.7. By interpolation, for 99 degrees of freedom, t is 2.6 (or -2.6). If the .05 level of significance is used, t is 2.0 for as few as 29 degrees of freedom as well as for any number between 29 and infinity. (These values of t are for nondirectional tests.)

Since the test of significance yields a t value less than $(-)2.6$, viz., a value of $(-)2.14$, the inference made is *not* to reject the null hypothesis. In other words, it is very possible that the parameter mean of the parent population is an I.Q. of 100. Although it does not necessarily follow that the parameter mean is 100, *it could be*. This possibility is accepted. This is the statistical inference. Its general implication is that the third grade population may very well be an average I.Q. (100) population insofar as its mean I.Q. is concerned.

The information at hand would support a different interpretation, however, if one should wish to increase the risk of rejecting a true null hypothesis. The use of an *alpha* significance level of .05 would have led to the rejection of the null hypothesis. This is the case, since the critical criterion for this level of significance is a t value of ± 2.0, which is *less than* the value of the obtained t of $(-)2.14$.

Strategy of Choice of *Alpha*

The question may again be asked, as it was in the last chapter: What level of significance should be chosen at the beginning of an investigation? The strategy employed depends very much on the size of the sample. If the sample is very large, it may not make too much difference whether *alpha* of .01 or of .05 is chosen, since the scale range of sampling variation between their confidence criteria, 2.57 and 1.96, will be small. But when samples are not large, especially if they are less than approximately 25 cases, the choice of significance level will more often make a difference in the character of the statistical inference. This is the case because the smaller the small sample, the larger the scale range of sampling variation.

If a strict (small) *alpha* level of significance is used to protect against the error of rejecting true null hypotheses, such a decision will be made at the cost of making it difficult to discover *new facts, real experimental effects,* etc. A *general rule of thumb* for choice of alpha is this: If in research nothing is to be lost, so to speak, and much may in the long run be gained by the rejection of the null hypothesis, use a large value of *alpha*, such as .05 or even .10. On the other hand, when the rejection of the null hypothesis has costly consequences, either in terms of money or psychological theory, a smaller value of *alpha* should be used, such as .01 or even .001.

The error of accepting the null hypothesis when false is called a type II error, or *beta error*. A type I, or *alpha error*, arises from rejecting the null hypothesis when true. Compared with .05, an *alpha* level of significance of .01 reduces the risk of type I error: When α is smaller, the null hypothesis will be rejected less frequently. Consequently, should it be a true hypothesis, it will not be rejected as often with $\alpha = .01$ as with $\alpha = .05$. Contrariwise, an *alpha* level of significance of .05 reduces the risk of the type II error: When α is larger, the null hypothesis will be rejected more frequently. Thus, should it be a false hypothesis, it will be rejected more frequently when $\alpha = .05$ than when $\alpha = .01$.

Comparison of Significance Testing with Estimation of a Parameter Mean

The student may already have mentally compared the procedure for testing the null hypothesis with the procedure of Chapter 8 for estimating the parameter mean. The level of significance should, of course, be the same for any such comparison. For $\alpha = .01$, the confidence criterion was found to be a t of 2.6 for 99 d.f.'s. Hence with $\hat{\sigma}_{\bar{x}} = 1.39$:

Estimation of μ:

$$97 - 2.6(1.39) > \mu > 97 + 2.6(1.39) \qquad 93.4 > \mu > 100.6$$

Perhaps the most significant aspect of this confidence interval of 93.4 to 100.6 is that within its range is the value of a parameter mean I.Q. of 100. Hence the confidence interval itself indicates very clearly that a parameter mean of 100 is not unlikely. Only if 100 were outside the range of the confidence interval would the significance test have led to its rejection.

Which procedure should be used, when a choice is possible: the significance *test* or the *parameter estimation?* Should one test the null hypothesis or should one obtain the broader estimate of value possibilities from the confidence interval? Either procedure may be used, but that of parameter estimation certainly provides more "information," even if the information is inferential rather than empirical. Furthermore, unless care is exercised, faulty inferences may be made when the null hypothesis cannot be rejected. Thus it has been emphasized that failure to reject the null hypothesis does not signify that it is true. The confidence interval method of parameter estimation serves to give emphasis to the fact that the numerical value of the null hypothesis may be only one of many values that cannot be rejected. Hence all values within the confidence interval are candidates, so to speak, for the true parameter value. It should therefore be remembered that the nonrejection of the null hypothesis does not preclude or rule out of the running the possibility that values other than that of the null hypothesis may be the true parameter mean. These other possibilities emphasize that the "acceptance" of the null hypothesis, by virtue of its nonrejection, is often a hazardous inference to make.

Once the student is thoroughly aware of the preceding implications of a test of significance, there should be little risk that he will make faulty inferences when he uses a significance test rather than estimate a parameter value. In practice, one ordinarily proceeds with the significance test when there is a specific parameter value relevant to test, i.e., relevant to some theory, as is the case with an I.Q. of 100. More often, however, for hypotheses about means of single variables, there are no particular parameter values supplied by theory. In such instances it is therefore usually more meaningful to proceed by estimating the parameter mean with an appropriate confidence interval. This is illustrated by the following example:

Let it be assumed that the same population of third-graders whose I.Q.'s were sampled also took a spelling test of 50 items. The only information available about the spelling test are the mean and variance of the same sample of 100 pupils whose mean I.Q. was found to be a 97. Their spelling test data are found to be:

$$\overline{X} = 35 \qquad s^2 = 25 \qquad s = 5 \qquad \hat{\sigma}_{\bar{x}} = \frac{5}{\sqrt{100}} = .50$$

In this situation there obviously is no relevant parameter value to test. There is no theory to supply a value analogous to a population mean I.Q. of 100. Various spelling test score values within the range of possible values could be tested. Thus, if the spelling test were scored by giving one unit credit for each of the 50 items responded to correctly, the limiting values would be zero and 50. Obviously neither of these values would be used as a value for the null hypothesis. Nor would there be any point in using any particular value in between. There just is no rationale for setting up a null hypothesis for any particular spelling test score.

Hence in all such situations the best procedure is to set up the confidence interval for the estimation of the parameter value. Actually, of course, when a parameter estimate is made, it is a short-cut procedure in the sense that it obviates the necessity of testing any particular null hypothesis. If α significance level of .01 is used, the confidence interval for the parameter mean of the spelling test scores is

$$35 - 2.6(.50) > \mu > 35 + 2.6(.50) \qquad 33.7 > \mu > 36.3$$

This result signifies in effect that all values above 36.3 and below 33.7 have been tested and rejected by the .01 alpha criterion of significance. All hypotheses whose values are within the limits of the confidence interval have been tested, in effect, and not rejected. Consequently the statistical inference made is that the parameter mean of the parent population's spelling test performance is most likely a value between 33.7 and 36.3.

t Tests for Small-Sample Means

The preceding results for a random sample of 100 observations will now be contrasted with mean I.Q. results for another independently obtained random sample of only nine third-grade children drawn from the same finite population:

$$\overline{X} = 108 \qquad s^2 = 144 \qquad s = 12 \qquad \hat{\sigma}_{\bar{x}} = \frac{12}{\sqrt{9}} = 4$$

The *t* criterion for the 1% level of significance is found in Table B for 8 degrees of freedom $(n - 1)$ to be 3.4, instead of 2.6 (as it was for 99 d.f.'s). The difference between these *t* criteria of 3.4 and 2.6 arises from the fact, discussed in Chapter 8, that the sampling distributions of *t* differ noticeably in form as the number of d.f.'s decrease to only 8 or so. When so small, the sampling distribution of *t* is markedly leptokurtic. There is therefore a greater concentration of results in both tails of the distribution than is characteristic of the normal distribution. For 8 d.f.'s the middle 99% range of the sampling distribution is much more extended than it is when the samples are based on 30 or more d.f.'s.

That there will be much greater sampling variation in the means of small samples than in the means of large samples is quite logical and intuitively comprehensible. This fact alone is taken into account by the estimate of such variation, $s/\sqrt{n}$, since the smaller the *n*, the larger this measure of random variation. But that the *form* of the probability distribution changes as the d.f.'s decrease below 25 or 30 is not intuitively perceptible. As earlier indicated, the mathematical formulas for the leptokurtic sampling distributions of *t* were published during the first decade of this century by "Student" (1908). Critical values of Table B were set up in convenient reference form from Student's work by R. A. Fisher (1925).

If the population is again hypothesized as having a parameter mean I.Q. equal to the theoretical average of 100, then the *t* test of the null hypothesis is as follows (the finite multiplier isn't necessary because the sampling fraction is only 9/5000):

For *H*₀: *μ* = 100:

$$t = \frac{\overline{X} - \mu}{\hat{\sigma}_{\bar{x}}} = \frac{108 - 100}{4} = \frac{8}{4} = 2.0 \qquad (10.5)$$

Since the t criterion for the 1% level of significance is 3.4, and hence considerably larger than the t statistic of 2.0, the null hypothesis is not rejected. It is therefore quite reasonable to conclude that this sample mean *could be* a random variation from a parent population whose mean I.Q. is 100. Note again that this inference is in the form of a *could be* rather than an *is*.

Nondirectional (Two-Tailed) vs. Directional (One-Tailed) Significance Tests

As was indicated in the preceding chapter, the use of both tails of a probability model in significance testing, as well as in parameter estimation, is a statistical procedure often referred to as *two-tailed probability*. When used in a test of significance, the test itself is *nondirectional*. *Two critical regions*, rather than only one, are set up for the rejection of the null hypothesis, as in Fig. 10.1. A sample result may be expected to occur in either direction from the parameter value of the null hypothesis; hence the *nondirectionality* of the test.

One-tailed, or *directional*, tests are sometimes relevant and are illustrated in Fig. 10.2. They are employed whenever a proposition whose implications are being tested has alternative hypotheses in one direction only rather than in either direction from the null hypothesis. Since such hypotheses are directional, they were referred to in the preceding chapter as *delta* hypotheses. The following example will illustrate a *delta* hypothesis for a mean.

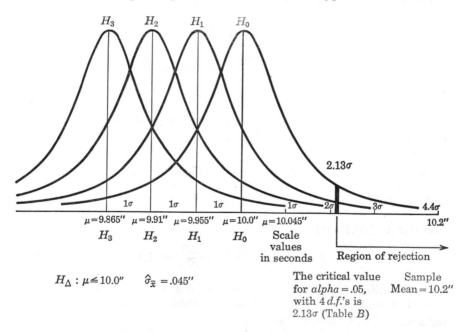

Fig. 10.2. Probability Model for a Directional (One-Tailed) Significance Test of a *Delta* Hypothesis, viz., $\mu \leq 10.0$ Seconds
(Since d.f. = 4, these sampling distributions are markedly leptokurtic.)

Delta (Directional) Hypothesis for a Mean

An athlete, A, makes the following official record for the 100-yd dash during the first half of the track season: 1st race, 10.2 seconds; 2nd = 10.1 seconds; 3rd = 10.3 seconds; 4th = 10.1 seconds; and 5th = 10.3 seconds. A's coach wishes to decide whether there is much hope that A will have the capacity to achieve the magic goal of at least one race in 10 seconds or better during the season. Being also a statistician, the coach decides to test a *delta* hypothesis, viz., $H_\Delta: \mu \leq 10$ seconds. If the facts indicate that this has to be rejected, then A's parameter time for the dash would be inferred to be *greater than* 10 seconds. The information obtained from A's five official races is used as a random sample of A's capacity for the 100-yard dash under conditions of competition.

The coach does not wish to be unduly optimistic about A's chances. Therefore, to be on the "safe side," he uses an *alpha* criterion of .05 instead of .01. That is, he doesn't wish to fail to reject the *delta* hypothesis if there is much likelihood of its being false. He would rather risk the acceptance of the alternative hypothesis as true, viz., a parameter value in excess of 10 seconds. The directional test is illustrated in Fig. 10.2. Interest is directed toward that tail of the higher values of the sampling distribution of means for a parameter mean of 10 seconds. A's record is entirely in that range.

The mean and the variance of A's time for the five races are:

$$\overline{X} = \frac{51}{5} = 10.2 \text{ sec}$$

$$s^2 = \frac{.04}{(5-1)} = .01 \text{ sec}$$

$$s = .1 \text{ sec}$$

Since theoretically the population (of dashes) sampled is indefinitely large, the finite multiplier is not used. Hence:

$$\hat{\sigma}_{\bar{x}} = \frac{.10}{\sqrt{5}} = .045 \text{ sec}$$

and therefore

For $H_\Delta: \mu \leq 10.0$ sec:

$$t = \frac{10.2 - 10.0}{.045} = \frac{.20}{.045} = 4.4 \tag{10.6}$$

The probability of obtaining a *t* equal to or greater than 4.4 when there are only four degrees of freedom is seen in Table B to be less than 1 in 100 for a one-sided, or directional, test:

$$t = 2.132 \text{ for } \alpha = .05; \quad t = 3.747 \text{ for } \alpha = .01$$

The coach therefore rejects the *delta* hypothesis that A's parameter mean is 10 seconds or less. He concludes that A will have to come up with one of those long-shot "miracles" to do the 100-yard dash in 10 seconds or better.

SIGNIFICANCE TESTS FOR DIFFERENCES BETWEEN MEANS OF INDEPENDENT SAMPLES

The tests of significance so far developed in this chapter have been for means of single variables. Procedures will now be presented to test hypotheses about differences between *two* means. They also will be compared with confidence-interval techniques for parameters of differences between means. In the next chapter the statistical technique known as *analysis of variance* will be presented to test the significance of the difference among *three or more means*.

The analysis of the significance of differences between means perhaps best illustrates the marriage of statistics and experimental method in research. The statistical technique for testing the significance of the difference between the mean of a control group and the mean of an experimental group, or between the means of matched groups, is one of the most frequent applications of statistical method to research. Mean results between two groups are nearly always different. The question to be evaluated is whether the manifest difference is plausibly explained by random variation in sampling and measurement, or whether the difference is too marked to be entirely explained as a random variation. If the former, both groups are inferred to have the same parameter mean. If the latter, then two different parameter means are involved; presumably the experimental conditions had real effects on the mean results. In all such significance tests, the null hypothesis is the hypothesis of no experimental effect, i.e., no difference between the parameter means of the parent populations.

Before the test of significance is made, three decisions that affect the statistical procedures and the interpretation of the results of the test are necessary. These three decisions concern:

1. *Alpha* level of significance.
2. One-tailed (directional) vs. two-tailed (nondirectional) tests.
3. Homogeneity of variances of groups whose means are to be compared.

Although the first two have been previously considered, they will again be discussed and related to significance tests for mean differences.

Alpha Level of Significance

Again the first decision to be made is that of an appropriate level of significance. Will *alpha* be taken as .10, .05, .02, .01, or .001? One of these five values is usually employed. *When samples are very small*, the risks of type I and type II errors may not be too great either way if *alpha* is taken as .05. The *power* of the significance test will be considerably greater for .05 than for .01. (See pp. 315 ff.)

When samples are large, the decision about significance level is not so critical because the scale values of sampling variations may not differ appreciably for the various criteria. If the theoretical or practical consequences of a rejection of a null hypothesis are greater or more important than those of its nonrejection, then it may be desirable to "lean over backwards," so to speak, and not reject the hypothesis unless it can be done with very high confidence. Hence the *alpha* value may be .001. On the other hand, if one is exploring the possible side (adverse) effects of a tranquilizing drug, it is better to recognize the existence of possible effects rather than overlook them. In such cases, a significance level of .01 or larger would be used instead of .001.

Some researchers have suggested the usefulness of an *alpha* of .10 in small sample research to ensure, so to speak, that nothing of possible significance will be overlooked. This should increase the *power* of the test in the sense that the likelihood of rejecting false null hypotheses is increased.

Directional (One-Tailed) vs. Nondirectional (Two-Tailed) Tests

In psychological measurement, however, the theoretical implications of parameter mean differences are sometimes one-sided affairs. That is to say, if there is a mean difference that has any practical as well as statistical significance, it should be in one direction rather than in either direction. Thus the possible experimental effect of a new training method in a shop would be tested by a coefficient of risk related to only one tail of the probability model. The null hypothesis of *no effect* between the old and the new methods would be as follows:

$$H_0: \mu_2 - \mu_1 = 0 \tag{10.7}$$

where the subscript 2 refers to the new method and subscript 1 refers to the old. The alternative hypothesis of an effect in favor of the new method would be

$$H_a: \mu_2 - \mu_1 > 0 \tag{10.8}$$

But this is the hypothesis whose acceptance the researcher is attempting to establish. Hence the relevant *delta* hypothesis to test is the following:

$$H_\Delta: \mu_1 - \mu_2 \geq 0 \quad (\text{or } \mu_2 - \mu_1 \leq 0) \tag{10.9}$$

This hypothesis is in the direction of inferiority for the new method of training. In testing this hypothesis, the researcher gives the experimental results (*facts*) the opportunity to *nullify* that hypothesis which he is interested in rejecting. If rejectable, then an inference can be logically made to support the hypothesis favoring the new method, viz., $\mu_2 - \mu_1 > 0$, i.e., that $\mu_2 > \mu_1$.

This directional test is illustrated in Fig. 10.3, in which it is noted that all alternative results are insignificant results.

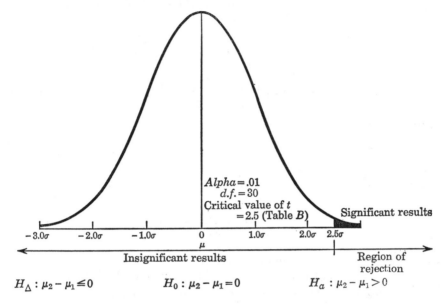

Fig. 10.3.   **Critical Region on a Probability Model for a Directional Significance Test of a *Delta* Hypothesis for Mean Differences, viz., H_Δ: $\mu_2 - \mu_1 \leq 0$**

Unless there are stated or compelling reasons to the contrary, significance tests for mean differences are interpreted as nondirectional, or two-tailed. This signifies in effect that alternative hypotheses in either direction from the null hypothesis are significant to theory.

Critical Criterion and d.f.'s

The critical criterion (c.c.) for a significance test of mean differences is usually taken in terms of the t statistic instead of a normal z deviate. Once decisions have been made (1) about the *alpha* level of significance to be employed and (2) whether the test is directional or nondirectional, the value of c.c. in terms of t is found by entering Table B with the appropriate degrees of freedom. When the samples whose means are compared are *independent*, the total d.f.'s will be the sum of the d.f.'s of each sample. Since the d.f.'s per sample are $n - 1$, the d.f.'s of two independent samples are $(n_1 + n_2 - 2)$. On the other hand, when samples are not independent but are (1) matched pair by pair or (2) the same sample is used for a second series of observations or measurements, the total d.f.'s will be the number of pairs minus 1. If, for example, there were 12 pairs of observations, the d.f.'s are 11. If *alpha* is taken as .05 and the test is nondirectional, or two-tailed, the critical criterion is found in Table B to be a *t* value of 2.20.

A useful rule of thumb concerning the value of c.c. in terms of *t* is that the value of *t*, compared with a normal *z* deviate criterion, will be greater for any given significance level. Hence, when a significance test yields a *t* statistic of a value *less than* that of the *z* deviate criterion for the *alpha* level of significance, the correct decision is *not to reject* the null hypothesis.

As applied to a significance test for mean differences, *t* is equal to the following:

$$t = \frac{(\overline{X}_1 - \overline{X}_2) - 0}{\hat{\sigma}_{(\overline{X}_1 - \overline{X}_2)}} \qquad (10.10)$$

Critical Ratio (C.R.)

Oftentimes the null hypothesis is unexpressed and the difference between sample means is symbolized by $\overline{D}$ (read as bar *D* or as "mean difference") to give what has been called the *critical ratio*, as follows:

$$t = \frac{\overline{D}}{\hat{\sigma}_{\overline{D}}} \qquad (10.11)$$

where $\overline{D}$ is the sample mean difference.

It may be apparent that other tests of the null hypothesis for differences between two statistics can be set up as a critical ratio, as for example, for proportions:

$$z = \frac{\overline{D}}{\hat{\sigma}_{\overline{D}}} \qquad (10.12)$$

These ratios have been called *critical ratios* because the decision to reject or not to reject the null hypothesis depends on the value of this ratio considered in relation to c.c., the critical criterion. The null hypothesis is rejected in a nondirectional test when

$$\frac{\overline{D}}{\hat{\sigma}_{\overline{D}}} > \pm \text{ c.c.} \qquad (10.13)$$

(read as plus *or* minus c.c.)

F Test for Homogeneity of Variance

One more decision needs to be made before the significance of the difference between two mean statistics is tested, when the means are based on *independent* samples. Independent samples, by definition, are drawn in such a way that the sampling units of one sample are in no way determined or affected by the selection of the sampling units of the other sample. A decision needs to be made for means of *independent* samples: whether to treat the statistical results as if obtained from *parent populations with equal variances*, or as if from parent populations with different variances. The estimated standard error of the sampling distribution of mean differences will depend on whether equal variances, i.e., *homogeneity of variance*, can be assumed. The null hypothesis tested is therefore

$$H_0: \sigma_1{}^2 = \sigma_2{}^2 = \sigma^2 \tag{10.14}$$

This null hypothesis can be written in two other ways:

$$\sigma_1{}^2 - \sigma_2{}^2 = 0 \tag{10.15}$$

$$\frac{\sigma_1{}^2}{\sigma_2{}^2} = 1.0 \tag{10.16}$$

Each population variance is estimated from the single unbiased value of its sample variance, $s_1{}^2$ and $s_2{}^2$, where

$$s_1{}^2 = \frac{\sum x_1{}^2}{n_1 - 1} \qquad \text{and} \qquad s_2{}^2 = \frac{\sum x_2{}^2}{n_2 - 1} \tag{10.17}$$

The ratio of the two sample variances yields the F *statistic:*

$$F = \frac{s_1{}^2}{s_2{}^2} \quad \text{or} \quad \frac{s_2{}^2}{s_1{}^2} \tag{10.18}$$

The larger of the two sample variances is used in the numerator so that the ratio will not be less than 1.0.

Sampling Distributions of F Statistics

The sampling distributions of F statistics are skewed. Their form varies with the number of d.f.'s for the numerator variance and with the number of d.f.'s for the denominator variance of the F ratio. Since there is a separate sampling distribution for every combination of d.f.'s, the F statistic has a tremendously large family of sampling distributions. The values of F are always positive, since sample variances are positive.

Tables of critical values for the distribution of the F statistic were developed by R. A. Fisher (1925) for the variance ratio symbolized as e^{2z}. G. W. Snedecor later published a set of tables with critical values of F at $F_{.95}$ and $F_{.99}$. He gave the name F *ratio* to the variance ratio in honor of Fisher. Critical values for the variance ratio at $F_{.95}$, $F_{.99}$, and $F_{.999}$ are given in Table F in the Appendix, having been adapted from Pearson and Hartley's tables (1958). The body of Table F consists of three critical F statistics, as just indicated, with the number of d.f.'s for the numerator and denominator of the F ratio indicated by the column heading and row entry, respectively, of the margins. Of the three values in each *cell* of Table F, the first (top) one is the critical value of $F_{.95}$ and is always the smaller of the three entries (except at d.f.'s of infinity, where all equal 1.0). The middle entry in italics is for $F_{.99}$ and the third or bottom entry of

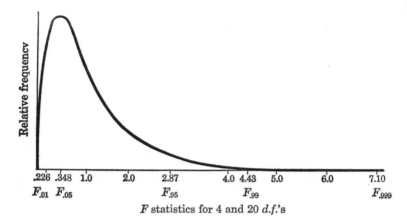

Fig. 10.4. Sampling Distribution (Probability Model) of the F Statistic
(When d.f.'s of Numerator = 4 and d.f.'s of Denominator = 20)
Statistical Inference, Helen M. Walker and Joseph Lev, Copyright © 1953, Holt, Rinehart and Winston, Inc. By Permission.

each cell is for $F_{.999}$. All critical values are thus at the upper tail of the sampling distributions of F.

An F distribution is illustrated in Fig. 10.4* for variance ratios whose numerator variance has four d.f.'s and denominator has 20 d.f.'s. The critical value for an F statistic at $F_{.95}$ is 2.87; at $F_{.99}$, the critical value is 4.43; and at $F_{.999}$, it is 7.10. Critical values for the lower end of the F distribution are indicated at $F_{.01}$ and $F_{.05}$. They are obviously not needed in tests of the homogeneity of variance because such tests are set up for the F ratio not to be less than 1.0. But they are sometimes relevant to analysis of variance (next chapter) and can readily be obtained from Table F, since they are equal to the reciprocal values of $F_{.99}$ and $F_{.95}$. Thus, for 4 and 20 d.f.'s

$$F_{.01} = \frac{1}{4.43} = .226 \quad \text{and} \quad F_{.05} = \frac{1}{2.87} = .348$$

Since only the critical values of the upper end of the F sampling distributions (as in Table F) are ordinarily used in a test of homogeneity of variance, their *alpha* probability values are doubled to .10, .02, and .002. This is done because the F test for homogeneity of variance is two-tailed, or nondirectional, i.e., the variance ratio may be written with either value in the numerator. The reason the ratio is taken with the larger variance

*Adapted from Walker and Lev (1955), p. 208.

in the numerator is to permit the use of tables of F values set up for only the extended end of the sampling distributions of the F statistics, and hence for values greater than 1.0.

For two-tailed probability and *alpha* of .05 and .01, values at $F_{.975}$ and $F_{.995}$ would be needed. On the other hand, if F were written with smaller variances in the numerator, then a table of $F_{.005}$ and $F_{.025}$ critical values for the lower end of the sampling distributions would be needed. A significance test for homogeneity of variance will be illustrated for the data of Table 10.1.

t Test for Mean Difference When Population Variances Are Not Significantly Different and Samples Are Independent

The learning ability of monkeys was tested in the Columbia University laboratories on a problem box consisting of an inner circular cage that contained food and an outer circular cage with the entrance at one end and three circular electric-circuit-closing floor discs or plates at 90°, 180°, and 270° between the two circular cages. The hungry monkeys had to learn to touch first one disc and then two, etc., in various stepped-up combinations in order for a door to the inner cage to open and admit the animals to food. H. A. Field tested 17 rhesus monkeys and A. M. Koch tested 6 cebus monkeys, with the results of Table 10.1 independently reported. The mean difference in average performance is 25.3 trials for the simplest problem.

For the data of Table 10.1, there are five degrees of freedom for the numerator (larger) variance of the F statistic, and 16 d.f.'s for the denominator (smaller) variance. F is equal to 1.49. Table F for the respective d.f.'s of 5 and 16 gives a critical value for $F_{.95}$ of 2.85; therefore the hypothesis that the population variances of the parent populations are equal is not rejectable by an *alpha* significance level of .10 (twice .05). Since the hypothesis of homogeneity of variance is not rejected, it is thus acceptable. The consequence of this acceptance is the fact that the null hypothesis for the mean difference will be tested by t, *which uses a common variance* for the estimated variance of the sampling distribution of mean

Table 10.1 Performance of Monkeys on Problem Box

Subjects	n	Number of trials to learn Problem 1		
		$\overline{X}$	s^2	s
Rhesus	17	162.5	9,460.30	96.23
Cebus	6	137.2	14,103.28	118.76

Mean difference $= 162.5 - 137.2 = 25.3$ trials.

$$F = \frac{14,103}{9,460} = 1.49$$

differences. Had the hypothesis of homogeneity of variance been rejected, then the population variances would have been estimated from the separate sample variances (as in the next sections, Formulas 10.21 and 10.22).

The cebus monkeys appear to be smarter on this particular problem than their "cousins" the rhesus monkeys. The question to be answered is whether the difference is reasonably explainable as a random variation from a parameter mean difference of zero, i.e., $\mu_1 - \mu_2 = 0$. Should this mean difference between average performances of the two types of monkeys be judged too large to ascribe to random variation, then the difference would be inferred to be statistically *significant*. The consequences for theory would also be quite significant. Hence it will be well to select an *alpha* level of significance that will tend to minimize the risk of rejecting a *true* null hypothesis (type I error). Therefore, .01 instead of .05 will be used. The significance test is nondirectional, or two-tailed, inasmuch as theory is wide open to evidence for superiority (or inferiority) in the direction of either type.

t for Independent Samples:

$$t = \frac{(\overline{X}_1 - \overline{X}_2) - 0}{\hat{\sigma}_{(\bar{x}_1 - \bar{x}_2)}} = \frac{(\overline{X}_1 - \overline{X}_2) - 0}{\sqrt{\dfrac{s^2}{n_1} + \dfrac{s^2}{n_2}}} = \frac{\overline{X}_1 - \overline{X}_2}{\sqrt{s^2 \left(\dfrac{1}{n_1} + \dfrac{1}{n_2} \right)}} \qquad (10.19)$$

Since the variances of the parent populations are taken as equal, s^2 represents the single variance estimate of the parent population and is based on the sample variances, taken however from their respective means (instead of from an overall mean of means) and combined as follows:

$$s^2 = \frac{(n_1 - 1)s_1{}^2 + (n_2 - 1)s_2{}^2}{(n_1 - 1) + (n_2 - 1)} \qquad (10.20)$$

$$s^2 = \frac{16(9,460.3) + 5(14,103.3)}{(17 - 1) + (6 - 1)} = 10,566.$$

It may be apparent that when n's are equal, the common variance is simply the average of the two variances. The test of significance for the mean difference is as follows:

$$t = \frac{(162.5 - 137.2) - 0}{\sqrt{10,566.(.0588 + .1667)}} = \frac{25.3}{\sqrt{2383.}} = \frac{25.3}{48.8} = .52$$

Since $t = 2.8$ for *alpha* of .01 and 21 d.f.'s $(17 + 6 - 2 = 21)$, it should be clear that the mean difference in the number of trials required to learn the task by the rhesus and the cebus monkeys is well within the range of expected random variation. Thus the null hypothesis cannot be rejected. It is therefore reasonable to conclude that no difference other than a chance difference has been demonstrated in the average learning ability on this problem for these two kinds of monkeys. Obviously this result has not established the truth of any new "fact."

Confidence Limits for Mean Differences

Confidence limits can be established for mean differences as well as for means, since differences between sample means will be distributed normally if the respective sampling distribution of means are normally distributed. For the problem box data, the parameter mean difference, δ, would be estimated to be as follows ($\alpha = .01$):

Interval Estimate of δ:

$$\overline{D} - \text{c.c.}\, \sigma_{\overline{D}} < \delta < \overline{D} + \text{c.c.}\, \sigma_{\overline{D}} \qquad (10.21)$$

$$25.3 - 2.8(48.8) < \delta < 25.3 + 2.8(48.8)$$

$$-111 \text{ trials} < \delta < +162 \text{ trials}$$

Thus the confidence interval by the 1% coefficient of risk ($\alpha = .01$) ranges from a difference of -111 through zero to $+162$. The t test of the null hypothesis has, of course, already indicated that *zero is a likely hypothesis.* This is always an implication of not being able to reject the null hypothesis. The possible parameter values from zero to -111 indicate that further sampling may yield results favoring *not* the cebus monkeys, as in the sample data of Table 10.1, but the rhesus monkeys. Certainly the estimate is not a very precise one. It is typical of the indecisive character of results that often accompany such small-sample experimentation.

The interval estimate of the parameter mean difference is not only lacking in precision; it is also pointless in that any inference is possible, so to speak:

1. Cebus monkeys are superior, on the average.
2. Rhesus monkeys are superior, on the average.
3. There is no difference, on the average, between them.

The probability of the correctness of one of these statements is 1.0, but it says precisely nothing that couldn't have been inferred about these species before the particular individuals were born. This is, of course, no reflection on the authors of the studies: Each conducted an independent investigation on the separate groups. But this kind of result in the comparison of two means does point to the crucial significance of the test of the null hypothesis. If the hypothesis cannot be rejected with satisfactory confidence, there is no point to establishing a confidence interval. On the other hand, when the hypothesis can be rejected, the confidence interval will then have significance inasmuch as it will include a range of parameter mean differences, *all* of which will favor one of the two groups whose means are being compared inasmuch as the confidence interval will not include a zero difference.

Tests for Mean Difference When Population Variances Are Unequal and Samples Are Independent and Large

The means and variances of the data of Table 6.8 on premature infants are summarized in Table 10.2. The variance of the 67 infants who died is considerably larger than that of the 182 infants who survived. The null hypothesis for these data asserts that their parameter variances are the same. Stated for an *F* significance test of homogeneity of variance, the null hypothesis takes the form of the *F* ratio:

$$\text{For } H_0: \frac{\sigma_1{}^2}{\sigma_2{}^2} = 1.0: \qquad F = \frac{\sigma_e{}^2}{\sigma_s{}^2} = \frac{150,245.}{95,304.} = 1.58 \tag{10.22}$$

where the subscripts *e* and *s* signify the "expired" and "survivor" groups.

Table 10.2. Means and Variances of the Birth Weights of Premature Infants Who Survived and Who Expired
(From Table 6.8)

Premature Groups	n	Mean Birth Weight, Grams	s^2
Expired	67	1108.	150,245.
Survived	182	1553.	95,304.

$$F = \frac{150,245.}{95,304.} = 1.58$$

$$\mathbf{P}(F \geq 1.58) < .05$$

The *F* test of significance for equal population variances is based on 66 d.f.'s in the numerator and 181 d.f.'s in the denominator. The critical values of *F* for this particular probability model of 66 and 181 d.f.'s are not given in Table F. By interpolation, however, for $\alpha = .02$ (twice the tabled significance level of .01), it can be inferred that this critical value of *F* is close to the obtained value of 1.58. Hence the null hypothesis can be rejected at an *alpha* level of .05. That the survivors are less variable in birth weight than are the expired appears not to be a matter of chance.

The point biserial correlation of .51, obtained in Chapter 6 for these data and summarized in Table 10.2, indicated a fairly marked mean difference between the two groups. The null hypothesis for a parameter mean difference of zero can now be tested. In this case, the null hypothesis asserts that premature infants delivered in hospital X and taken to the premature nursery immediately after birth have equally good chances of survival *regardless* of birth weight.

A test of this hypothesis will show whether prematures that weigh more at birth have a significantly better chance, on the average, of survival. In the one-year sample investigated, those prematures who survived had a mean birth weight of 1553 grams; those who expired had a mean birth weight of only 1108 grams.

The t statistic is based on the condition of a common population variance. Hence it cannot be used for the test, unless certain adjustments are made, as in the next section. However, since both samples are fairly large, the normal probability model may be used to test the null hypothesis: $\mu_e = \mu_s = \mu$. The normal z deviate formula for the significance test is as follows:

$$z = \frac{(\overline{X}_1 - \overline{X}_2) - 0}{\sqrt{\hat{\sigma}_{\bar{x}_1}{}^2 + \hat{\sigma}_{\bar{x}_2}{}^2}} = \frac{\overline{X}_1 - \overline{X}_2}{\sqrt{\dfrac{s_1{}^2}{n_1} + \dfrac{s_2{}^2}{n_2}}} \qquad (10.23)$$

For the data of Table 10.2, z is found to be equal to 8.5:

$$z = \frac{(1553. - 1108.) - 0}{\sqrt{\dfrac{95{,}304}{182} + \dfrac{150{,}245}{67}}} = \frac{445.}{52.6} = 8.5$$

Since a normal z deviate of 8.5 has a very small probability of occurring in random sampling for a parameter mean difference of zero, the null hypothesis is rejected with great confidence. (For a nondirectional test and *alpha* of .001, the critical value of z is 3.3.) Thus the mean difference between the birth weights of prematures who expired and those who survived cannot reasonably be explained simply as the result of chance variation.

Test for Mean Differences When Population Variances Are Unequal and Samples Are Independent and Small

A significance test for small samples will have sampling distributions more appropriately described by the probability models of t than of the normal z deviate. The *form* of the test is the same as for Eq. 10.23. It will be observed, however, that the number of degrees of freedom for t will not be $n_1 + n_2 - 2$ as it is for t when parameter variances can be taken as equal. This is the case because the sampling distributions of t are based on the assumption that population variances are equal. Therefore, in order to use the probability values of Table B to obtain the desired t critical criterion for a significance test, an adjustment will have to be made either (1) in the number of degrees of freedom to be used to enter Table B, or (2) in the critical value of t for a given significance level. The latter adjustment can be made simply by averaging the t critical criteria for each sample considered separately, with each t value weighted by the variance of its respective sampling distribution of means. (Cochran and Cox, 1957, p. 101.)

t' for Independent Samples When $\sigma_1{}^2 \neq \sigma_1{}^2$:

$$t' = \frac{\hat{\sigma}_{\bar{x}_1}{}^2 t_1 + \hat{\sigma}_{\bar{x}_2}{}^2 t_2}{\hat{\sigma}_{\bar{x}_1}{}^2 + \hat{\sigma}_{\bar{x}_2}{}^2} \tag{10.24}$$

When $n_1 = n_2$, the value of t' will be the same as t_1 or t_2; hence, the number of d.f.'s is equal to $n_1 - 1$ (or $n_2 - 1$), or exactly half the d.f.'s of $n_1 - n_2 - 2$.

When $n_1 \neq n_2$, the value of t', weighted by each sample's estimated variance of the hypothetical sampling distribution of means, will be an average between t_1 for n_1 and t_2 for n_2. As an example: If $n_1 = 10$ and $n_2 = 20$, and $s_1{}^2 = 400$ and $s_2{}^2 = 100$, then $F = 400/100 = 4.0$. By Table F, $F_{.99}$ is 3.52 for 9 and 19 d.f.'s. Hence the hypothesis of equal population variances is rejected at the $\alpha = .02$ (twice .01) level of significance. The adjusted value of t as a critical criterion for the significance test about *means* therefore is as follows, with the critical value of t taken at $\alpha = .05$:

$$t' = \frac{(40)(2.262) + 5(2.093)}{40 + 5} = 2.243$$

where $\hat{\sigma}_{\bar{x}_1}^2 = 400/10 = 40$, and $\hat{\sigma}_{\bar{x}_2}^2 = 100/20 = 5$; t_1 for n_1 (9 d.f.'s) $= 2.262$ (Table B), and t_2 for n_2 (19 d.f.'s) $= 2.093$.

If a significance test of the difference between means of these data yields a $t > \pm 2.243$, the null hypothesis can be rejected with considerable confidence (at the 5% level of significance).

SIGNIFICANCE TESTS FOR DIFFERENCES BETWEEN MEANS OF RELATED SAMPLES

The t tests so far described have been based on differences between means derived from independent samples. When, however, the samples of two or more groups are drawn in such a way that membership in one sample is determined by, or related to, membership in another one, then the samples are related, or dependent, rather than independent. If they should be positively correlated on the dependent variable being studied, the standard error of the sampling distribution of mean differences will be less (and hence t will be larger) than if there were no such correlation. This is the case because the higher the correlation, the less the possible role of random variation on the variance of the differences between the measures of the two groups.

Experimental designs in psychology and the biological sciences make extensive use of *control groups*, along with one or more experimental groups. Members of a control group are often *matched* with corresponding members of one or more experimental groups so as to give the researcher at the end of the experiment an index (by virtue of the control group's results) of what the experimental group(s) would have done had its members not been subjected to the conditions of the experimental variables. The statistical problem, therefore, is to determine whether it is likely that the final mean differences between them are significant, i.e., whether the null hypothesis can be rejected with confidence.

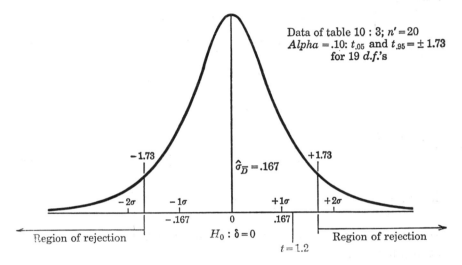

Data of table 10 : 3; $n' = 20$
Alpha $= .10$: $t_{.05}$ and $t_{.95} = \pm 1.73$
for 19 $d.f.$'s

-1.73

$+1.73$

$\hat{\sigma}_{\bar{D}} = .167$

-2σ -1σ $+1\sigma$ $+2\sigma$

$-.167$ 0 $.167$

Region of rejection $H_0 : \delta = 0$ Region of rejection

$t = 1.2$

Fig. 10.5.   Nondirectional Test of Significance of Mean Differences of Related Samples*

---

*With but 19 d.f.'s, this probability model is slightly leptokurtic.

Individuals are often tested and later retested after having been experimented upon. In this design, the group is its own "control." Again the problem is to determine whether there has been a significant change in mean performance (or in variance, for that matter). Thus the data of Table 10.3 (displayed in Fig. 10.5) are the results obtained from the administration of a digit-span test to a sample of 20 college students, who were then retested on the same task several weeks later. There is some change: The mean number of digits that could be reproduced by the group on the first testing was 7.45; on the retest, the mean is 7.65. Is the amount of change significant, either statistically or psychologically? Psychologically the answer is a NO; statistically the answer can be obtained from a test of the null hypothesis. It is to be emphasized, however, that aside from didactic reasons, there ordinarily would be no point to a test of *statistical* significance of psychological data when an obtained mean difference has no *psychological* significance.

Instead of working with the difference between group means, as in the *t* tests of independent samples, it will be arithmetically simpler to work with the mean of the paired differences, $\overline{D}$, where $\overline{D}$ equals

$$\overline{D} = \frac{\Sigma D}{n'} = \frac{4.0}{20} = .2 \tag{10.25}$$

where n' is the number of pairs. The standard deviation of the difference is as follows:

$$s_D = \sqrt{\frac{\Sigma(D^2) - \frac{(\Sigma D)^2}{n'}}{n' - 1}} \tag{10.25a}$$

$$= \sqrt{\frac{11.3125 - \frac{(4.0)^2}{20}}{20 - 1}} = .7438$$

t for Related Samples:

$$t = \frac{\overline{D} - \delta}{\hat{\sigma}_{\overline{D}}} = \frac{\overline{D}}{\hat{\sigma}_{\overline{D}}} = \frac{\overline{D}\sqrt{n'}}{s_D} \tag{10.26}$$

where δ, the parameter difference of the null hypothesis, is zero; and $\hat{\sigma}_{\overline{D}} = s_D/\sqrt{n'}$

For the data of Table 10.3, the significance test for the mean difference between test and retest is therefore 1.2, as follows:

$$t = \frac{\overline{D}\sqrt{n'}}{s_D} = \frac{.2\sqrt{20}}{.7438} = 1.2$$

The mean of paired differences, $\overline{D}$, is arithmetically the same as the difference between means. Similarly, the sum of the paired differences is equal to the difference between the sums of the first and second set of measures. This fact serves as a check on the computations in Table 10.3:

$$\Sigma X_2 - \Sigma X_1 = \Sigma D$$

$$153.0 - 149.0 = 4.0$$

The use of the paired differences for the *t* test of significance greatly simplifies the computations. For otherwise, this significance test would require the computation of Pearson's *r* for the estimate of the standard error of the mean differences, as follows:

$$\hat{\sigma}_{(\bar{x}_1 - \bar{x}_2)} = \sqrt{\hat{\sigma}_{\bar{x}_1}^2 + \hat{\sigma}_{\bar{x}_2}^2 - 2r_{12}\hat{\sigma}_{\bar{x}_1}\hat{\sigma}_{\bar{x}_2}} \tag{10.27}$$

Table 10.3.   Test and Retest Differences in Digit-Span Scores

Subjects	X_1 First Test	X_2 Retest	D (Difference)	D^2
A	8.5	8.25	−.25	.0625
B	6.75	8.25	1.50	2.25
C	6.0	5.5	−.50	.25
D	6.25	7.75	1.50	2.25
E	7.0	7.25	.25	.0625
F	9.25	9.25	0	0
G	5.5	5.75	.25	.0625
H	9.25	8.25	−1.00	1.00
I	7.75	6.75	−1.00	1.00
J	5.0	5.25	.25	.0625
K	6.5	7.25	.75	.5625
L	7.75	8.5	.75	.5625
M	9.0	8.0	−1.00	1.00
N	7.5	8.25	.75	.5625
O	7.0	7.75	.75	.5625
P	7.75	8.25	.50	.25
Q	5.75	5.75	0	0
R	8.75	9.5	.75	.5625
S	8.75	8.5	−.25	.0625
T	9.0	9.0	0	0
$n' = 20$ Σ	149.0	153.0	4.0	11.3125

The product-moment correlation, r_{12}, between test and retest scores is .84. The standard errors of the means are .30 and .28, respectively. Hence:

t for Related Samples:

$$t = \frac{(7.65 - 7.45) - 0}{\sqrt{.09 + .0784 - 2(.84)(.30)(.28)}} = \frac{.20}{.165} = 1.2$$

It should thus be clear that the first method (10.25), based on the variance of the differences between pairs, takes into account the correlation between the dependent variables. That the computations are much simpler than those required for Formula 10.26 is obvious.

With a t of 1.2 the null hypothesis cannot be rejected with confidence at any level of significance ordinarily used in psychological measurement. This test is nondirectional, or two-tailed. Even though one might expect an improvement, i.e., an increased mean digit-span score, from the first to the second testing, the digit-span performance of young adults is more likely to be at a plateau of achievement such that achievement levels from one testing to another are random rather than directional.

It is to be noted that the number of degrees of freedom is not $n_1 + n_2 - 2$, but $n' - 1$, the number of paired measurements less one, with n' used to symbolize the n of pairs. This is the case because there is only one degree of freedom within each pair of measurements.

TESTS OF SIGNIFICANCE FOR r CORRELATIONS

In the application of inferential statistics to the data of r correlations, there is always a relevant parameter value to hypothesize for a test of significance. It is the hypothesis that parameter *rho* (ρ) equals zero. The information derived from sample data is given the opportunity to nullify this null hypothesis. If it can be reasonably rejected as untenable in the light of the facts available, then the inference can be made that at least *some* of the observed correlation is attributable to real effects, as opposed to *chance* effects. The rejection of the null hypothesis signifies that the obtained correlation cannot reasonably be "explained" as entirely a result of random variations from a parameter value of zero.

Null Hypothesis for $\rho = 0$ vs. *Delta* Hypothesis for $\rho \leq 0$

The sampling distributions of Student's t statistic describes the expected variation for values of r when $\rho = 0$. Fisher and Yates (1938, p. 2) give the exact test of significance, with d.f. $= n' - 2$, as follows:

t for $\rho = 0$ (or $\rho \leq 0$):

$$t = \frac{r - \rho}{\sqrt{\dfrac{1 - r^2}{n' - 2}}} = \frac{r\sqrt{n' - 2}}{\sqrt{1 - r^2}} \tag{10.28}$$

where n' is the number of pairs on which the correlation is based. If r is .84 (as for the test-retest variables of Table 10.3) and n' is 20, a test of the null hypothesis yields the following value of t:

$$t = \frac{.84\sqrt{20 - 2}}{\sqrt{1 - (.84)}} = \frac{3.5638}{.5426} = 6.6. \qquad \mathbf{P} \ (t \geq 6.6) < .001$$

Is this particular significance test nondirectional or directional? In view of the psychological nature of the measurements, the test is directional. The question here is one of determining whether parameter *rho* is positively greater than zero. Hence a *delta* hypothesis is the one tested:

$$H_\Delta: \quad \rho \leq 0 \tag{10.29}$$

Many tests of r for psychological data are similarly directional, since *true* negative correlations are alien to psychological theory of abilities. When there is no relevant theory from which to predict positive parameter *rho*'s, the test of the null hypothesis will ordinarily be nondirectional.

It will again be noted that if a bivariate distribution consists of only two pairs of observations and there is variation within each variate, *r* will be 1.0 or −1.0. In other words, *r* has no freedom for variation unless *n'* is at least 3; hence the loss of two d.f.'s in Formula 10.28.

It will also be noted that if the researcher prefers, he may continue with the *t* statistic in testing the null hypothesis for *rho* of zero, even when samples are large. Since this is the case, the *z* deviate method for sampling distributions assumed to be normal will not be presented. The *t* test is quite satisfactory for any *n'*. (As earlier indicated, the critical values of *t* in the bottom row of Table B are also the critical values of the normal *z* deviates.)

Advantage of an Interval Estimate for ρ

When one tests the null hypothesis of $\rho = 0$, or the *delta* hypothesis of $\rho \leq 0$ is tested, one is still left with the problem of parameter estimation when either hypothesis can be rejected. The significance test doesn't provide any information about the likely value of the parameter correlation coefficient. Since more "information" is usually desirable, an interval estimate of ρ by the method described in Chapter 8 is recommended. Thus *r* is converted to *Z* (by Table E) because *Z*'s are approximately normally distributed whereas high values of *r* are not. Confidence limits are established for *zeta*, ζ, and the ζ values of the confidence limits are converted to ρ values for the parameter estimate. For alpha of .01, two-tailed probability, $n' = 36$, c.c. = 2.6, $Z = 1.19$ when $r = .832$, and the standard error of the sampling distribution of $Z = 1/\sqrt{n' - 3}$. The estimate of ρ from the estimate of ζ is as follows:

Interval Estimate of ζ (zeta):

$$Z = 2.6\sigma_z < \zeta < Z + 2.6\sigma_z \qquad (10.30)$$

$$1.19 - 2.6\frac{1}{\sqrt{33}} < \zeta < 1.19 + 2.6\frac{1}{\sqrt{33}}$$

$$1.02 < \zeta < 1.36$$

and therefore, converting the *Z* limits to ρ limits (by Table E),

Estimate of ρ:

$$\rho = .77 < \zeta < .88$$

It is thus inferred that ρ is at least .77 but not greater than .88.

The Fisher and Yates (1938) table for significant values of *r* for various size samples is given in Table EE of the Appendix. By use of this table it is quickly possible to ascertain whether a sample *r* of any value is large enough to warrant the rejection of the null hypothesis at five different levels of significance, viz., $\alpha = .10, .05, .02, .01,$ and $.001,$ and for bivariate distributions of $n' - 2 = 1$ to 100. Furthermore, one can readily see how large *r* needs to be for a given *alpha* and a given n' in order to reject the null hypothesis at a chosen confidence level. Thus for a sample of 52 bivariate pairs and $\alpha = .01,$ *r* needs to be at least .35 in order that the null hypothesis may be rejected at this significance level.

It may be apparent that if the confidence interval were set up in the first place, it would have been unnecessary to test the null hypothesis of $\rho = 0$. All parameter values of ρ not within the confidence interval are in effect rejected. It is true that *the ρ value of zero is a critical one* inasmuch as the researcher cannot infer any correlation other than chance for a bivariate distribution unless $\rho = 0$ is rejectable. However, the confidence interval will include a value of zero when this hypothesis is not rejected by the test of significance (assuming the same *alpha* level of significance). If the confidence interval includes a value of zero, it will usually also include negative as well as positive values. They all are possibilities for the parameter correlation of the parent population. Again the student is warned that failure to reject the null hypothesis does not prove the null hypothesis to be the correct one. It's simply a case of having no evidence that will *exclusively* support parameter alternatives greater than zero.

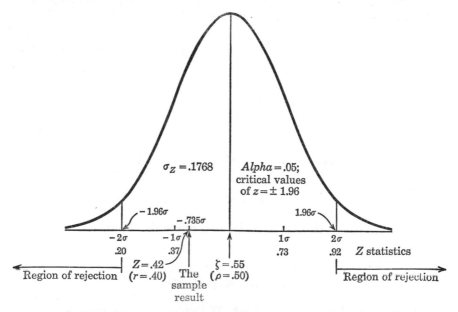

Fig. 10.6. Probability Model for Nondirectional Test of the Hypothesis that *Rho* = .50

(By Means of Fisher's *Z* Transformation Function)

Tests of Significance for Hypotheses of ρ Other Than Zero

Only a null hypothesis of $\rho = 0$ or a *delta* hypothesis of $\rho \geq 0$, or $\rho \leq 0$, should be tested by t of Formula 10.8. This is the case because, as pointed out in Chapter 8, the sampling distributions of r when ρ departs from zero become increasingly skewed, especially so for ρ values beyond $+.50$ and $-.50$.

If one wishes to test a hypothesized value of ρ other than zero, the simplest correct procedure involves the use of Fisher's Z transformation. The test of significance is made for a parameter value of ζ equivalent to the hypothesized value of ρ.

Correlations close to .50 have been reported in a number of studies that have measured the relation between the traits of parents and their children. If an r of only .40 is obtained in a random sample of 35 families of city A, it may be desirable to determine whether this result may be interpreted as a random variation from a parent population whose parameter correlation could well be .50. The answer may be obtained by a test of significance for the ζ equivalent of a $\rho = .50$. By Table E, r of .40 is equal to Z of .42, and ρ of .50 is equal to ζ of .55:

For H_0: $\zeta = .55$:
$$z = \frac{Z - \zeta}{1/\sqrt{n' - 3}} \tag{10.31}$$

$$z = \frac{.42 - .55}{\dfrac{1}{\sqrt{35 - 3}}} = -.13(\sqrt{32}) = -.735$$

This test is illustrated in Fig. 10.6. The z deviate is $-.735$; alpha is taken at .05.

Since the sampling distribution of Z is approximately normal, the z deviate value of $-.735$ signifies that the sample Z value of .42 is only about three-quarters of a standard deviation from the parameter mean of .55 of the sampling distribution of Z values. Hence the hypothesis cannot be rejected, and the r statistic of .40 is not to be considered as unlikely for a parameter correlation of .50.

TESTS OF SIGNIFICANCE FOR DIFFERENCES BETWEEN r's

When Both Bivariate Distributions Are Independent of Each Other

The sampling distributions of differences between Z's (Fisher's transformations of r) are approximately normal in form when the bivariate distributions of two correlation coefficients to be compared are independent of each other. When two r's are obtained from samples of different populations, they are by definition independent of each other, and hence uncorrelated. The question is one of determining whether the parameter correlation coefficients of their respective populations may or may not differ significantly from each other. A test of significance will permit an inference as to whether the magnitude of the difference between the two *r*'s is or is not explainable by random variation (or chance). The hypothesis tested is the null hypothesis that the difference between the parameter correlation coefficients is zero:

$$H_0: \rho_1 - \rho_2 = 0; \quad \zeta_1 - \zeta_2 = 0$$

Or, on occasion, the more relevant hypothesis might be a *delta*, directional one such that $\rho_1 - \rho_2 \leq 0$. When the parameter values of ρ have been converted to ζ, the test of significance will be in terms of a normal z deviate as follows:

z for Independent Samples:

$$z = \frac{(Z_1 - Z_2)}{\sigma_{(Z_1 - Z_2)}} \tag{10.32}$$

If the null hypothesis is rejectable, then $H_0: \rho_1 - \rho_2 = 0$ is also rejectable. The standard error of the sampling distribution of differences between Z's is

$$\sigma_{(Z_1 - Z_2)} = \sqrt{\frac{1}{n'_1 - 3} + \frac{1}{n'_2 - 3}} \tag{10.33}$$

The grades of a sample of 40 graduating college seniors were analyzed for various correlative relations. It was found, for example, that the correlation between their freshman-year science grades and their freshman-year social studies grades was slightly negative: a product-moment r of $-.19$. Another sample of 63 students from a different graduating class had a correlation of .47 on similar grade variables. Is this difference reasonably explainable as random variation or should the null hypothesis of a zero difference be rejected?

The test of significance for the difference between an r of .47 and an r of $-.19$, derived from independent samples, is as follows: When

$$r = .47, Z = .51; \quad \text{when } r = -.19, Z = -.19$$

Therefore

For $H_0: \zeta_1 - \zeta_2 = 0$:

$$z = \frac{[.51 - (-.19)] - 0}{\sqrt{\dfrac{1}{63 - 3} + \dfrac{1}{40 - 3}}} = \frac{.70}{\sqrt{.0167 + .0270}} = 3.35$$

The null hypothesis is rejected with confidence, since the test is non-directional and the normal z deviate for $\alpha = .001$ is 3.29. There thus appears to be a very significant difference between the way science and social studies grades *hang together* for the one group ($r = .47$) and the way they *hang separately* for the other group ($r = -.19$). The latter correlation may be considered a random variation from a parameter value of zero, since

For H_0: $\zeta = 0$:

$$z = \frac{-.19 - 0}{\sqrt{\dfrac{1}{40 - 3}}} = -.19(\sqrt{37}) = -1.2 \qquad [10.31]$$

The null hypothesis for this sample cannot be rejected; hence the two variables *hang separately*, i.e., they are independent of each other. On the other hand, there is a *tendency* for the grades in science and social studies of the other sample to *hang together:*

For H_0: $\zeta = 0$:

$$z = \frac{.51 - 0}{\sqrt{1/(63 - 3)}} = .51(\sqrt{60}) = 3.95 \qquad [10.31]$$

Since the null hypothesis can be rejected with considerable confidence, the parameter correlation of the parent population should be greater than zero.

When Bivariate Distributions Are Not Independent of Each Other

The method used in the preceding section for testing the null hypothesis of a zero difference between r's cannot be employed when the bivariate distributions are not independent of each other. Such independence disappears whenever two correlation coefficients to be compared have a variable common to both bivariate distributions, as in the comparison of r_{xy} and r_{xz}. Correlations whose measures are based on the same sampling units are also not independent. This is the situation described in the data of Table 10.4.

A study was made of the predictive value of various freshman-year grades for the four-year college average. A sample of 79 students in a June graduating class had freshman-year grades in at least four of the five areas indicated in Table 10.4. The highest correlation with their general four-year average is seen to be an r of .67 for freshman-year mathematics grades. The lowest is an r of .45 for freshman-year English grades. The four-year general average variable is symbolized by g, and each of the five variables of the freshman year are symbolized by numbers.

Question: Is the maximum difference between $r_{1g} = .45$ and $r_{2g} = .67$ *significant* in the sense that it cannot be reasonably explained in terms of random variation from populations whose parameter coefficients are equal? Or, are freshman-year mathematics grades a more significant predictor of g

than are the freshman-year English grades? If the answer to the latter question is YES, how broadly can the generalization be made? These two questions will be considered before the method for the test of significance is described.

Table 10.4.   Correlation of Freshman-Year Grades
with Four-Year Averages

Areas of Freshman-Year Grades	Four-Year Averages, g
1. English	.45 (r_{1g})
2. Mathematics	.67 (r_{2g})
3. Foreign Language	.56 (r_{3g})
4. Social Studies	.49 (r_{4g})
5. Science	.58 (r_{5g})

Sampling and Parameter Estimation vs. Forecasting

The problem of generalization is discussed again at this point because this kind of research situation is rather common to the behavioral sciences. Perhaps the broadest generalization of all is this: Inferential statistics may be used to make conditional generalizations about populations that have been sampled by methods which will yield results amenable to the implications of probability theory. Sampling a population by *random selection*, or the random selection of a sample from a subpopulation, will yield information that can be utilized with confidence for either parameter estimation or for significance testing. Unless a population is specified (the frame) and sampled by appropriate methods, there can be no generalization about a "parent population." The only generalization permissible will be conditional and about hypothetical populations, as for example: *If* the sample of the particular graduating class is representative of students elsewhere, then mathematics grades earned during the freshman year may or may not be (depending on the particular results) more significant as forecasters of overall college achievement at time of graduation than English grades earned during the freshman year.

Hypothetical propositions are interesting, especially as related to the development of theory and as guides for further research. The reality character of the results are such, however, that any generalization beyond the "population" of this graduating class is an example of *forecasting* or *prophecy rather than of parameter estimation.* This is also the sort of situation the economist is up against when he wishes to generalize from past observations to the future. He *forecasts* market trends. He generalizes from experience and information at hand. He cannot estimate parameters of unsampled populations (viz., future behavior). The generalizations of behavioral scientists are frequently of this nature: They are forecasts or predictions inferred as best guesses from experience (which may be actuarial), current information, and pro and con judgments. A public opinion pollster is limited to *forecasting* what voters going to the polls on Election Day will do; no parameter estimates of such behavior can be made because the voting behavior that day cannot be sampled in advance of the event.*

Parameter estimation and significance testing can be used in the behavioral sciences when conditions of sampling and of measurement satisfy the requirements for statistical inferences. It is again emphasized that these requirements ordinarily will consist of (1) random sampling of defined populations or subpopulations and (2) the use of methods of observation and of measurement that will put a premium on the randomization of errors and rule out, as far as possible, the role of constant contaminating effects. These requirements arc often easier to satisfy in the natural sciences and in experimental psychology than in social psychology, sociology, and cultural anthropology.

Test of Significance for r Differences of Related Samples

The test of significance for the null hypothesis of a zero difference between parameter r's of dependent samples can be made by the following formula developed some years ago by Hotelling (1940). The subscript notation symbolizes the two r's of Table 10.4 that showed the greatest difference. They are usually written so that the difference in the numerator of Formula 10.34 will be positive, but it really does not matter because the sampling distributions of t are bilaterally symmetrical and the test is nondirectional. A difference can thus be stated either way.

$$t = \frac{(r_{2g} - r_{1g})\sqrt{(n' - 3)(1 + r_{12})}}{\sqrt{2(1 - r_{1g}^2 - r_{2g}^2 - r_{12}^2 + 2r_{1g}r_{2g}r_{12})}} \qquad (10.34)$$

The correlation r_{12} is that between the two predictor variables, viz., freshman-year mathematics grades and English grades. In this study the correlation was found to be .31. The test of significance yields a t value of 2.34, as follows:

$$t = \frac{.67 - .45\sqrt{(79 - 3)(1 + .31)}}{\sqrt{2[1 - (.45)^2 - (.67)^2 - (.31)^2 + 2(.45)(.67)(.31)]}} = 2.34$$

*Jerzy Neyman (1960) envisages a new level of applied statistics. In an address to the annual meeting of the American Statistical Association, he contrasts *static indeterminism* with *dynamic indeterminism* and stresses the need for "stochastic models" (chance mechanisms) for the biological and social sciences that will permit the generation of sound inferences about the dynamics of statistical populations ever coming into being as well as not yet arrived. Unfortunately the needed techniques are only in the development stage. For the present, therefore, most researchers will have to do with (1) conditional inferences about more or less static statistical populations that have been sampled, and (2) speculations about future populations, based on as much relevant "evidence" as can be marshaled as pertinent to the dynamics of change.

As a two-tailed test with *alpha* significance level of .05, the critical value of t is found in Table B to be 2.0 for $(n' - 3) = 76$ degrees of freedom. Hence the null hypothesis can be rejected with confidence. For this student population, then, freshman-year mathematics grades were a more significant predictor than freshman-year English grades of overall college achievement as measured by grade average at time of graduation.

TESTS OF SIGNIFICANCE FOR OTHER CORRELATION COEFFICIENTS

For correlations other than product-moment r, procedures are available for testing the null hypothesis that the correlation of the parent population is zero. Significance tests for ϕ and for C, the contingency coefficient, were presented at the end of Chapter 9. Tests of significance for biserial r and tetrachoric r, rank correlation and point biserial r coefficients described in Chapter 6 are given here.

In the case of both biserial r and point biserial r, estimates of parameters can be made. Students interested will find the methods developed by Walker and Lev (1953, pp. 262 ff.).

Biserial r, r_b

A test of the null hypothesis for a parameter biserial correlation of zero can be made with the following measure of its sampling variation, provided both p and q are larger than .10 and $n' > 30$:

Standard Error of r_b:

$$\hat{\sigma}_{r_b} = \frac{\sqrt{pq}}{y\sqrt{n'}} \tag{10.35}$$

where, as in Chapter 6, p is the proportion of cases in the one dichotomized class of the x variable and q is the proportion in the other class, and y is the ordinate value in the normal curve at the point dividing the distribution into the p and q proportions, obtained from Table A (Appendix).

For the biserial r of .72 of Table 6.1, the standard error is as follows:

$$\sigma_{r_b} = \frac{\sqrt{(.47)(.53)}}{(.398)\sqrt{133}} = \frac{.499}{4.590} = .109$$

The test of the null hypothesis of a parameter correlation of zero is therefore equal to 6.6:

$$z = \frac{r_b - \rho_b}{\sigma_{r_b}} = \frac{.72 - 0}{.109} = 6.6 \tag{10.36}$$

The null hypothesis is obviously rejectable with extreme confidence, irrespective of the directionality or nondirectionality of the significance test.

(In view of the data of Table 6.1, this test is directional: The pertinent *delta* hypothesis, $H_\Delta: \rho_b \leq 0$, is, of course, also rejectable.)

Tetrachoric r, r_t

The sampling variations for a tetrachoric r of zero are measured fairly well by the following formula, provided $n' > 30$ and the dichotomies are such that any differences between p_1 and q_1, and between p_2 and q_2, are not large:

Standard Error of r_t: $\qquad \dfrac{\sqrt{p_1 q_1 p_2 q_2}}{y_1 y_2 \sqrt{n'}}$ $\qquad\qquad$ (10.37)

where p_1, q_1, p_2 and q_2 are the proportions of the frequencies in the dichotomies of the two variables and y_1 and y_2 are the ordinate values (from Table A) of each variable at their respective points of dichotomy.

A significance test for the tetrachoric r of Table 6.2, where r_t was found to be .75, is a z test as follows:

$$z = \frac{r_t - 0}{\dfrac{\sqrt{p_1 q_1 p_2 q_2}}{y_1 y_2 \sqrt{n'}}} = \frac{r_t(y_1 y_2 \sqrt{n'})}{\sqrt{p_1 q_1 p_2 q_2}} \qquad (10.38)$$

$$= \frac{.75(.398)(.399)\sqrt{133}}{\sqrt{(.48)(.52)(.51)(.49)}} = \frac{1.37}{.25} = 5.5$$

With a z of 5.5, the null hypothesis of zero correlation is rejected with confidence. For the data of Table 6.2, it is concluded therefore that some of the observed relationship between clerical skill and the clerical proficiency test scores is attributable to the operation of behavioral or psychological functions common to both variables.

When and if tetrachoric r is used as a timesaver for the computation of many intercorrelations of fully distributed variables, the student should bear in mind that r_t is not so *sensitive* a measure for significance testing as is r. This is the case because, for given n's, the expected sampling variation of r_t is at least 50% larger than that of r. Hence it takes values of r_t larger than those of r to nullify the zero hypothesis. Put in another way, r correlation has *more power* than r_t because, other things being equal, false null hypotheses will be more frequently rejected.

Rank Correlation, r_r

To test the null hypothesis for the rank correlation of .87, obtained earlier in Table 6.7, the sampling distribution of r_r for ten degrees of freedom is needed. Unfortunately this is not readily obtainable. Generally, for such small samples, r_r needs to be *larger* than r to have similar significance levels.

An approximation can be made of the standard error of r_r for sample sizes of about 25 or more, for the null hypothesis of zero ρ_ρ, viz.,

$$\hat{\sigma}_{r_r} \cong \frac{1}{\sqrt{n' - 1}} \tag{10.39}$$

Hence the normal z deviate for a significance test of the null hypothesis is as follows:

For H_0: $\rho_\rho = 0$:

$$z = \frac{r_r - 0}{\hat{\sigma}_{r_r}} \tag{10.40}$$

$$\cong \frac{.87 - 0}{1/\sqrt{11 - 1}} \cong \sqrt{10}\,(.87) \cong 2.8$$

C.c. for the z deviate with $\alpha = .05$ and a two-tailed test, is 1.96. Since z is 2.8, the obtained correlation of .87 deviates far enough from the zero value of the null hypothesis to warrant its rejection with satisfactory confidence. The emphasis is on the *approximation*, since this is not an exact test.

An exact test can be made but it is laborious. For small samples the exact sampling distribution of $r_r = 0$ is bimodal and discrete. It can be obtained by an enumeration of the number of permutations of ranks for each possible value of the r_r statistic when there are n' pairs of ranks (Kendall, 1948.) The number of permutations for 11 ranks is 39,916,800.

Point Biserial r, r_{pb}

The null hypothesis of zero correlation for point biserial correlation may be tested with the t statistic, where

$$t = \frac{r_{pb} - 0}{\sqrt{\dfrac{1 - r_{pb}^2}{n' - 2}}} = \frac{r_{pb}\sqrt{n' - 2}}{\sqrt{1 - r_{pb}^2}} \tag{10.41}$$

For the data of Table 6.8, r_{pb} was found to be .51, with $n' = 249$. Hence,

$$t = \frac{.51\sqrt{249 - 2}}{\sqrt{1 - (.51)^2}} = \frac{8.02}{.86} = 9.3$$

The null hypothesis is rejected with confidence, since *alpha* of .01 for a nondirectional, or two-tailed, test is equal to 2.6 for 247 d.f.'s (Table B).

ALPHA AND *BETA* ERRORS AND THE STRATEGY OF RISKS

The decision made in the testing of a hypothesis involves a strategy of choice between two types of risks of an incorrect inference. These were earlier indicated as two types of errors that may be made: Type I, or *alpha error*, occurs when a true null hypothesis is rejected; type II, or *beta error*, occurs when a false null hypothesis is not rejected. An error of the first type is called an *alpha error* because the likelihood of its occurrence is directly related to the value of the *alpha* level of significance used in the test. An error of the second type is called a *beta error* because *beta* is the next letter in the Greek alphabet after *alpha*, the first letter. The likelihood of a *beta*, second-type error, depends on a number of factors, including the value of the *alpha* level of significance. These factors are discussed in the next section on *the power of a test*.

Consequences of a Decision in Significance Testing

The four possible consequences of a decision made in a test of significance are summarized in Table 10.5.

Table 10.5   The Consequences of a Decision in Significance Testing

| | THE NULL HYPOTHESIS | |
DECISION MADE	True	False
To Reject the Null Hypothesis:	*Alpha* Error (I)	Correct Decision
Not to Reject the Null Hypothesis:	Correct Decision	*Beta* Error (II)

From a hypothetical, deductive point of view, each of these four possible results has a probability value. Inductively, the decision made is either correct or incorrect, and there is no way at the time of decision to ascertain which it may be. The likelihood of error, as well as the likelihood of a correct decision, are related to probability in the same way that the confidence interval is related. That is, there is no probability of a correct decision or of an incorrect decision. Irrespective of whether probability is considered deductively or inductively, the basis for a probability value lies in what happens in the long run. There is no probability of a single result, or of a single decision, a fact that is overlooked by players of Russian roulette and similar "games."

Hypothesized situations can be examined, however, deductive probabilities stated, and the strategy of risks of *alpha* and *beta* errors considered in relation to the realities of empirical data. A basic consideration lies in the complementary relationship of *alpha* and *beta* errors. The risk of *alpha* errors can be decreased by decreasing the value of *alpha*, but this increases the risk of *beta* errors, especially in small samples. On the other hand, the risk of *beta* errors can be decreased by increasing the value of *alpha*, but this increases the risk of *alpha* errors. There is only one way to *decrease* the risk of *beta* errors and not at the same time increase the risk of *alpha* errors and that is to *increase the size of randomized samples*. Oftentimes, however, this is not feasible because of cost and time limitations.

Knowing this complementary relationship of *alpha* and *beta* error risks, and seeing how these risks are related to the test situation, the researcher's strategy is to minimize the risk of that type of error *that is best to minimize*. A decision about what is "best" is not a matter of whim or caprice but a matter of working within the framework of scientific methodology and the demands of practical situations.

Thus an *exploratory* investigation of drugs that may increase mental tranquillity may be designed with the usual experimental procedures of matched groups, controls, etc., and the results can be evaluated by appropriate tests of significance. In a research situation of this kind, which strategy is more desirable, to minimize the risk of *alpha* error or to minimize the risk of *beta* error? Since the research is exploratory, the researcher ordinarily will prefer to minimize the risk of *beta* error. He is exploring the field, so to speak, and consequently he does not wish to make the mistake of ruling out drugs that may eventually be found to be satisfactory tranquilizers. Naturally he does not wish to make either an *alpha* or a *beta* error, but *if* an error should be made, he would prefer it to be the *alpha* type, i.e., he would prefer to risk the rejection of a true null hypothesis (no drug effect) rather than to fail to reject it when false (a drug effect).

How, then, can he adjust the basis for decision so that it will harmonize with this objective? The answer resides in the value taken for the *alpha* level of significance, aside from increasing the number of observations. When the value of *alpha* is decreased, say, from .05 to .01, the risk of failing to reject a false null hypothesis (*beta* error) is increased. When the value of *alpha* is increased, say, from .05 to .10, the risk of failing to reject a null hypothesis is decreased. The latter is what is ordinarily desirable in the exploratory phases of drug research and most research. The researcher does not wish to overlook any "good bets." Even though an increase in the size of *alpha* increases the risk of rejecting true null hypotheses, at the early stages of a research investigation the researcher will not be too concerned about *alpha* errors; he is exploring.

Assume that drugs A, B, and C have by an *alpha* criterion of .10 been earmarked as having tranquilizer possibilities. Now further tests will be made for more information about A, B, and C, not only about their effects as tranquilizers but also about their possible side effects, harmful or otherwise. Before any of these drugs is marketed, the manufacturer and the medical profession will wish to be very sure of any claim made. So, in the experimental work that follows, *real* tranquilizing effects should be inferred only at a very small risk of *alpha* error. Now the risk of rejecting a true null hypothesis (no drug effect) is to be minimized. The *alpha* level of significance used will be .01 or .001. Note, however, that the situation in this definitive stage of research still has its exploratory aspects in that the researcher needs to be on a continual alert to the possibility of harmful side effects—for which an *alpha* of .05 or .10 rather than of .01 will be the criterion for the preferred risk.

Deductive Probability and *Alpha* and *Beta* Errors

Given the probability models and the true parameters, it is possible to *deduce* what the probability is for each of the four types of results of Table 10.5. Obviously this will be entirely a theoretical business, since the truth or falsity of the null hypothesis is not known and the probability values are derived from purely hypothesized sampling distributions. Hence the extent to which these implications of theory actually apply to any particular research results is not known.

1. *Alpha errors* occur when a *true* null hypothesis is rejected. The probability of this occurrence is deduced from a hypothetical situation in which the null hypothesis is taken as true. If the *alpha* level of significance is .05 and the test is nondirectional, or two-tailed, then 5% of the results of randomized samples will yield statistics beyond the critical values that mark off the middle 95% of the sampling distribution. All such results will lead to *alpha* errors. Hence, when the null hypothesis is true, the probability of *alpha* errors is equal to *alpha* (.05, or .01, etc., as the case may be).

2. The probability of a correct decision when the null hypothesis is true is therefore $1 - \alpha$. This value is used by some statisticians as a coefficient of confidence.

3. The probability of not rejecting the null hypothesis when it is taken as false is the probability of the occurrence of *beta* errors. The probability value of *beta*, however, is contingent on several variables and thus does not have a single probability value as *alpha* has. In general the larger the value of *alpha*, the smaller will be the value of *beta*, and *vice versa*. In small samples, the differences may be very sizeable.

4. The probability of a correct decision in the rejection of a *false* null hypothesis is a measure of *the power of the test of significance*. The probability is equal to $1 - \beta$. This is discussed in the following section.

POWER OF A TEST OF SIGNIFICANCE

The power of a test of significance is measured *hypothetically* by the probability of rejecting the null hypothesis when an alternative hypothesis is true; in other words, when the null hypothesis is false and correctly rejected. This probability, as indicated above, is equal to $1 - \beta$. The value of *beta* depends on four conditions, each of which may vary.

1. *The value of true hypotheses alternative to the null hypothesis:* If the value of an alternative true hypothesis is well within the range of the sampling variation to be expected for the null hypothesis, then the test

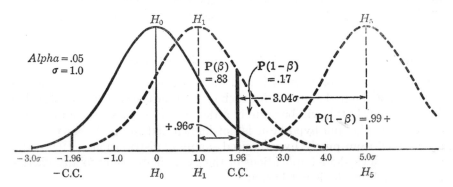

Fig. 10.7.   Illustration of the Power of a Nondirectional Test of Significance of the Null Hypothesis*
(With the Normal Probability Model)

*Two hypotheses, alternative to the null hypothesis, are indicated: H_1, which is one standard deviation from the null hypothesis of zero, and H_5, which is five standard deviations from the null hypothesis. The power of the test $(1 - \beta)$ is equal to the area of the distribution of an alternative hypothesis that is subtended by a vertical line extending from c.c. to the curve of the alternative hypothesis. Thus, for H_1, the power is .17, since that much of the area of the H_1 probability model is subtended beyond the c.c. point of 1.96. The power of the test is .99+ when the alternative H_5 is considered, since the most of the area of its probability model is beyond the c.c. point of 1.96.

will have little power. For the hypothetico-deductive model, the probability value of $1 - \beta$ will be small. This is illustrated in Fig. 10.7 for the hypothesis $H_1 = 1.0$, taken as a true alternative hypothesis to the null hypothesis of zero, and also with a second true alternative hypothesis, $H_5 = 5.0$. When the true alternative is $H_1 = 1.0$, the power of the test, $1 - \beta$, is only .16. When the true alternative is 5.0, the power of the test is .99+; in other words, in the latter instance the odds are greatly increased that the false null hypothesis will be rejected.

2. *The size of the alpha significance level:* Other things equal, the larger the value of *alpha*, the more powerful the test. This is the case because the likelihood is increased that a false null hypothesis will be rejected. But, as already pointed out, an increase in the size of *alpha* also increases the likelihood of *alpha* error.

3. *The size of the sample:* Increases in the size of the sample do not affect the likelihood of *alpha* error, but they do decrease the likelihood of *beta* errors and hence increase the power of the test of significance. Thus *the best way to increase the power of a test of significance is to increase the size of randomized samples.* The power is increased because the sampling variation for the null hypothesis is decreased, and hence fewer values of al-

ternative true hypotheses and their sample statistics will be within the hypothesized 95% or 99% range of sampling variation for $H_0 = 0$.

4. *The directional character of the test of significance:* A one-tailed directional test is considered to be more powerful, other things equal, than a two-tailed, nondirectional test. The argument for this is illustrated in Fig. 10.8.

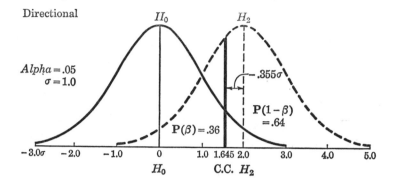

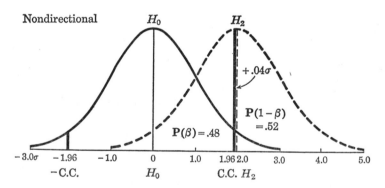

Fig. 10.8.   Illustration of the Power of a Directional vs. a Nondirectional Test of Significance of the Null Hypothesis
(Within the Normal Probability Model)

One alternative hypothesis to the null hypothesis is represented by its hypothetical probability model and parameter mean 2.0σ's above the mean of the null hypothesis (0). On both sets of distributions, vertical lines are extended from the c.c. values for the null hypothesis to the surfaces of the curve of the probability model of the alternative hypothesis H_2. For the directional test, the power is .64; for the nondirectional it is .52.

Since the normal z deviate value for $\alpha = .05$ is smaller (1.645) for a one-tailed test than for a two-tailed one ($z = 1.96$), the critical value for the rejection of the null hypothesis is nearer the parameter of the null hypothesis (zero). Therefore the likelihood of a *beta* error is decreased (from about .48 to .36) and the likelihood of rejecting a false null hypothesis is correspondingly increased (from about .52 to .64).

It is to be emphasized that whether a significance test is directional or nondirectional is not a matter of choice. Rather it is a question of the logical significance and relevance of alternative hypotheses. If hypotheses in *both* directions from the null hypothesis are relevant to a theory or research formulation of a problem, then, willy-nilly, the significance test is nondirectional, or two-tailed.

Power Function

Curves that relate the power of a test to the preceding four variables are referred to as power functions of a test of significance. They illustrate in hypothetico-deductive detail for given sets of circumstances what has been described in the preceding paragraphs. (See Walker and Lev, 1953.)

Importance of Suspended Judgment and Replication

The student may have noticed that this author is inclined to interpret a significance test that points to "no effect" or "no difference" as a case for *not rejecting* the null hypothesis. Some authors, however, do *accept* the null hypothesis under exactly the same set of circumstances. This may be proper as long as such acceptance connotes no more than a reconciliation to the fact that the null hypothesis cannot be rejected by the specified criterion of confidence. *Not reject* is preferred to *accept* in relatively isolated, nonreplicated research studies because *not reject* has no implication that the result demonstrates the truth of the null hypothesis. Logically it is, of course, impossible to prove the truth of the null hypothesis; nor can it be conclusively disproved.

This is not to deny that many statements which circulate as knowledge are based on inability to reject null hypotheses. Is there, for example, a significant difference in the intellectual capacities of boys and girls of a given culture? If test after test of the capacities of sample after sample fail to evoke results that permit the rejection of the null hypothesis, then such replications may justify acceptance and the generalization of no sex difference, at least until someone comes along with evidence really to the contrary. The point emphasized here is that a body of knowledge should not be generated on the acceptance of a null hypothesis unless there has also been a substantial body of replicated research by independent investigators.

Thus a key concept in research is replication of observations and measurement over many samples. The results of a single investigation do not justify the acceptance of the null hypothesis. When it cannot be rejected with confidence, then judgment had best be suspended until the research can be replicated. If additional evidence continues to fail to refute the null hypothesis, then there is the logical possibility of at least a tentative generalization about "no difference" or "no effect." Unfortunately too many generalizations of this kind are based on too *little* "lack of evidence."

ANALYSIS OF VARIANCE AND EXPERIMENTAL DESIGNS

*It should be noted that the null hypothesis
is never proved or established, but is possibly disproved,
in the course of experimentation.
Every experiment may be said to exist only in order to
give the facts a chance of disproving the null hypothesis.*

R. A. Fisher

EXPERIMENTAL research is often designed in such a way that mean results from the measurables of more than two groups or subsamples need to be evaluated by a significance test. The tests for means described in the preceding chapter are useful for the evaluation of a *pair* of mean results at a time. In this chapter the F significance test will be developed for the simultaneous evaluation of more than two means. F, it will be recalled from the preceding chapter, is a statistic based on the ratio of two variances. The critical values for F are related to an enormous family of probability models (Table F of Appendix), each of which is a function of the degrees of freedom (d.f.) of the numerator variance and of the d.f.'s of the denominator variance of the F variance ratio.

F for Two Different Classes of Hypotheses

1. The F statistic was used in the preceding chapter to test the hypothesis of equal variances of two populations; the hypothesis of homogeneity of variance:

$$H_0: \sigma_1^2 = \sigma_2^2; \qquad \frac{\sigma_1^2}{\sigma_2^2} = 1.0 \qquad (11.1)$$

When F is 1.0, therefore, the variances are equal and the null hypothesis of equal variances cannot be rejected. When F is 1.0 for sample variances, the population variances are inferred to be equal even though, logically, other hypotheses (within appropriate limits) are tenable, such that $\sigma_1^2 > \sigma_2^2$, or $\sigma_1^2 < \sigma_2^2$. In other words, the failure to reject the null hypothesis of equal population variances should not imply that this hypothesis is the only candidate for the true state of affairs; rather, the implication is that a significance test about mean differences can proceed *as if* the parameter variances are equal, at least until demonstrated otherwise. In very small samples this procedure may be somewhat hazardous, since not enough information may have been assembled to give the facts a real opportunity to nullify the hypothesis of equal variances. As repeatedly emphasized, the remedy for this is to employ larger samples.

2. In this chapter, F will also be used to test a different class of hypothesis. Instead of testing only for homogeneity of population variances, F will be used to test the hypothesis that *population means are equal:*

$$H_0: \mu_a = \mu_b = \mu_c = \cdots = \mu_k = \mu \tag{11.2}$$

But how is this possible, one may well ask, if F is a ratio of two variances rather than of means? The answer to this question will be developed shortly.

SOME EXPERIMENTAL DESIGNS

Analysis of variance has been developed as a tool especially useful for the statistical analysis of experimental results. It is especially helpful with small samples and just as useful with large samples. In order, however, that this technique may be properly employed, the researcher needs to design his experiments according to certain specifications. In this introductory text it is not feasible to attempt to describe the many possible variations in experimental designs, the results of which are evaluated by analysis of variance.* Three of the most commonly used designs for experimental research will be described in subsequent paragraphs.

Randomized Group Design

The essential characteristic common to most experimental designs is the requirement of randomization of subjects among the various groups or subsamples. If a particular population of persons is to be studied, a randomized sample of sufficient size is drawn from that population and then each person is randomly assigned to one of the groups needed for the experiment. More often, however, in experimental research, the interest is directed toward the possible *effects* of experimental variations of a factor, or factors. Experimental research is usually focused on experimental effects

---

*Students are urged to read at least the first two chapters of *The Design of Experiments* by R. A. Fisher (1935).

rather than on the study of the behavior of populations, as is done in survey research. The persons who serve as subjects are more or less literally taken as "guinea pigs," serving as organic vehicles for the manifestation of effects in response to experimental manipulation. In zoology, psychology, and the behavioral sciences, unlike physics and chemistry, experimental effects depend on organisms to reveal them.

Perhaps too little attention has been paid in experimental research to the possible roles of organismic factors, such as age and sex, and environmental factors such as socio-economic status in "experimental behavior." The assumption is often implicit that if x factor works successfully with the college sophomore, it should work well with all the Joes and Josephines who either couldn't get into college or didn't want to. Why the college sophomore? He is generally available on university campuses. Perhaps more of his class than freshman or upperclassmen are to be found in the introductory courses in psychology, etc. Possibly the allusion to the college sophomore is in itself apocryphal. Certainly the exact statistics are not available. But the reference is relevant in emphasizing that a great deal of university research, in psychology at least, is based on observations and measurements derived from the behavior of college students.

Various incentives to learning may be the subject of an experimental investigation. What may be found to work with college students should be limited in its generality to college populations until and unless other kinds of populations are also properly sampled and studied. Praise may be effective with some populations and not with others. Various kinds of punishment may work with some populations and not with others. Although the objectives of a piece of experimental research may be broad, the inferential implications of the results may really be quite limited in scope. (See Cronbach, 1957.)

Leon Festinger (1953) has emphasized the importance of an active association between laboratory experimentation and the study of "real life" situations. From the latter oftentime come the hunches and ideas and hypotheses about causes and effects that lead to the formulation of new hypotheses and the trek to the laboratory for their significance testing under the controlled conditions of experimental methodology. He takes the view that

a laboratory experiment need not, and should not, be an attempt to duplicate a real-life situation. If one wanted to study something in a real-life situation, it would be rather foolish to go to the trouble of setting up a laboratory experiment duplicating the real-life condition. Why not go directly to the real-life situation and study it? The laboratory experiment should be an attempt to create a situation in which the operation of variables will be clearly seen under special identified, and defined conditions. It matters not whether such a situation could ever be encountered in real life. In most laboratory experiments such a situation would certainly *never* be encountered in real life. In the laboratory, however, we can find out exactly how a certain variable affects behavior or attitudes under special or "pure" conditions.

In laboratory research, one hopes therefore to discover *significant factors*, i.e., factors whose *effects* on behavior in the laboratory setting have been established by significance testing. The possible and proper application of laboratory findings to real life situations depends, *then*, on further research into the role of significant factors in the general state of affairs of real life. Too often, in the past, researchers made their generalizations about human nature without leaving the quadrangle or cloister. The significant trend since World War II has been not only to explore and test the applicability of experimental results of the laboratory to real life situations but also to study intensively the latter under conditions of systematic and unbiased observation and to evaluate the significance of the findings with the aid of statistical "know-how."

Random Assignment of Subjects. The randomized group design consists essentially, then, in the randomized assignment of subjects to the various subsamples needed for an experiment. Were three or more dosages of a drug to be tested, at least four subsamples would be required, one being the *control* group, which would think it was getting the drug but which would receive a placebo instead. All dosages of the drug and the control would, of course, be constructed in tablet or capsule form so as to look and taste as much alike as possible.

Although a control group would be needed in the foregoing type of experiment, there is much research for which control groups are not needed. The general purpose of a control group is to have a subsample result that will serve as a yardstick of behavior not subjected to experimental treatments or conditions.

In a drug experiment the control and the experimental variations of a drug factor represent the *independent variables*. The *dependent variable* would be some measurable aspect of behavior relevant to the study of drug effects. If the drug were supposed to sharpen the acuity of visual perception, then the dependent variable would consist of measures of such activities for each subject of each of the four subsamples. The null hypothesis tested by analysis of variance would be that of equal parameter means (Formula 11.2).

The random assignment of members to the various subsamples is best done with the aid of a table of random numbers. Each member of the original, undivided sample is numbered from 1 to n. If the total sample consists of less than 100 sampling units (in this case, persons), then two-place numbers will be sufficient when using the table of random numbers. Persons are assigned to subsamples in sequence. A randomly selected starting point is located in the table and the person whose number shows first is assigned to the first subsample, the second person to have a number show is assigned to the second subsample, etc., through the jth person of the kth subsample. Then a new cycle of assignments is begun, and the process is repeated so that the person whose number shows next is assigned the first subsample, etc.

It is very helpful, computationally as well as analytically, in analysis of variance to have all subsamples equal in size. In some experimental designs, such as the factorial, it is essential. If n_j signifies the size of a subsample and k is the number of subsamples, then the original, undivided sample should have n_jk members.

Randomized Blocks or Matched Groups Design

This experimental design is generally a more powerful method for experimental research than is the randomized group design. It is generally more powerful in the sense that the odds for rejecting false null hypotheses are increased for samples of the same size. This is done by separating out the variations between block means from the "within-groups" sampling error variations and thereby reducing the estimate of *error variance*. As will be seen shortly, the estimate of error variance is used in the denominator of the F variance ratio. It provides a measure of results arising from random variations around a common population mean. The numerator of the F ratio provides a measure of results arising not only from random variation but also of effects possibly arising in consequence of the experimental variation of the independent variable(s), such as a drug factor.

The Matching Variable. As in the case of the randomized group design, the researcher begins with a randomized sample size n_jk of a specified population if he wishes his results to have a generality beyond the particular persons whose behavior is observed and measured. The sampling units (persons) are then *ordered from* 1 to n on a matching variable. A matching variable is one known to be or thought to be significantly related to the dependent variable, i.e., the behavior to be studied. If the dependent variable were visual acuity, as in the foregoing account, then the best matching variable would be the measures from a test of visual acuity given to the members of the sample at the outset of the experiment and, of course, before their assignment to subsamples. Each subject's result would be used as the basis for the ranking of from 1 to n.

When a control and three treatment groups are needed and $n = 60$, each *block* consists of four persons and each subsample of 15 persons. The four persons with the four highest acuity measurements (ranks of 1, 2, 3, and 4) are randomly assigned to the four subsamples. These four constitute the first block, or *matched tetrad* (when four). The next four persons, with rank orders of 5, 6, 7, and 8, are randomly assigned to the second block, or matched tetrad. The randomizing process within each tetrad continues until all 15 are set up. The last one, of course, consists of persons ranking 57, 58, 59, and 60 on the acuity test. The S.U.'s are thus *randomized within* blocks but systematically *ordered* on a matching variable from block to block.

Table 11.1 illustrates what may work out with such random assignments into matched tetrads, each number in the table being a person's identification number with respect to his rank on the measures of the matching variable (acuity test). Even though the members within each tetrad may not have measures exactly the same, especially those with extreme ranks in the beginning and ending blocks, it should be apparent that this experimental design will necessarily yield four subsamples more homogeneous on the matching variable than could be expected from simple randomization, as in the randomized group design. The means and variances of their measures on the matching variable should be approximately the same.

Random Assignment of Order to Equal Measures. Should two or more persons have the same measures on the matching criterion, then their rank positions with respect to each other should be randomly determined before they are assigned their numbers in the ordinal series of 1 to n. The order for simple ties could be settled by a toss of a coin; triple ties up to six-way ties, by a toss of a die. A table of random numbers would, of course, take care of more than six ties as well as the lesser number; for example, odd and even numbers for two-way ties.

Table 11.1 Randomized Block Design with Matched Tetrads

| | SUBSAMPLES | | | |
| | For Control | For Experimental Factor | | |
BLOCKS	c	a_1	a_2	a_3
Matched Tetrads				
First	3	2	1	4
Second	6	5	7	8
Third	12	9	11	10
. . . . . .	. .	. .	. .	. .
Fifteenth	58	60	59	57
15 Tetrad Blocks	$n_c = 15$	$n_{a_1} = 15$	$n_{a_2} = 15$	$n_{a_3} = 15$

Randomized Treatment Design on Same Subjects. It may be noted that the matched group design is sometimes not used because of no satisfactory matching variable or too few subjects. Instead, what might be called a randomized treatment design over each person is employed. Each block consists of a single person rather than of several matched persons. The *order* of the several treatments of variations of the experimental factor is randomized for each subject.

This method hasn't much to recommend it unless there is good evidence that there are no carryover effects from one experimental variation to another. Human beings as well as infrahumans are so constituted, however, that it is ordinarily safer to assume that there will be some carryover effects rather than there will be none. The randomized block design assumes that treatment effects *within each block*, as well as between blocks, are independent of each other. When one person is substituted for the several matched persons of a block, this assumption is difficult to satisfy. Whenever it does appear reasonable, however, to infer independence, then the analysis of variance for mean differences is carried out in the same way as for the randomized block design.

A Simple Factorial Design

One of the compelling aspects of analysis of variance is the fact that it provides a way for testing the possible significance of *interaction effects* on the dependent variable of two or more factors. Factorial designs may become somewhat complicated to work with, but some of the basic principles can be illustrated with a 2 by 3 factorial design. Thus a dependent variable, such as visual acuity, may be measured with respect to the experimental variations of two factors (the independent variables) such as structure of tachistoscopically presented material and color of the material. The structure of the material may vary two ways: numbers vs. letters. The color of the material could be varied in more than three ways, but if the purpose of the study were related to traffic signals and signs, three colors, viz., red, blue-green, and amber might be more relevant. If it were found that numbers were more clearly seen when red, and letters more clearly seen when amber, then the possible statistical significance of such a contrasting result could be analyzed by an F test for interaction of these effects.

The subjects for a factorial design may be assigned to each subsample, as in the randomized group design; however, the method of the randomized block design is also oftentimes used. There should be the same number of subjects in each subsample. The number of subsamples required is a product of the number of experimental variations or treatments in the one factor and the number of variations in the other. Thus six subsamples are required for a 2 by 3 factorial design:

$$A_1B_1, \quad A_1B_2, \quad A_1B_3, \quad A_2B_1, \quad A_2B_2, \quad \text{and } A_2B_3$$

where A represents one factor and B the other factor, and the numerical subscripts are the different treatments or variations. In a 2 by 3 by 2 design, six additional subsamples would be required. The number of sampling units (persons) required for a factorial design is n_jk, where (as before) k is the number of subsamples and n_j is the number of sampling units per subsample.

Nonexperimental Factors. Not all factors in a factorial design need be experimental in the usual laboratory sense of the term. A second or third factor may be organismic, such as sex or age differentials (youngsters vs. middlers vs. oldsters), or it might be a social factor, such as urban people vs. suburban vs. rural. Were a dichotomy such as sex used as a third factor to give a 2 by 3 by 2 factorial design, there would be the following 12 subsamples, each designated by its combination of factors:

$$A_1B_1C_1, \quad A_1B_2C_1, \quad A_1B_3C_1, \quad A_1B_1C_2, \quad A_1B_2C_2, \quad A_1B_3C_2$$
$$A_2B_1C_1, \quad A_2B_2C_1, \quad A_2B_3C_1, \quad A_2B_1C_2, \quad A_2B_2C_2, \quad A_2B_3C_2$$

where C_1 and C_2 would represent the dichotomy of the third factor.

The introduction of organismic or social factors into an experimental design is analogous to stratification of these factors in survey sampling. With analysis of variance one can determine not only the significance of mean differences between sexes, for example, but also the significance of the effects on the dependent variable of possible *interactions* among the factors: A and B (structure with color), A and C (structure with sex), B and C (color with sex), as well as ABC (all with each other).*

When one or more factors is organismic or social rather than experimental, the randomized group design is more likely to be employed than is the randomized block design because of the problem of matching "unmatchables." Thus, if there is a marked difference in the visual acuity of youngsters and oldsters, they couldn't very well be matched on such a variable. Or, in a learning experiment for which the matching variable is often I.Q. (an index of ability to learn), matching might be difficult because of language differences; for example, New York public school children born in New York City vs. those born in Puerto Rico.

A combination of both the randomized group and the randomized block designs can be used with a factorial design: the randomized group design initially with the organismic or social factors; and then the randomized block design, with the aid of a matching variable, but only *within* the subsamples of each of the organismic or social subgroupings.

THREE ADVANTAGES OF ANALYSIS OF VARIANCE

From the foregoing account of three experimental designs, three general advantages may be described as accruing to analysis of variance technique that are not characteristic of a series of t tests of significance for mean differences taken two at a time. These advantages may be summarized as follows:

1. The possible significance of mean differences can be analyzed simultaneously by an overall test of significance. When there are many mean results to be compared, the use of analysis of variance is a time saver and also involves less risk of a type I, or *alpha*, error; i.e., the error of rejecting a true null hypothesis. Thus, if the first experimental design (randomized

---

*Interested students will find the following texts very useful for more advanced work in analysis of variance: Cochran and Cox (1957), Edwards (1960), and Walker and Lev (1953).

groups) were employed with six subsamples, there would be six means. Taken two at a time and tested for the significance of their differences by t would require a series of 15 such tests, since

$$\binom{n}{r} = \frac{n!}{r!(n-r)!} = \frac{6!}{2!4!} = 15 \qquad [7.9]$$

Such a series of tests would require much more time than an overall test of their significance by analysis of variance. Furthermore, for the argument, it will be assumed that the null hypothesis is *true;* i.e., that all sample means are random variations from a common parameter mean. If an *alpha* significance level of .05 is used as the criterion for a decision to reject or not reject the null hypothesis, for a *true* null hypothesis this is in effect a *tolerance level* of one wrong decision in every 20 decisions made (on the average). With six means to be compared by 15 t tests, 15 decisions would have to be made. By chance, therefore, a *true* null hypothesis may very well be rejected simply because a long-shot result could be expected to occur within the 15 comparisons. With analysis of variance, however, a single overall analysis of the significance of the differences among means is made, and hence the risk of a type I, or *alpha*, error is lessened.

2. The second advantage arises in the use of the randomized block design. This method tends to lessen the risk of a type II, or *beta*, error; i.e., failing to reject a false null hypothesis. This is the case (as pointed out in the discussion of this experimental design) because the estimate of sampling error is usually smaller when the variance associated with differences among the means of the blocks (matched persons, or persons) has been eliminated from it. This advantage thus makes for an increase in the power of the test of significance, since it leads to higher values of the variance ratios of F and hence, for given n_j's, it increases the likelihood of the rejection of false null hypotheses.

3. The third advantage arises in the use of the factorial experimental design. As already indicated in the preceding discussion, this design permits a significance test for the possible interaction of the effects of the factors on the dependent variable. Thus two methods of teaching (A factor) may show significant interaction with the particular teacher (B factor) in that method A_1 may work out well in the hands of teacher B_1 but not for teacher B_2, and method A_2 may work well for teacher B_2 but not for B_1.

On the other hand, if there is no significant interaction between factors, and one method has been found to be significantly superior to the other, the superiority is presumably independent of the particular teachers B_1 and B_2. Note, however, that this generalization would have to be restricted to these two teachers. Even if they had been selected randomly from a large population of teachers, the margin of possible sampling error when $n = 2$ is too great to risk a general inference about the efficacy of either method with the "average" teacher.

BASIC REQUIREMENTS FOR ANALYSIS OF VARIANCE

The use of the variance ratio technique to assess the significance of differences among means is based on three general requirements:

1. Independence of the variance estimates.
2. Normality of the sampled populations.
3. Homogeneity of their variances.

Each of these will be considered in turn.

Independence of Variance Estimates

The variance ratio for F needs to consist of two independent estimates of population variance. As will be seen in Formulas 11.12 and 11.13, such independent estimates may be provided from variations *within* groups (Formula 11.7), on the one hand, and from variations or differences among groups (Formula 11.8), on the other. The basic components of Formulas 11.5 and 11.6 have to be independent of each other, for unless they are, the ratio of the variances obtained from them will not have an F distribution.

Independence here means that the value of one of these components in a sample result is not predictable from the value of the other component, or vice versa.

A neat example of such independence is given by Walker and Lev (1953, p. 210). Students computed the sum of squares of each component for 46 examples drawn from the same population and consisting of 4 subsamples of 5 cases each. The correlation between the respective component sum of squares for the 46 sets of sample results was $-.05$, a value well within the range of random variation for the hypothesis of zero correlation (Table EE).

Normality of Sampled Populations of Measurements

It is assumed that each subsample of measurements obtained for analysis of variance are drawn from normally distributed populations of measurements. Whether this assumption is satisfied is often difficult to determine, especially with small samples. Unless, however, there is significant evidence to the contrary, this requirement is usually assumed to be satisfied.

Homogeneity of Variance

It is assumed that the populations of measurements sampled have equal variances. In other words, it is assumed that the variances of the subsample results in an experiment are random variations from a common population variance. This assumption is explicit to the use of the *combined within-group variances of k subsamples* as the estimate of the error variance for the null hypothesis of a common population mean (Formula 11.5).

This second assumption is that of *homogeneity of variance* described in the preceding chapter and used there in connection with a t test of significance. F and t are based on the same set of assumptions. This is quite logical inasmuch as t is a special case of F. Were analysis of variance used to test the significance of the difference between the means of only two samples, the numerator of the F ratio would have only one d.f. (since $k - 1 = 1$). Under such circumstances F is equal to t^2, or $t = \sqrt{F}$. The critical values in the first column of Table F are therefore t^2 values.

From a number of studies reported in the statistical literature, it appears that both t and F are satisfactory to use even though samples may not be in themselves very normal looking, provided all subsample distributions tend to diverge in the same manner from normality. If all tend to be negatively skewed, for example, such a divergence from symmetry may not seriously affect the usefulness of t or F (Box, 1953). F will ordinarily be more sensitive to mean differences than to skewness differences. However, the assumption of homogeneity of variance is not so flexible. Therefore the variances of subsample results should be tested for equal population variances whenever they appear very dissimilar.

Hartley's Maximum F-Ratio Test for Homogeneity of Variance

The assumption made for subsamples a, b, c, $\cdots$, k is as follows:

Homogeneity of Variance:

$$\sigma_a{}^2 = \sigma_b{}^2 = \sigma_c{}^2 \cdots = \sigma_k{}^2 = \sigma^2 \tag{11.3}$$

If the variances of the several subsamples were compared, a pair at a time, one would encounter the same two difficulties already mentioned for the comparisons with t of means, a pair at a time: (1) a lot of labor would be involved, and wastefully so, were none of the mean differences significant; and (2) the likelihood of a type I, or *alpha*, error would be increased for a given significance level such as an *alpha* of .05.

H. O. Hartley (1950) has devised a procedure to surmount both difficulties: the first by its simplicity and the second by adjusting the significance criteria as the number of subsamples increases, in order to lessen the risk of rejecting true null hypotheses. These criteria for various values of k are given in Table H of the Appendix.

Hartley's procedure consists in finding the maximum difference between subsample variances (from the smallest and largest variances), and then giving the F ratio of these two variances the opportunity to nullify the null hypothesis of equal population variances. The use of his procedure will be illustrated with the six subsample variances for the data of Table

11.10. The largest is 13.5 and the smallest is 3.5. This is a rather large range, but the samples are small. Hartley's Maximum F test is as follows:

Hartley's Maximum F Test:

$$F_{max} = \frac{s^2_{max}}{s^2_{min}} = \frac{13.5}{3.5} = 3.86 \qquad (11.4)$$

Reference to Table H for the critical values of F_{max} for α of .05, 4 d.f.'s, and $k = 6$ gives an F of 29.5. Hence the null hypothesis of equal population variances is not rejected, and consequently the sample results may be used in analysis of variance for differences among means *as if* obtained from populations with equal variances.

Table 11.2. Hartley's Maximum F Ratio Significance Test for the Variances of the Six Distributions of Table 11.10

Subsamples	Sum of Squares	d.f.	s^2
A_1B_1	26	4	6.5
A_2B_1	16	4	4.0
A_3B_1	54	4	13.5
A_1B_2	34	4	8.5
A_2B_2	50	4	12.5
A_3B_2	14	4	3.5

$$F_{max} = \frac{s^2_{max}}{s^2_{min}} = \frac{13.5}{3.5} = 3.86$$

Had there been only two groups whose variances were to be compared (as for a t test, in which case reference would have been made to Table F instead of Table H) an $F_{.95}$ for 4 and 4 d.f.'s is 6.39. Thus the critical value of $F_{.95}$ more than quadruples to 29.5 when k is 6 instead of only 2. What Hartley's method does, therefore, is to increase the *protection level* against the rejection of true null hypotheses (*alpha* errors) as the number of multiple comparisons of variances increases. It should be evident, therefore, that whenever F_{max} has a value *less than* the critical value given in Table F for the degrees of freedom of the two maximally different variances, the null hypothesis will not be rejected regardless of the value of k.

From the foregoing discussion it may be apparent that Hartley's Maximum F test is developed on the assumption of subsamples equal in size. All examples of analysis of variance developed in this chapter are developed with this requirement of subsamples of equal size, for the reasons earlier indicated, viz., computational and analytical advantages. The use of Hartley's test is an instance of the latter.

Other techniques available for significance testing of homogeneity of variances include that of Bartlett (1937) and a method by Cochran (1941).

ANALYSIS OF VARIANCE WITH RANDOMIZED GROUP DESIGN

Analysis of variance is based on two essential mathematical facts:

1. The sum of the squared deviations can be partitioned or divided into component parts, each sum of which, when divided by its appropriate number of degrees of freedom, will provide *independent* estimates of population variance.

2. The F ratio of these two independent estimates of population variance is a significance test of the differences among the means of the several groups in the randomized group design (or some other design).

If the value of F is about 1.0, this may signify that the differences among the means are no greater than differences to be expected from sampling variation (sampling error). If the value of F is sufficiently greater than 1.0, then the null hypothesis may be rejected, since such results may signify that the differences among means are too large to attribute simply to random sampling variation around a common population mean.

Basic Components

When a measure is one of a subsample k in a randomized group design, then it may be expressed as a deviation with two components parts:

$$x = (X_j - \overline{X}) = (X_j - \overline{X}_j) + (\overline{X}_j - \overline{X}) \qquad (11.5)$$

In other words, the deviation of this measure from the overall mean $\overline{X}$ can be broken down into the two components, its deviation from its subsample mean $(X_j - \overline{X}_j)$ and the deviation of the subsample mean from the overall mean $(\overline{X}_j - \overline{X})$. This fact leads to the following equation, after squaring and summing over all measures:

$$\sum (x^2) = \sum_{}^{k} \sum_{}^{n_j} (X_j - \overline{X})^2 = \sum_{}^{k} \sum_{}^{n_j} (X_j - \overline{X}_j)^2 + n_j \sum_{}^{k} (\overline{X}_j - \overline{X})^2$$

$$(11.6)$$

This is the *foundation equation* for analysis of variance.

The double notation of Formula 11.6 for summation, $\sum\sum$, signifies that a summing of two or more sums is made. Thus the equation is read, as follows: The sum of the squared deviations from the overall mean is equal to the sum of the sums of the squared deviations of the measures of each subsample from their respective subsample means, *plus* the sum of the squared deviations of each subsample mean from the overall mean, multiplied by the number of measures in each subsample.

The total sum of squares is thus composed of *two additive* parts, the first of which consists of the variations of the measures about their respective subsample means. This is often referred to as *within-group* variation. The second component consists of the variations of the subsample means about the overall or total mean. It is often referred to as the variation *among means*, or among groups, or between groups.

It may be apparent that if there were no differences among the mean results in an experiment, the value of the second component would be zero; *all* the variation would be *within* the subsamples. *F* would be zero, an unlikely result because means of subsamples can be expected to vary about a common population mean when individual measures do. In other words, means as well as individual measures exhibit random variation or sampling error. The critical question is whether these sample means have parameters that are the same. If most of the variation were among the sample means and very little (relatively) within the subsamples, the differences among means might be sufficiently substantial to warrant a decision to reject the null hypothesis of equal parameter means. The usefulness of the *F* test of significance in the randomized group design (and other designs) lies in the fact that it provides a statistic which permits a decision on this question.

SS as Sum of Squares (Sum of Squared Deviations)

The sum of the squared deviations within groups is often symbolized as SS_w. It measures the variations to be expected from the operation of randomized errors of sampling and measurement with individual measures. The sum of the squared deviations of subsample means from the overall mean multiplied by n_j is often symbolized as SS_a. It also measures sampling variation, but (and this is the test!) SS_a may also measure additional variation associated with different parameter mean values, presumably as the result of the *effects* of the experimental treatments or variations.

The way in which the squared deviations, usually referred to simply as the *sum of squares*, are partitioned into the two components is illustrated schematically in Fig. 11.1. A sample of nine subjects is randomly divided into three groups, A_1, A_2, and A_3, each equal in size with n_j of three members. Measures of a dependent variable are scaled at the left of the chart and range from 14 to 6, with only one frequency for each of the nine measures listed. The means of the three subsamples are seen to be 7, 10, and 13, respectively. The overall mean of 10 is represented by the horizontal line across the middle of the chart.

The sum of squares of all the measures from the overall mean is obtained from the computations at the right side of the chart. It is equal to 60. An examination of the contents of the chart shows this sum to have two component sums of squares, as follows:

$$60 = (2 + 2 + 2) + (27 + 0 + 27) = 6 + 54$$

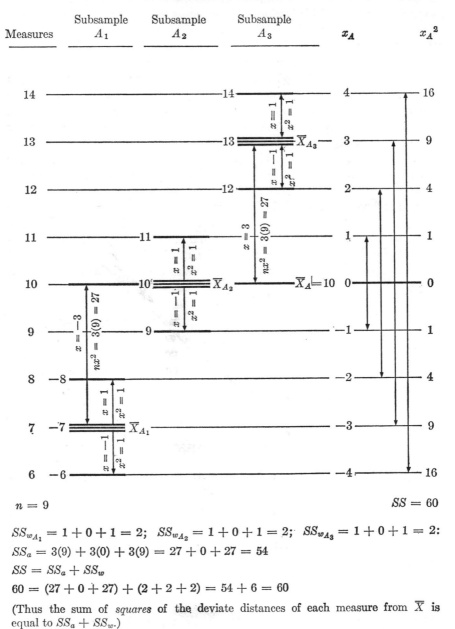

Distribution of Nine Measures Over the Experimental Factor A

$n = 9$ $SS = 60$

$SS_{wA_1} = 1 + 0 + 1 = 2$; $SS_{wA_2} = 1 + 0 + 1 = 2$; $SS_{wA_3} = 1 + 0 + 1 = 2$:

$SS_a = 3(9) + 3(0) + 3(9) = 27 + 0 + 27 = 54$

$SS = SS_a + SS_w$

$60 = (27 + 0 + 27) + (2 + 2 + 2) = 54 + 6 = 60$

(Thus the sum of *squares* of the deviate distances of each measure from $\overline{X}$ is equal to $SS_a + SS_w$.)

Fig. 11.1. Partitioning of the Sum of Squares in Two Components for Analysis of Variance

Thus, of the sum of squares of 60, only 6 are obtained from the within-groups component. The remainder, 54, are for the other component, between groups (among means).

Independent Estimates of Population Variance (n_j's Equal)

If the two sums of squares are divided by their respective degrees of freedom, there will be available two independent point value estimates of population variance, one based on sampling error sums of squares and the other based on the sum of squares among means. The number of d.f.'s for the former is $n - k$; for the latter, $k - 1$ (one less the number of subsamples whose means are compared).

The two estimates of population variance can be made from the sums of squares of the components by the *long method* of computation, as follows:

Variance Estimate from Within-Groups:

$$s_w^2 = \frac{SS_w}{\text{d.f.}} = \frac{\sum\limits^{k}\sum\limits^{n_j} (X_j - \overline{X}_j)^2}{n - k} \tag{11.7}$$

Variance Estimate from Among Means (Between Groups):

$$s_a^2 = \frac{SS_a}{\text{d.f.}} = \frac{n_j \sum\limits^{k} (\overline{X}_j - \overline{X})^2}{k - 1} \tag{11.8}$$

The latter estimate is based on an estimate of the standard error of a sampling distribution of means. This was seen in the preceding chapter to be equal to:

$$\hat{\sigma}_{\bar{x}} = \frac{s}{\sqrt{n}} \cdot \sqrt{\frac{N - n}{N - 1}} \tag{10.3}$$

This of course becomes simply $s/\sqrt{n}$ when the finite multiplier makes little or no difference, as in small sampling or in sampling with replacement. The estimate of the variance of the means is therefore usually taken as equal to:

$$\hat{\sigma}_{\bar{x}}^2 = \frac{s^2}{n} \tag{11.9}$$

and the population variance can be estimated from the standard error of the sampling distribution of means, since

$$s^2 = n\hat{\sigma}_{\bar{x}}^2 \tag{11.10}$$

But this is exactly the estimate of variance already presented in Formula 11.8:

$$s_a^2 = n\hat{\sigma}_{\bar{x}}^2 = \frac{n_j \sum\limits^{k} (\overline{X}_j - \overline{X})^2}{k - 1}$$

F Test of Significance for the Differences Among Means

If the two independent estimates of population variance are the same, except for differences attributable to random variation, or chance, then the ratio of these variances generally should be within the range of the critical values of the appropriate probability model of the F statistic:

F for Randomized Group Design:

$$F = \frac{\text{variance among-groups}}{\text{variance within-groups}} = \frac{s_a{}^2}{s_w{}^2} \qquad (11.11)$$

This is a one-tailed, or directional, test and hence the critical values of F given in Table F are taken at $F_{.95}$, $F_{.99}$, and $F_{.999}$ for $\alpha = .05, .01,$ and .001.

The denominator of the F test of significance in analysis of variance is always taken as an estimate of population variance based on random variation (sampling error). In the case of the randomized group design, this will be the variance based on the sum of squares *within-groups*. The parameter expectation of $s_w{}^2$ is σ^2:

Expectation of Variance from Within-Groups:

$$E(s_w{}^2) = \sigma^2 \qquad (11.12)$$

The parameter expectation of $s_a{}^2$, however, is σ^2 *plus* possible variation attributable to real differences among parameter means:

Expectation of Variance from Among Means:

$$E(s_a{}^2) = \sigma^2 + n_j \frac{\sum(\mu_j - \mu)^2}{k - 1} \qquad (11.13)$$

When the obtained F statistic is less than the critical value of $F_{.95}$, $F_{.99}$, or $F_{.999}$, depending on which significance level is chosen in advance of the experiment, then the second term of Formula 11.13 is inferred to be equal to zero since for the null hypothesis it is zero. When the F statistic is larger than the critical value of F, the null hypothesis is rejected because it is reasonable to infer that the population variance is equal to σ^2 *plus* variations attributable to *real effects* (second term of Formula 11.13).

Design vs. Chance

The relationship between analysis of variance and experimental design is perhaps most succinctly summarized from the implications of Formulas 11.12 and 11.13. When the null hypothesis of equal parameter means for k subsamples cannot be rejected, then F may be interpreted as the ratio of population variances estimated from the variations of purely chance or uncontrolled effects. Thus, if $\alpha = .05$:

When $F < F_{.95}$:

$$F = \frac{s_a^2}{s_w^2} = \frac{\text{estimate of variance from chance effects}}{\text{estimate of variance from chance effects}} \quad (11.14)$$

But when the null hypothesis can be rejected, then the role of the effects of experimental design is inferred to have entered into the results by producing effects on the dependent variable not entirely explainable in terms of random (chance) variations from a common population mean.

When $F > F_{.95}$:

$$F = \frac{s_a^2}{s_w^2} = \frac{\text{estimate of variance from effects of chance PLUS DESIGN}}{\text{estimate of variance from chance effects}}$$
$$(11.15)$$

Analysis of Variance for Schematic Data of Fig. 11.1

The value of the F statistic is calculated to be 27.0, as follows:

$$F = \frac{s_a^2}{s_w^2} = \frac{SS_a/\text{d.f.}_a}{SS_w/\text{d.f.}_w} = \frac{54/2}{6/6} = 27.0$$

The critical values of $F_{.95}$, $F_{.99}$, and $F_{.999}$ in Table F for 2 and 6 d.f.'s are 5.14, 10.92, and 27.0 respectively. Thus, an F of 27.0 is such an extreme value on the sampling distribution of the F probability model that it is most unlikely to occur simply as the result of random variation for the hypothesis of equal parameter means. The rejection of the null hypothesis is therefore a reasonable decision to make. It is consequently also reasonable to infer that the experimental variables, whatever they might have been in an actual experiment, had *real effects* on the measures of the dependent variable. These effects show up, on the average, among the means, which have different values from subsample to subsample. It does not necessarily follow, however, that *all* the differences among subsample means, considered two at a time, are significant in the sense that they are to be associated with different parameter means in each case. *The F test of significance shows whether there is any significant or real effect, not whether all means differ significantly from each other.*

Multiple Comparisons of Means

When an F test yields a result that leads to a decision to reject the null hypothesis of a common parameter mean, the researcher will wish to know the source of the experimental effects. In a drug experiment, for example, with a control group and several experimental groups, the main interest may be in the direction of comparing the mean result of each experimental group with the mean result of the control group, rather than of comparing all means with each other, taken two at a time or in larger combinations. C.W. Dunnett (1955) has developed a set of *Studentized* tables with critical values of t increased systematically as the number of mean comparisons increases. These adjusted values help to lessen the risk of *alpha* errors (other conditions remaining constant) as the number of mean comparisons with the control mean increases. Thus, if there were four experimental groups, each to be compared with the control, the critical value of t for *alpha* of .05 and a nondirectional, or two-tailed, test would be 2.55 for 60 d.f.'s instead of 2.00, as in a single comparison with the t criteria of Table B.

J. W. Tukey (1949), D. B. Duncan (1955), and H. Scheffé (1952) have developed various techniques for systematically lessening the risk of *alpha* errors for different values of k, the number of groups whose means are to be compared, when comparisons of many mean differences need to be made. In some experimental designs it is very important to test for the possible effects of various combinations of subsample results, as well as pairs of means at a time, in the process of exploring and testing out the sources of *experimental effect*.

ANALYSIS OF VARIANCE FOR A RANDOMIZED GROUP DESIGN WITH A SINGLE EXPERIMENTAL FACTOR

The several examples for analysis of variance to be presented in this chapter will be based on simplified sets of data so that the computational steps and relationships will be clearer than might otherwise be the case. The partitioning of the sum of squares for the nine measures of Fig. 11.1 was done by the *long method* of computation. That is to say, the actual deviations (x) were obtained from the overall mean as well as from the three subsample means, and between-means, in order to obtain the various sums of squares needed. The use of the *short method*, hereafter to be employed, is to be strongly recommended because of its greater simplicity. It is timesaving and it is practically always used in analysis of variance because the same set of squared values of the original measures used for the calculation of the total sum of squares can be used in the other sums of squares computations.

Steps in Partitioning Squared Deviations (for Data of Table 11.3)

1. The total sum of squares (SS). Before the squared deviations are divided into the two components of the single experimental factor of the randomized group design, the overall sum of squares is obtained. It will serve as a check on the accuracy of the sums of squares of the components, since the sum of the latter should equal the total sum of squares (equation of Formula 11.6).

Table 11.3. Sum of Squares for the Analysis of Variance of a Single Factor, Randomized Group Experimental Design
(With three Variations on the Experimental Factor A)

	Variations on the Experimental Factor					
	Measures of the Dependent Variable			Squares of the Measures		
	A_1	A_2	A_3	$A_1{}^2$	$A_2{}^2$	$A_3{}^2$
Subjects (15)	5	6	7	25	36	49
Randomly Assigned	4	5	6	16	25	36
to three Subsamples	3	4	5	9	16	25
($n_j = 5$)	1	3	5	1	9	25
	2	2	2	4	4	4
$\sum X_j =$	15	20	25	$\sum X_j{}^2 =$ 55	90	139
$\bar{X}$	3	4	5	2		

$$\sum\sum X = 15 + 20 + 25 \qquad \sum\sum X^2 = 55 + 90 + 139$$
$$= 60 \qquad\qquad\qquad\qquad = 284$$

THE SUM OF SQUARES

Step I: $\quad SS = \sum^{n}(X^2) - \dfrac{(\sum^{n} X)^2}{n} = 284 - \dfrac{60^2}{15} = 284 - 240 = 44$

Step II: $\quad SS_a = \dfrac{1}{n_j} \sum^{k} (\sum X_j)^2 - \dfrac{(\sum X)^2}{n} = \dfrac{15^2 + 20^2 + 25^2}{5} - \dfrac{60^2}{15}$

$\qquad\qquad = 250 - 240 = 10$

Step III: $\quad SS_w = \sum^{k}\sum^{n_j}(X_j{}^2) - \dfrac{\sum^{k}(\sum X_j)^2}{n_j}$

$\qquad\qquad = 55 + 90 + 139 - \dfrac{15^2 + 20^2 + 25^2}{5} = 284 - 250 = 34$

Each original measure is squared (Table M of the Appendix is convenient for this) and summed. This is done by subsample in the three columns of the right half of Table 11.3. When an adding machine is available, the squares of the measures are usually punched into the machine and then the entries are again checked against the adding machine tape. Two sums are needed for the sum of the squared deviates from the overall mean:

Total Sum of Squares:

$$\sum x^2 = \sum(X - \bar{X})^2 = SS = \sum^{n}(X^2) - \dfrac{(\sum^{n} X)^2}{n} \qquad (11.16)$$

where n is equal to the total number of measures and $\overline{X}$ without a subscript is the mean of the n measures.

For the data of Table 11.3, SS equals 44, as indicated by the first row of calculations below the body of the table.

2. *The sum of squares among means* (SS_a). It will be recalled that the recommendation was made that the subsamples be equal in size because, if all n_j's are equal, the computations are simpler. Sometimes, however, an experimental design may require subsamples unequal in size; as, for example, a larger single control group as against several experimental groups, smaller but equal in size to each other. (See Dunnett, 1955.) If groups are unequal in size, then the sum of squares is equal to the following:

Sum of Squares Among Means:

$$SS_a = \sum^k \frac{(\sum X_j)^2}{n_j} - \frac{(\sum X)^2}{n} \tag{11.17}$$

where k, as usual, symbolizes the number of groups, j is the jth subgroup, and n_j is the size of the subsamples (each experimental group). As in Formula 11.16, those symbols without subscripts relate to the total set of measures: $\sum X$ and n.

When the subsamples are equal in size, as in Table 11.3 and as ordinarily would be the case for the randomized group design, one division is sufficient for the sum of the measures for the first term of Formula 11.17, as follows:

SS_a, When n_j's Are Equal:

$$SS_a = \frac{1}{n_j} \sum^k (\sum X_j)^2 - \frac{(\sum X)^2}{n} \tag{11.17a}$$

For the data of Table 11.3, the sum of squares among means is 10, as indicated by the second row of calculations at the bottom of the table.

3. *Sum of squares within-groups*. This final step in the partitioning of the squared deviations consists essentially in computing the sum of squares (squared deviations) for each subsample and then adding these sums to obtain SS_w:

Sum of Squares Within-Groups:

$$SS_w = \sum^k \left[\sum^{n_j} (X_j{}^2) - \frac{(\sum X_j)^2}{n_j} \right] \tag{11.18}$$

SS_w, When n_j's Are Equal:

$$SS_w = \sum^k \sum^{n_j} (X_j{}^2) - \frac{1}{n_j} \sum^k (\sum X_j)^2 \tag{11.18a}$$

For the data of Table 11.3, the sum of the squares within groups is 34, as indicated in the third row of computations at the bottom of the table.

Table 11.4. Analysis of Variance for the Data of Table 11.3

Source of Variation	Sum of Squares (SS)	Degrees of Freedom (d.f.)	Mean Square Estimate of Variance	F
Between-Groups (Among Means)	10	2	5	1.77
Within-Groups	34	12	2.83	
Total (check)	44	14		

$F_{.95}$ for 2 and 12 d.f. = 3.89 (Table F)

$$P (F \geq 1.77) > .05$$

Analysis of Variance

Now the two independent estimates of population variance can be made from SS_a and SS_w. This is usually done in a summary table such as Table 11.4. The sources of variation are listed, and the sum of squares and the respective number of degrees of freedom of each are entered into the table. The sums of these entries should agree with the total sum of squares and the total number of d.f.'s equal to $n - 1$. The variance estimates are often referred to simply as the *mean squares* (being the means of the squared deviations, with the proviso that the latter have been divided by their respective d.f.'s which are equal to $k - 1$ and $n - k$).

The null hypothesis tested by analysis of variance in Table 11.4 is for no experimental effects of the A factor, as follows:

$$H_0: \mu_{A_1} = \mu_{A_2} = \mu_{A_3} = \mu \tag{11.19}$$

The variance estimates are given in the next to last column of Table 11.4 and are 5 and 2.83, respectively. The F ratio of these two variance estimates is found to be 1.77. In *small sample* experimentation, *alpha* of .05 gives considerably more *power* to the test of significance than does an *alpha* of .01, in the sense discussed in the preceding chapter, viz., a greater likelihood that false null hypotheses will be rejected and *beta* errors thus avoided. The larger value of *alpha* is therefore often used.

By Table F, $F_{.95}$ for 2 and 12 d.f.'s is equal to 3.89. Since the obtained F statistic is *less than* this critical value, the decision is made not to reject the null hypothesis. It is therefore reasonable to infer that the differences between the three means of the three experimental variations of the A

factor, viz., 3, 4, and 5, *could be* random variations from a single population mean.

Significance of *Eta* Correlation by Analysis of Variance

The significance of the *eta* correlation coefficient obtained on p. 134 can now be tested for the null hypothesis of no correlation. The hypothesis actually tested will be that of equal parameter means on the measures of the y variable for the three classes of the trichotomized validity criterion (Table 6.3) rather than $\eta = 0$. In effect this is the same hypothesis because, if the parameter means of y on x are equal, the slope of a line of best fit will be zero, and hence *eta* will be zero:

$$H_0: \mu_{y_l} = \mu_{y_c} = \mu_{y_h} = \mu \tag{11.20}$$

(in effect, the null hypothesis for *eta* correlation of zero).

This is the same hypothesis just tested by analysis of variance for mean differences in the randomized group design. The sums of squares needed, therefore, for the analysis of variance test are SS_a and SS_w. In Table 6.3, SS was 90.3 and SS_a was 70.0; hence $SS_w = SS - SS_a = 90.3 - 70.0 = 20.3$. The number of d.f.'s for SS_a is 2; for SS_w, the d.f.'s are $n' - k = 27$. The F significance test is therefore as follows:

$$F = \frac{SS_a/k - 1}{SS_w/n' - k} = \frac{70/2}{20.3/27} = \frac{35}{.75} = 46.7$$

$$\mathbf{P}(F \geq 46) < .001$$

When there are 2 and 27 d.f.'s, $F_{.95}$ by Table F is 3.35; $F_{.99} = 5.49$; and $F_{.999} = 9.02$. Thus the null hypothesis of equal parameter means can be rejected with a great deal of confidence, and as indicated, this is tantamount to the rejection of the null hypothesis for zero correlation.

F Test for Linearity of Regression

Walker and Lev (1953, p. 278) present a method for testing the linearity of regression by means of the F statistic of the following variance ratio:

$$F = \frac{\dfrac{(\eta_{yx}^2 - r^2)s_y^2}{k - 2}}{\dfrac{(1 - \eta_{yx}^2)s_y^2}{n' - k}} = \frac{\eta_{yx}^2 - r^2}{1 - \eta_{yx}^2} \cdot \frac{n' - k}{k - 2} \tag{11.21}$$

The numerator variance has $k - 2$ d.f.'s, and the error variance of the denominator has $n' - k$ d.f.'s.

For the somewhat nonlinear, bivariate distribution of Table 6.3 and Fig. 6.2, *eta* correlation was found to be .88. Pearson's r was also calculated for the data of Table 6.3 by the product-moment method: A value of 1.0

was assigned to the measures in the *low* criterion group, a value of 2.0 to those in the *average* group, and a value of 3.0 to those in the *high* criterion group. The value of r was found to be .84.

Is this difference of an *eta* correlation of .88 and a Pearson correlation of .84 significantly different? The relevant hypothesis to test is that parameter *eta* is equal to parameter *rho*. Formula 11.21 for the pertinent variance ratio is as follows:

$$F = \frac{(.88)^2 - (.84)^2}{1 - (.88)^2} \cdot \frac{27}{1} = \frac{.0688(27)}{.2256} = 8.2$$

For 1 and 27 d.f.'s, $\mathbf{P}(F \geq 8.2) < .01$. Hence the hypothesis of linearity is rejected with confidence at an *alpha* significance level of .01. In other words, it is very likely that the regression of y on x in the parent population is nonlinear.

ANALYSIS OF VARIANCE FOR A RANDOMIZED BLOCK DESIGN WITH A SINGLE EXPERIMENTAL FACTOR

The same measures of the three subsamples used in Table 11.3 are employed in Table 11.5. The context, however, is quite different. It now is that of the randomized block design. Each row is to be read as a *block* of three measures: either for a triad of persons *matched* on a relevant criterion or from the same person *when and if* it can be assumed that a subject's behavior on A_1 is independent of his behavior on A_2 and his behavior on A_3 is independent of both A_1 and A_2.

As indicated early in this chapter, the randomized block (*matched group*) design is ordinarily a more powerful experimental method than is the randomized group design because the source of variation attributable to mean differences among blocks can be eliminated from the error sum of squares and hence from the estimate of error variance. This will ordinarily reduce the size of the latter and therefore increase the size of the F statistic, thereby giving the F test more *power* to reject false null hypotheses.

The error variance is now based on measures of a more homogeneous nature, since the heterogeneity of mean measures from block to block is subtracted out and segregated. This cannot be done in the randomized group design with a single experimental factor inasmuch as the *only* basis for an estimate of error variance lies in the variations *within* each subsample. In the randomized block design, the estimate of sampling error (the error variance) is based on the sums of the squares of the *residual variations, as a third component*.

Since the total sum of squares is the same for the data of Table 11.5 as for those of Table 11.3, the squared values of each measure are not repeated in Table 11.5. However, the five blocks of matched triads are numbered in the column at the left of the body of the table.

Table 11.5.   Sum of Squares for Analysis of Variance of Single Factor, Randomized Block (Matched Group) Design

Blocks	No.	A_1	A_2	A_3	Σ_r	n_r	$\overline{X}_r$	$(\overline{X}_r - \overline{X})$
(Matched Triads)	1	5	6	7	18	3	6	2
''	2	4	5	6	15	3	5	1
''	3	3	4	5	12	3	4	0
''	4	1	3	5	9	3	3	−1
''	5	2	2	2	6	3	2	−2

$$\Sigma_c = \quad 15 \quad 20 \quad 25 \qquad \Sigma\Sigma X = 15 + 20 + 25 = 60$$

$$n_c = \quad 5 \quad 5 \quad 5 \qquad n = 15$$

$$\overline{X}_c = \quad 3 \quad 4 \quad 5 \qquad \overline{X} = 4$$

$$(\overline{X}_c - \overline{X}) = -1 \quad 0 \quad 1$$

$$SS = (5^2 + 4^2 + 3^2 + \cdots + 5^2 + 2^2) - \frac{60^2}{15} = 284 - 240 = 44$$

$$SS_c = \frac{(15^2 + 20^2 + 25^2)}{5} - \frac{60^2}{15} = 250 - 240 = 10$$

$$SS_r = \frac{(18^2 + 15^2 + 12^2 + 9^2 + 6^2)}{3} - \frac{60^2}{15} = 260 - 240 = 30$$

$$SS_{res} = SS - SS_c - SS_r = 44 - 10 - 30 = 4$$

Notation for Column and Row Measures and Means

Since the analysis of variance will now be concerned with the sums and means of rows (the blocks) as well as with the sums and means of the columns (experimental variations of the experimental factor), the symbols r (rows) and c (columns) will be used instead of k to designate which set of means is referred to in the various equations needed. Furthermore, the symbols i and j will be used to designate individual measures as well as subsample statistics: i for rows and j for columns. As indicated in Table 11.6, numerical subscripts are used to locate particular measures of a column and row. Thus:

1. X_{ij} signifies the ijth measure.
2. $X_i.$ signifies a measure in the ith row.
3. $X._j$ signifies a measure in the jth column.
4. $\overline{X}_i.$ signifies a mean of a row.
5. $\overline{X}._j$ signifies a mean of a column.
6. n_i signifies the number of measures in a row.
7. n_j signifies the number of measures in a column.

8. $\overline{X}$ and n (without subscripts) signify (as before) the overall mean and the total number of measures.

Table 11.6.   Double Subscripts for Entries of Column and Row Measures in Analysis of Variance

| Blocks | Experimental Factor | | | | |
	1	2	. . .	j	$\overline{X}_r$
1	X_{11}	X_{12}	. . .	X_{1j}	$\overline{X}_{1.}$
2	X_{21}	X_{22}	. . .	X_{2j}	$\overline{X}_{2.}$
. . .	. . .	. . .	. . .	. . .	
. . .	. . .	. . .	. . .	. . .	
i	X_{i1}	X_{i2}	. . .	X_{ij}	$\overline{X}_{i.}$
$\overline{X}_c$	$\overline{X}_{.1}$	$\overline{X}_{.2}$		$\overline{X}_{.j}$	$\overline{X}$

The measure in any cell is designated by two numerical subscripts, the first of which identifies the row; the second, the column. Thus X_{21} is the measure in the cell of the second row and the first column. The symbols i and j are used generically to identify a measure. A dot notation is used to identify means. Thus the mean of the second row (block) is $\overline{X}_{2.}$; the mean of the second column (second variation of the experimental factor) is $\overline{X}_{.2}$.

The Three Components

The total sum of squares can be partitioned into three components instead of only two inasmuch as each measure may now be expressed as a deviation divided into three parts, as follows

$$x_{ij} = (X_{ij} - \overline{X}) = [X_{ij} - (\overline{X}_{i.} + \overline{X}_{.j} - \overline{X})] + (\overline{X}_{i.} - \overline{X}) + (\overline{X}_{.j} - \overline{X})$$

$$= (X_{ij} - \overline{X}_{i.} - \overline{X}_{.j} + \overline{X}) + (\overline{X}_{i.} - \overline{X}) + (\overline{X}_{.j} - \overline{X}) \qquad (11.22)$$

The first component is the deviation of the individual measure from the difference between the sum of that measure's row and column means *and* the overall mean. The second component is the deviation of the measure's row mean from the overall mean. The third component is the deviation of the measure's column mean from the overall mean.

Squaring and summing over all measures give the following fundamental equation for sums of squares with three components:

Sum of Squares for Three Components:

$$\sum x^2 = \sum^c \sum^r (X_{ij} - \overline{X})^2$$

$$= \sum^{cr} (X_{ij} - \overline{X}_{i.} - \overline{X}_{.j} + \overline{X})^2$$

$$+ n_c \sum^r (\overline{X}_{i.} - \overline{X})^2 + n_r \sum^c (\overline{X}_{.j} - \overline{X})^2 \qquad (11.23)$$

where n_c is the number of column means and n_r is the number of row means.

The total sum of squares is thus equal to the sum of the sum of squares of the residual variations (error) plus the sum of squares among column means plus the sum of squares among row means. From these sums of squares three *independent* estimates of population variance can be made.

Calculation of the Sum of Squares

1. *The total sum of squares:* as in Table 11.3, $\sum x^2 = SS = 44$.

2. *The sum of squares among means of columns:* as in Table 11.3, $SS_a = 10$, this being the sum of squares among the means of the three variations of the single experimental factor A.

3. *The sum of squares among means of rows (blocks):* among the means of the triads of Table 11.5.

This source of variation is attributable to differences among the mean measures of the 5 blocks. The mean of each such triad of measurements is given at the right of the body of Table 11.5. They range from 2 to 6 and in order of size (as if there might be a high correlation between these schematic results for the dependent variable of the experiment and the matching variable used initially to establish the 15 triads). The sum of squares among blocks is found by exactly the same method used to find the sum of squares among the subsample means of the experimental factor. Only the notation and consequently the computations are different.

Sum of Squares Among Row Means:

$$SS_r = \sum^r \frac{(\sum X_{i.})^2}{n_i} - \frac{(\sum X)^2}{n} \qquad (11.24)$$

When n_i's are equal, the arithmetic can be simplified as before:

$$SS_r = \frac{1}{n_i} \sum^r (\sum X_{i.})^2 - \frac{(\sum X)^2}{n} \qquad (11.24a)$$

and therefore for the data of Table 11.5,

$$SS_r = \frac{18^2 + 15^2 + 12^2 + 9^2 + 6^2}{3} - \frac{(60)^2}{15} = 270 - 240 = 30$$

4. *The sum of squares of the residual variations* for an estimate of the error variance, either by subtraction (as in Eq. 11.25) or by computation as in Table 11.7.

By subtraction, the sum of squares for the residual variation is as follows:

$$SS_{\text{res}} = SS - SS_c - SS_r = 44 - 10 - 30 = 4 \qquad (11.25)$$

The accuracy of this sum of squares so easily obtained by subtraction obviously depends on the accuracy of SS, SS_c, and SS_r. Either the original computations should therefore be carefully rechecked or (better) an independent calculation of the residual sum of squares should be made. That this procedure would be quite tedious for many measures is evident from the computations in Table 11.7 for the 15 measures of Table 11.5. As indicated, the square of the residual variations is equal to the following:

Sum of Squares of Residual Variations:

$$SS_{\text{res}} = \overset{cr}{\sum} (X_{ij} - \overline{X}_{i.} - \overline{X}_{.j} + \overline{X})^2 \qquad (11.26)$$

**Table 11.7. Computation of the Residual Sum
of Squares for the Data of Table 11.5**

$$SS_{\text{res}} = \overset{cr}{\sum} (X_{ij} - \overline{X}_{i.} - \overline{X}_{.j} + \overline{X})^2 = 4$$

Experimental Group		
Block 1		X_{res}^2
	A_1	$= (5 - 6 - 3 + 4)^2 = 0$
	A_2	$= (6 - 6 - 4 + 4)^2 = 0$
	A_3	$= (7 - 6 - 5 + 4)^2 = 0$
Block 2		
	A_1	$= (4 - 5 - 3 + 4)^2 = 0$
	A_2	$= (5 - 5 - 4 + 4)^2 = 0$
	A_3	$= (6 - 5 - 5 + 4)^2 = 0$
Block 3		
	A_1	$= (3 - 4 - 3 + 4)^2 = 0$
	A_2	$= (4 - 4 - 4 + 4)^2 = 0$
	A_3	$= (5 - 4 - 5 + 4)^2 = 0$
Block 4		
	A_1	$= (1 - 3 - 3 + 4)^2 = 1$
	A_2	$= (3 - 3 - 4 + 4)^2 = 0$
	A_3	$= (5 - 3 - 5 + 4)^2 = 1$
Block 5		
	A_1	$= (2 - 2 - 3 + 4)^2 = 1$
	A_2	$= (2 - 2 - 4 + 4)^2 = 0$
	A_3	$= (2 - 2 - 5 + 4)^2 = 1$
	(Check) $\sum = 4$	

Analysis of Variance for Experimental Effects

Two null hypotheses will be tested, one for equal parameter means among experimental groups (Table 11.8) and the other for zero interaction (Table 11.9).

The degrees of freedom for the independent estimate of population variance based on the differences among the means of the rows (blocks) are equal to one less the number of row means: $r - 1 = 5 - 1 = 4$. The d.f.'s for the estimation of population variance based on the sum of squares of the residual variation is equal to $(r - 1)(c - 1)$, one less the number of row means times one less the number of column means. For the data of Table 11.5, $(r - 1)(c - 1) = 4 \times 2 = 8$ d.f.'s.

The analysis of variance is presented in Table 11.8. With the variation among the means of the blocks eliminated from the error variance, the significance of the mean differences of the three variations on the experimental factor A is marked by an $F = 10$. With 2 and 8 d.f.'s, the critical value of F at $F_{.95}$ is 4.46. Therefore the decision is made to reject the null hypothesis.

Table 11.8. Analysis of Variance for Differences Among Means of Experimental Groups

(Data of Table 11.5)

Source of Variation	SS	d.f.	Mean Squares (Variance Estimates)	F
Between Experimental Groups (columns)	10	2	5	10.0
Between Blocks (triads of rows)	30	4	7.5	
Residual	4	8	.50	
Total (check)	44	14		

$$F_{.95} \text{ for 2 and 8 d.f.'s } = 4.46; \quad (F_{.99} = 8.65)$$

$$P(F \geq 10) < .01$$

$$F = \frac{SS_r}{SS_{res}} = \frac{7.5}{.5} = 15; \quad F_{.95} \text{ for 4 and 8 d.f. s } = 3.84; \quad (F_{.999} = 14.39)$$

The greater power of the randomized block design over the randomized group design should now be clear. With exactly the same set of measures, but with the variations among the block means eliminated from the estimate of the error variance, the null hypothesis that all experimental groups have the same population mean is now rejected.

Significance Test for Interaction

The extent and direction of the experimental effects for the data of Table 11.5 are nearly alike for each block. If they were all patterned the same, this would signify *no interaction* effects of the three variations of the experimental factor and the matched triads on the measures of the dependent variable in the body of the table. Only the 5th block shows no "experimental effect," but the 4th block shows a somewhat accentuated effect compared with the 1st, 2nd, and 3rd blocks.

The randomized block, matched group design assumes that the variations of an experimental factor will have similar effects from block to block. The members within each block are *by design* relatively homogeneous in the functions on which they are matched. The matching variable should (if it is to be of any use) have a fairly high correlation with the dependent variable. Otherwise, the possible improvement over the randomized group design may not occur. This requirement is analogous to that in survey research in which stratification is employed: To be useful, the stratifying criteria or factors need to correlate with the behavior to be studied (the dependent variable). That it is satisfied for the fictional data of Table 11.5 is evident from the mean results of the blocks. They correlate perfectly with the order set up by the matching variable, viz., a mean of 6 for the 1st triad, 5 for the 2nd, 4 for the 3rd, 3 for the 4th, and 2 for the 5th.

Research data do not ordinarily lend themselves to such an easy interpretation about interaction, such that it can be made from an inspection of the data as in Table 11.5. Here it is clear that there is very little interaction, and consequently the effects of the experimental variations of factor A can be generalized, at least over the range of the matching variable. In other words, those in the high echelons (triads in this case) of the matching variable are affected by the experimental variations in about the same way as those in the low echelons of the matching variable.

In order to test for interaction by analysis of variance, the residual sum of squares needs to be partitioned into two components; interaction and the remainder sum of squares.

Residual Sum of Squares = Interaction SS + Remainder SS

The Sum of Squares for Interaction:

$$SS_{\text{Interact}} = \frac{[\sum^c \sum^r (X_{ij})(\overline{X}_r - \overline{X})(\overline{X}_c - \overline{X})]^2}{\sum^c (\overline{X}_c - \overline{X})^2 \sum^r (\overline{X}_r - \overline{X})^2} \qquad (11.27)$$

The necessary computations for this sum of squares for interaction are presented in Table 11.9. The interaction sum of squares for the data of Table 11.5 is equal to .20. With one d.f., the analysis of variance for the significance of the possible differential effects on the measures of the matched triads of the three variations of the experimental factor is seen to result in an F of less than 1.0:

$$F = \frac{.20}{.54} = .37$$

where .54 is the error variance based on the remainder sum of squares and 7 d.f.'s.

Remainder Sum of Squares (SS$_{rem}$):

$$SS_{rem} = SS_{res} - SS_{Interact} \tag{11.28}$$

$$SS_{rem} = 4.0 - .20 = 3.8$$

Had the interaction effect been *significant*, this would have meant that the effects of the three variations of the experimental factor A on the dependent variable differed among the various matched triads of persons. This in turn would have limited the generality of the effects of the experimental variable, since this would have meant that variation A_1 would affect some subjects one way and other subjects another; likewise for variation A_2, and also for A_3. If the experimental variable had been three color variations, such as red, blue-green, and amber, and the dependent variable had been a measure of visual acuity, then *significant interaction* would have meant that some triads of subjects have sharper vision with one color, others with another color, etc. But on *average* for the group of subject's as a whole, the effects of the three experimental variations would nevertheless be significant (as indicated by the analysis of variance in Table 11.8).

When the test for interaction yields a result that does not warrant a decision to reject the null hypothesis of *zero interaction*, then the *residual* rather than the *remainder* sum of squares will ordinarily give a *more sensitive* measure of error variance in that it may be less in magnitude because of the additional degree of freedom. Thus, for the data of Table 11.8, the estimate of error variance from the residual mean square was .50 with 8 d.f.'s, whereas the estimate of error variance from the remainder mean square in Table 11.9 was slightly larger, being .54 and with one less d.f., viz., 7.

When the analysis of variance significance test for interaction indicates that its null hypothesis is tenable (as with the results in Table 11.9), and when analysis of variance has indicated that the null hypothesis for no experimental effects is rejectable (as in Table 11.8), then the generality of the experimental effects is at least as broad as the nature of the sample as a whole.

**Table 11.9.   Sum of Squares and Analysis of Variance for
Interaction of Experimental Effects with Matched Groups**
(Data from Table 11.5)

$$SS_{\substack{\text{Interact} \\ \text{(with 1 d.f.)}}} = \frac{[\sum\limits^{c}\sum\limits^{r}(X_{ij})(\overline{X}_r - \overline{X})(\overline{X}_c - \overline{X})]^2}{\sum\limits^{c}(\overline{X}_c - \overline{X})^2 \sum\limits^{r}(\overline{X}_r - \overline{X})^2} = \frac{2^2}{(2)(10)} = .20$$

COMPUTATIONS FOR NUMERATOR OF SS_{Interact}

For Variations of Experimental Factor A

Blocks	A_1	A_2	A_3	Σ
1	$5(-1)(2)$	$6(0)(2)$	$7(1)(2)$	4
2	$4(-1)(1)$	$5(0)(1)$	$6(1)(1)$	2
3	$3(-1)(0)$	$4(0)(0)$	$5(1)(0)$	0
4	$1(-1)(-1)$	$3(0)(-1)$	$5(1)(-1)$	-4
5	$2(-1)(-2)$	$2(0)(-2)$	$2(1)(-2)$	0
Σ_c	-9	0	11	$\Sigma = 2$

COMPUTATION FOR DENOMINATOR OF SS_{Interact}

$$\sum^{c}(\overline{X}_c - \overline{X})^2 = (-1)^2 + (0)^2 + (1)^2 = 2$$

$$\sum^{r}(\overline{X}_r - \overline{X})^2 = (2)^2 + (1)^2 + (0)^2 + (1)^2 + (2)^2 = 10$$

ANALYSIS OF VARIANCE

Source of Variation	SS	d.f.	Variance Estimate	F
Interaction	.20	1	.20	.37
Remainder	3.80	7	.54	
Residual (Table 11.7)	4.00	8		

Significance of Mean Differences
Among the Matched Triads (Blocks)

Analysis of variance for differences among the means of the matched triads of persons is obviously not a significance test of an experimental result. Hence this test is usually not made. If $F = s_r^2/s_{\text{res}}^2$ is significantly large, as it is in Table 11.8 with $F = 15$ and $F_{.999}$ for 4 and 8 d.f.'s equal to 14.39, the implication is clear that individual differences *among* triads are significantly greater than individual differences within triads, as they should be if the matching procedure was effective.

ANALYSIS OF VARIANCE FOR A SIMPLE FACTORIAL DESIGN

One of the simplest factorial designs is presented in Table 11.10. Each of the six subsamples represents a random assignment of n_j sampling units (subjects); hence the randomized group design is employed in this factorial design. The total sample of $n = n_j k = 30$, and thus there are five subjects in each subsample. The six subsamples are identified as follows:

$$A_1 B_1, \quad A_2 B_1, \quad A_3 B_1, \quad A_2 B_1, \quad A_2 B_2, \quad \text{and} \quad A_3 B_2$$

where A and B are the independent variables in an experiment in which the A factor is set up with three variations and the B factor with two variations. The five measures for each of the six subsamples in Table 11.10 are the measures of the dependent variable.

Three hypotheses will be tested as follows:

1. H_0: $\mu_{A_1} = \mu_{A_2} = \mu_{A_3} = \mu$ (for A factor effects)   (11.29)

2. H_0: $\mu_{B_1} = \mu_{B_2} = \mu$ (for B factor effects)   (11.30)

3. H_0: $\mu_{AB} - \mu_A - \mu_B + \mu = 0$ (for AB interaction effects)   (11.31)

Computation of the Sum of Squares

The sums of squares are calculated as before except that the sum of squares for interaction will be obtained by subtraction and its accuracy will be checked against the sum of squares for all six experimental variations considered independently of the two experimental factors.

1. Total Sum of Squares:

$$SS = 7914 - \frac{455^2}{30} = 7914 - 7053 = 861 \qquad [11.16]$$

2. Sum of Squares for Error Variance (Within-Groups):

$$SS_w = SS_{A_1 B_1} + SS_{A_2 B_1} + SS_{A_3 B_1} + SS_{A_1 B_2} + SS_{A_2 B_2} + SS_{A_3 B_2}$$

$$= \left[431 - \frac{45^2}{5} \right] + \left[996 - \frac{70^2}{5} \right] + \left[1859 - \frac{95^2}{5} \right] \qquad (11.32)$$

$$+ \left[639 - \frac{55^2}{5} \right] + \left[1330 - \frac{80^2}{5} \right] + \left[2659 - \frac{115^2}{5} \right] = 194$$

3. Sum of Squares for Differences Among Means of Factor A:

$$SS_A = \frac{100^2 + 150^2 + 210^2}{10} - \frac{460^2}{30} = 7660 - 7053 = 607$$

4. Sum of Squares for Differences Between Means of Factor B:

$$SS_B = \frac{210^2 + 250^2}{15} - \frac{460^2}{30} = 7107 - 7053 = 54$$

Table 11.10. Distributions of Measures for a Simple Factorial Design

| | Experimental Factor A | | | | | Squares | | |
	A_1	A_2	A_3	Σ_r	$\overline{X}_r$	$A_1{}^2$	$A_2{}^2$	$A_3{}^2$
Experimental Factor B_1	11	16	25	52	17.3	121	256	625
	11	15	19	45	15 0	121	225	361
	10	15	18	43	14.3	100	225	324
	8	13	18	39	13.0	64	169	324
	5	11	15	31	10.3	25	121	225
$\overset{c}{\Sigma}$	45	70	95	210		431	996	1859
$\overline{X}_c$	9	14	19					

$\overline{X}_{AB_1} = 14\ 0$

	A_1	A_2	A_3	Σ_r	$\overline{X}_r$	$A_1{}^2$	$A_2{}^2$	$A_3{}^2$
Experimental Factor B_2	16	20	25	61	20.3	256	400	625
	11	19	24	54	18.0	121	361	576
	10	16	23	49	16.3	100	256	529
	9	13	23	45	15.0	81	169	529
	9	12	20	41	13.7	81	144	400
$\overset{c}{\Sigma}$	55	80	115	250		639	1330	2659
$\overline{X}_c$	11	16	23					

$\overline{X}_{A_1B} = 10 \qquad \overline{X}_{A_2B} = 15 \qquad \overline{X}_{A_3B} = 21 \qquad \overline{X}_{AB_2} = 16.7$

Total:
$\sum\sum X = 45 + 70 + 95 + 55 + 80 + 115 = 460$
$\sum\sum X^2 = 431 + 996 + 1859 + 639 + 1330 + 2659 = 7914$

$\overline{X} = 460/30 = 15.3$

Factor A: $\sum\sum X = (45 + 55) + (70 + 80) + (95 + 115) = 100 + 150 + 210 = 460$
$\overline{X}_A = 100/10,\ 150/10,\ \text{and } 210/10 = 10,\ 15,\ \text{and } 21$

Factor B: $\sum\sum X = (45 + 70 + 95) + (55 + 80 + 115) = 210 + 250 = 460$
$\overline{X}_B = 210/15 \text{ and } 250/15 = 14 \text{ and } 16.7$

5. Sum of Squares for Interaction of A and B (by Subtraction):

$$SS_{AB} = SS - SS_w - SS_A - SS_B \qquad (11.33)$$
$$= 861 - 194 - 607 - 54 = 6$$

6. Check Sum of Squares:

$$SS_A + SS_B + SS_{AB} = SS_a \qquad (11.34)$$

where SS_a is the sum of squares among means irrespective of the A and B factors (Formula 11.17a):

$$SS_a = \frac{45^2 + 70^2 + 95^2 + 55^2 + 80^2 + 115^2}{5} - \frac{460^2}{30}$$
$$= 7720 - 7053 = 667$$
$$\text{Check: } 607 + 54 + 6 = 667$$

Thus the value of the sum of squares of the three experimental components checks with the value of the sums of squares among all means considered as if they were variations on a single factor (as in the randomized group design).

Analysis of Variance for Significance of Differences

The analysis of variance is summarized in Table 11.11. F is 37.5 for the significance test of the differences among the means of the A factor. By Table F, for 2 and 24 d.f.'s, $F_{.999} = 9.34$. Therefore the first null hypothesis may be rejected with considerable confidence, and it is reasonable to ascribe *significant effects* to the experimental variations of the A factor.

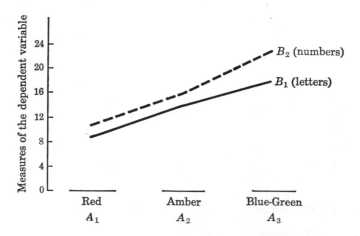

Fig. 11.2. Illustration of Insignificant Interaction in a Simple Factorial Design

(Data of Table 11.10)

Table 11.11. Comparison of Means and Analysis of Variance for Experimental Effects and Interaction

	Means of Subsamples			Means of Experimental Factor B
	A_1	A_2	A_3	
B_1	9	14	19	14.0
B_2	11	16	23	16.7
Means of Experimental Factor A	10	15	21	$\overline{X} = 15.3$

Analysis of Variance				
Source of Variation	SS	d.f.	Estimates of Variance	F
Experimental Factor A	607	2	303.5	37.5
Experimental Factor B	54	1	54.0	6.7
Interaction A and B	6	2	3.0	.4
Error (Within-Groups)	194	24	8.1	
Total (check)	861	29		

As for the B factor, F is equal to 6.7 for 1 and 24 d.f.'s. The critical value for *alpha* of .05 is $F_{.95}$ of 4.26. Therefore the second null hypothesis is also rejected with confidence although with not "so much" confidence perhaps as accompanied the rejection of the first null hypothesis. Thus B may also be considered a *significant factor* inasmuch as its two experimental variations are inferred to manifest significant effects.

The third hypothesis cannot be rejected. F is less than 1.0. In other words, there are no significant interaction effects of the experimental factors on the dependent variable. For the data of Table 11.10, the F test for interaction is hardly needed, since a comparison of the mean results in Fig. 11.2 shows practically no differential effects of the A factor variations with the B factor variations. If the interaction were exactly zero, the difference between the means of B_1 and B_2 on the A_1 variation would be the same as the differences between the means of B_1 and B_2 on the A_2 and the A_3 variations.

The less significant the interaction effect, the more generalized the significance of the experimental factors. This is the case because, with no significant interaction effects, the experimental effects of factor A can be generalized over factor B, and vice versa, the experimental effects of factor B can be generalized over A independently of its three variations.

Significant Interaction

Had the results for interaction been as illustrated in Fig. 11.3, with the hypothesis for zero interaction rejectable, then broad generalizations for each experimental factor could not be made. If, for example, the dependent variable were visual acuity, if factor A were three colors (red, amber, and blue-green), and if factor B were letter material versus number material, as in Figure 11.2,

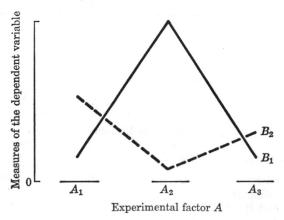

Fig. 11.3.   Illustration of Possibly Significant Interaction in a Simple Factorial Design

Note that this "scale" is purely schematic; the experimental variations of A are usually fixed (hence discrete) rather than continuous (with equal intervals).

the mean results plotted in Fig. 11.3 would indicate that letters show up much better in amber than in red or blue-green and that figures show up better in red.

Graphs of this kind for the data of experimental psychology were made long before the method of analysis of variance was invented. The great contribution to research of the marriage of experimental design and analysis of variance stems from the fact that the *significance* of experimental variations of experimental factors, and their possible interaction, can be tested and decisions can be made as to whether effects observed are most likely a matter of random variations from the null hypotheses tested or whether and how the effects of experimental design can be inferred as also entering into the results.

ANALYSIS OF COVARIANCE

An examination of a volume such as *Experimental Designs* by Cochran and Cox (1957) will show very clearly that this chapter is only an introduction to the area designated by its title. This is the intent. It is hoped that the serious student, having sampled these "tools of the trade," will want more. If he is going to be a researcher, he will need more.

Perhaps the wealth of experimental designs and techniques of statistical analysis that are the student's for the learning can be best exemplified by pointing to methods involving *analysis of covariance*. The covariance of a bivariate distribution is the mean of the crossproducts of the deviations:

$$Covariance = \frac{\sum(xy)}{n'} \tag{11.35}$$

Analysis of covariance is useful in research when random samples from different populations are such that they cannot possibly be matched. Thus, such samples of sexagenarians doubtless cannot be matched in speed of motor reactions with random samples of teen-agers. It is not that 25 such oldsters might not be found to pair off with 25 youngsters; rather, it is the case that random samples of their respective populations cannot be matched. For a function such as motor speed, therefore, the researcher has to deal with unmatchables.

Unmatchables and Intact Groups

The impossibility of matching *unmatchables* does not necessarily present a hopeless situation for research. On the contrary, something quite significant can often be done about it. An unmatchable factor related to age differences or to *state of origin* differences, for example, can be taken into account when and if relevant information, analogous to the information of a matching variable, is available for random samples of different populations or for the members of intact groups. In the latter instance, when random sampling is presumably out of the question, any generalizations from the results of an experimental investigation would need to be restricted to the intact groups.

In a learning experiment on the classroom effects of *praise* vs. *reprimand*, for example, it is possible to take into account I.Q. differences of two or more populations, possibly unmatchable, with different states of origin, such as the New York State born, the Puerto Rican born, and the Alabama born. That is to say, the researcher can determine whether significant mean differences from a *dependent variable* such as *speed of learning* simple tasks, under the variable conditions of praise and reprimand, are still significant *after* the several groups have had removed the possible effects of different I.Q. levels as a differentiating influence on the dependent variable. The differential effectiveness of praise and reprimand on learning may be more a function of I.Q. level than of state of origin.

Just as analysis of variance is developed from the partitioning of the squared deviations of single variables into two or more component parts, analysis of covariance is based on a partitioning of the sum of the crossproducts (xy) of bivariates into two or more components. Thus, most simply, the overall crossproducts from the overall means may be partitioned into (1) the crossproducts from the means of the measures of the respective bivariate subsamples, and (2) the crossproducts of the means of the bivariate subsamples from the overall means. Such partitioning into components makes possible by *regression estimation* (Chapter 5) to *determine how much* of the difference among the means of the dependent variable (speed of learning) may be attributed to the initial differences of a related variable (I.Q.). The means of the dependent variable can be adjusted or corrected accordingly, of course subject to errors characteristic of regression estimates. The null hypothesis of a common parameter mean can then be tested with the effects of the unmatchable variable thus taken into account.

McNemar (1960) has underscored the great usefulness of the covariance method to psychology and the behavioral sciences:*

The co-variance adjustment technique could be the most useful of all statistical methods. . . . It is a "natural" for the many situations where experimental control of variables is either not feasible or impossible. If the restrained use of analysis of variance has been a boon to certain laboratory experimentation, as I believe it has, the co-variance method can be a real godsend to those in social, child, clinical and educational psychology where frequent use must be made of intact groups.

---

*The interested student will find the development and application of the method of covariance described in McNemar (1955) and Walker and Lev (1953).

CHAPTER 12

SUMMARY: PARAMETRIC VS. DISTRIBUTION-FREE METHODS

Area of the Distinction: Significance Testing · Populations vs. Probability Models

Null and *Delta* Hypotheses for a Proportion · Null Hypothesis for Frequencies of Two Classes · Null Hypothesis for Frequencies of k Classes · Null Hypothesis for Goodness of Fit · Null and *Delta* Hypotheses for a Mean

Null and *Delta* Hypotheses for Difference Between Proportions · Median Test by Chi-Square · Versatility of the Median Test by Chi-Square · Mann-Whitney U Test · Expected Sum of Ranks · The U Statistic · z Deviate Test of Significance for U · Parametric Methods

Sign Test for Countables · Median Test by Chi-Square · Chi-Square for Differences Between Proportions of Related Samples · Wilcoxon Test of Signed-Ranks for Differences Between Matched Pairs · Comparison of Sign Test with Signed-Rank Test · Parametric Methods

Median Test by Chi-Square for k Groups · Kruskal-Wallis H Test of Ranks for k Independent Samples · Friedman's Rank Test by Chi-Square for k Related Samples · Relation of χ_r^2 to W · Parametric Methods ·

*It is always good
When a man has two irons in the fire.*

Beaumont and Fletcher

THE distinction between parametric and distribution-free (nonparametric) methods of inferential statistics was pointed to in the first chapter. In this final chapter, methods of each of these two categories that have been developed in the preceding chapters will be so identified, and several useful distribution-free methods not yet described will be presented.

The behavioral sciences have made increasing reference to distribution-free methods since World War II. This is because many of the populations of social psychology, sociology, and cultural anthropology appear not to fit in with the classical (over the past fourscore years) picture of normal variation. The normal probability model as a description of the distributions of various characteristics has evidently worked well with the data of the physical and biological sciences, including biopsychology. But as soon as the threshold of social psychology is crossed and the researcher extends his inquiries into the domains of the behavioral sciences, the observed distributions of measurables often appear contradictory to normal variation. Oftentimes the data themselves are those of countables and rankables whose populations are not hypothesized as normally distributed because of their very nature: two-class or multiclass populations in the case of enumeration statistics, and ordinal populations for rank statistics.

Among the "measurables" of the behavioral sciences there are distributions of the results of attitude and opinion studies. Very often results on such variables tend to distribute toward polar opposites rather than toward a unimodal bellshaped type of distribution. People's attitudes toward live issues apparently are inclined to channel themselves from middle-of-the-road or neutral positions toward strong feelings for or against. In fact the maintenance of a *neutral* position is often suspect, not only in international relations but also in interpersonal relations.

Area of the Distinction: Significance Testing

The distribution-free methods have been developed and used mainly for significance testing. Parametric methods are, of course, used for both aspects of sampling-inferential statistics, viz., the estimation of parameters and the testing of hypotheses. But some distribution-free methods are also used in parameter estimation, as, for example, the estimation of proportions (Chapter 8). Their estimation is obviously not conditional on normally distributed populations, since such statistics may come from two-class populations whose parameters are P and not-P. Hence the use of the word "nonparametric" to describe statistical techniques of this kind may be misleading; "distribution-free" is to be preferred. As a matter of even better nomenclature, it will be seen shortly that *population-distribution-free* may be more descriptive of these methods.

In descriptive statistics no distinction is ordinarily made between parametric and distribution-free methods. However, since the application of the methods of sampling-inferential statistics depends on the organization and summarization of statistical data by methods developed in Chapters 2 through 6, it is relevant to point to the following twofold distinction:

1. Descriptive statistics developed for COUNTABLES AND RANKABLES are those pertinent to the distribution-free methods: frequencies (counts), proportions, percentages, medians and other centile ranks, means and variances of ranks, and rank difference correlation.
2. Descriptive statistics developed for MEASURABLES are most pertinent to the parametric methods: means, variances, standard deviations, and Pearson r correlations.

Distribution-free methods have long been used for significance testing of the data of countables and rankables. Pearson developed chi-square for the data of countables at the turn of this century, and Spearman at about the same time developed rank difference correlation for bivariates with ordinal distributions.

The *semantic distinction* is fairly modern and has been emphasized in recent years especially for those situations in which the variables are presumably measurables but somewhat unsatisfactory measurables from the point of view of the normal distribution assumption. The "modern" distribution-free techniques have thus been developed as substitutes for some parametric methods of significance testing. Sign tests or rank tests of significance are used free of the condition or requirement of normally distributed populations of measurements.

Populations vs. Probability Models

Rather than have all distribution-free methods segregated into a single section of this book, the intent has been to include them as needed and as relevant to more inclusive categories such as sampling-inferential statistics, and in particular, to that of significance testing. Chapters 7 through 11 have been concerned with the development and application of sampling-inferential statistics for the three general classes of statistical data, viz., countables, rankables, and measurables. Chapter 7 laid the foundation in probability theory for some of the stochastic models (chance mechanisms) essential to inferential statistics. The two models presented in that chapter were the Bernoulli binomial and the Laplace-Gaussian curve of error. Two subsequent models essential to significance testing were the probability distribution of the chi-square statistic (Chapter 9) and those of the F statistic (Chapters 10 and 11), including the t statistics (which were seen to be the square root of F when the numerator of the variance ratio has only one d.f.).

All these probability models are essential to the estimation or calculation of random variation in the testing of null hypotheses. Three of them are used with both parametric and distribution-free methods: the binomial, chi-square and the normal probability. The fourth, F (and t), is based on the assumption of normally distributed populations and hence is generally used with the parametric methods of t and analysis of variance.

The distinction between the distributions of populations and sampling distributions is sometimes confused. The probability models of sampling-inferential statistics are hypothesized descriptions of the expected sampling variation. They are the sampling distributions. Distribution-free methods for significance testing are just as dependent on these hypothesized models as are the parametric methods. Both methods require *probability sampling* with the *randomization* of selections; otherwise, as emphasized at the end of Chapter 7, these probability models cannot be legitimately or safely hypothesized, and thus significance testing is precluded.

The student should therefore mark well what distributions the distribution-free methods are really free of: They are free of assumptions about the form and characteristics of population distributions. They are not free of an assumption about the expected nature of sampling variation. Under some circumstances, usually of large samples, the expected variation is that of the normal probability model; as, for example, in the significance testing of differences between sample results by the Mann-Whitney test, presented later in this chapter. Even for small random samples of about ten or more, it was shown on p. 167 that when $P = .50$, its binomial discrete sampling distribution may be closely approximated by the normal probability model.

On the other hand, parametric statistics such as means are not bound absolutely to the assumption of normally distributed populations. Mean statistics of large samples drawn randomly from very large skewed populations may nevertheless have a probability model of sampling variation closely approximated by the normal curve of error. (See Theorem II, p. 176.)

These considerations are thus made to emphasize that all methods for significance testing, whether parametric or distribution-free, have to be identified with a probability model of a sampling distribution appropriate to the statistic and size of sample. The general condition for their safe use in significance testing is that of RANDOMIZATION. This requirement of randomization for inferential statistics has no favorites: It is just as essential to the use of probability models in distribution-free methods as in the parametric ones.

SUMMARY OF METHODS OF SIGNIFICANCE TESTING FOR VARIOUS RESEARCH PROBLEMS

Methods developed in earlier chapters, whether parametric or distribution-free, will be identified and referred to by page number. The several new methods to be presented in this chapter will be introduced as needed. The frame of reference will be the *type of problem* requiring a significance test, as follows:

1. Single sample results of univariates.
2. Differences between results of two independent samples.
3. Differences between results of two paired or related samples.
4. Differences for results of more than two independent samples.
5. Differences for results of more than two related samples.
6. Correlation of bivariates.

SIGNIFICANCE TESTS FOR SINGLE SAMPLE RESULTS OF UNIVARIATES

Both distribution-free and parametric methods for significance testing of null hypotheses relevant to single sample problems were presented for the data of countables (Chapter 9) and of measurables (Chapter 10). Most of these methods are useful to survey research as well as experimental research. *Delta* hypotheses, which include the null hypothesis, were also presented.

Null and *Delta* Hypotheses for a Proportion

$$H_0: P = (1 - P) = .50 \qquad (12.1)$$

$$H_\Delta: P \geq .50 \quad \text{or} \quad \leq .50 \qquad (12.1a)$$

These are the hypotheses for two-class countables, such as YES OR NO, LIKE or DISLIKE, APPROVE, or DISAPPROVE. The probability models for these distribution-free tests vary with n, the size of the sample:

1. Very small samples: the exact distribution of the binomial is used (p. 234).

2. For sample sizes of $10 > n < 20$, the z deviate, corrected for continuity, is used with the normal probability model (pp. 167 and 234).
3. For samples larger than 20, the z deviate is used without the need for continuity correction (p. 233).
4. When samples are drawn from finite populations and the sampling fraction is greater than $1/20$ (5%), then the finite multiplier is used (p. 233).

Null Hypothesis for Frequencies of Two Classes

$$H_0: \mathbf{F}_1 = \mathbf{F}_0 \tag{12.2}$$

($\mathbf{F}$ = expected frequencies; see p. 245).

The preceding null hypothesis for a parameter proportion equal to .50, or $P = (1 - P)$, can also be stated in terms of the counts (frequencies) and tested by the following distribution-free method:

Chi-square (p. 247), when $n \geq 10$.

Null Hypothesis for Frequencies of k Classes*

$$H_0: \mathbf{F}_1 = \mathbf{F}_2 = \cdots = \mathbf{F}_k = \frac{n}{k} \tag{12.3}$$

The null hypothesis for the equiprobable distribution of frequencies of a univariate into more than two classes is tested by chi-square (p. 253). The size of the sample should be $n \geq 5k$, where k is the number of classes or categories. The method is distribution-free.

Null Hypothesis for Goodness of Fit

$$H_0: \text{an } \mathbf{F}_k \text{ distribution of frequencies for some hypothesis} \tag{12.4}$$

These are hypotheses set up for chi-square tests of the GOODNESS OF FIT of a sample result (p. 255). This distribution-free method is very useful to test the normal distribution assumption and hence the use of parametric methods, provided the number of hypothesized frequencies per class interval is about 5 or more (p. 257 ff.).

Null and *Delta* Hypotheses for a Mean

$$H_0: \mu_x = \nu \tag{12.5}$$

$$H_\Delta: \mu_x \geq \nu \text{ or } \leq \nu \tag{12.5a}$$

---

*While reading proof on this chapter, the author received a journal with an article by Alphonse Chapanis (1962) on an exact test of significance for proportions of small samples divided into more than two classes. This multinomial test becomes the usual exact test for a binomial when there are only the two classes Q and P. Chapanis shows some striking discrepancies between the exact test and chi-square (both uncorrected and corrected for continuity) for a null hypothesis of a multinomial of three classes, $H_0: Q_1 = P_1 = O_1$, when n is only 12.

(where x refers to the population of the sample and v refers to some hypothesized parameter value).

Hypotheses about the means of single samples are not very plentiful because the measurables of psychology and the behavioral sciences rarely have specific numerics of significance. One exception is the hypothesized parameter mean I.Q. of 100:

1. A normal z deviate test when $n \geq 30$ (p. 279 ff.).
2. A t test when $n \leq 30$ (pp. 284 ff.).

The latter test is definitely parametric. The former is usually considered so inasmuch as the sampling distributions of means of large samples approximate the normal probability model even though the parent populations of measurements may be skewed.

SIGNIFICANCE TESTS FOR DIFFERENCES BETWEEN TWO INDEPENDENT SAMPLES

The null hypothesis for this class of problems is that the difference between two parameter distributions, or measures thereof, is zero. These tests are indispensable to experimental research and are also used in survey research. *Delta*, or directional hypotheses, are also sometimes pertinent.

Null and *Delta* Hypotheses for Difference Between Proportions

$$H_0: P_1 - P_2 = 0 \tag{12.6}$$

$$H_\Delta: P_1 - P_2 \leq 0, \quad \text{or} \quad \geq 0 \tag{12.6a}$$

A distribution-free method was presented (pp. 263 ff.) for testing this null hypothesis of no difference between parameter proportions of two independent samples. It takes the form of a normal z deviate test and is satisfactory when the product of the smaller sample proportion and the smaller n is at least 5.

Median Test by Chi-Square

$$H_0: \text{MDN}_1 - \text{MDN}_2 = 0 \tag{12.7}$$

This is a distribution-free method not presented earlier. It is very useful for the data of measurables whose populations may be suspect, i.e., not normally distributed. The measurables are *ordered* into either one of two intervals: *above* the median of the combined sample results or *below* the median. When $n_1 + n_2 \geq 20$, the significance of the difference between two sample results (in effect, the differences between their medians) may be tested by chi-square. When, however, there are less than five hypothesized frequencies in two or more cells of the 2 by 2 crosstabulation of the data, *Fisher's exact test* (p. 272 ff.) should be used.

The median test is illustrated with the data of Table 12.1, which comprises the survival data of 249 premature infants (Table 6.8). The significance test is a test for the *independence of birth weight and survival.* The median birth weight of all 249 prematures is first calculated. For the distribution of Table 6.8, the median is 1450 grams, as follows:

$$\text{mdn} = 1400 + \frac{124.5 - 116}{17} \, 100 = 1450 \text{ grams}$$

Since the division of the frequencies at C_{50} in the interval of the median (1400 to 1499.9 grams) is exactly half, the respective frequencies in this interval of the separate distributions are divided in the same proportions, half to the *above* class and half to the class *below* the median of the whole. [Note that with small samples, the data for the combined groups are usually set up as an *array* (in order of size); the median is taken as equal to the value of the midmeasure when $n_1 + n_2$ is odd, and as the average of the two middle measures when $n_1 + n_2$ is even. The data of large samples may also be *arrayed* instead of tabulated into class intervals, as in Table 6.8.]

Chi-square may be computed as in Table 6.5, where the hypothesized frequencies were set up for each cell and the series of ratio values obtained, cell by cell. Or the following reshuffling of the arithmetic may be employed when there are the four cells of a 2 by 2 crosstabulation:

Chi-Square for a 2 by 2 Table:

$$\chi^2 = \frac{n'(bc - ad)^2}{(a + c)(b + d)(a + b)(c + d)} \tag{12.8}$$

For the Data of Table 12.1:

$$\chi^2 = \frac{249[(110)(52) - (15)(72)]^2}{(67)(182)(125)(124)} = 28.4$$

When n' is not large, *Yates' correction* (p. 272) may be used unless Fisher's exact test is called for. Applied to Formula 12.8, this correction consists in the subtraction of $\frac{1}{2}$ of n' from the *absolute* value of $(bc - ad)$:

$$\chi^2 = \frac{n' \left(|bc - ad| - \dfrac{n'}{2} \right)^2}{(a + c)(b + d)(a + b)(c + d)} \tag{12.9}$$

where the vertical bars indicate that the absolute value (without regard to sign) of $bc - ad$ is to be used.

Chi-square for the median test is 28.4, and since $\chi^2_{.999} = 10.8$ for one d.f., survival is evidently not independent of birth weight, and the null hypothesis of equal medians is therefore rejected with confidence. Among

**Table 12.1. The Median Test by Chi-Square
for the Significance of Median Differences of
Independent Samples**
(Data of Table 6.8)

| | SURVIVAL | | |
	Expired	Survived	n_r
Above Median (mdn = 1450 grams)	a 15	b 110	125
Below Median	c 52	d 72	124
n_c	67	182	$n' = 249$

$$\chi^2 = \frac{249[(110)(52) - [(15)(72)]^2}{(67)(182)(125)(124)} = 28.4$$

$$P(\chi^2 \geq 28.4) < .001$$

prematures, those who survive have a higher median birth weight than those who expire.

This result is in harmony with that obtained with the parametric method for the difference between the means of these two groups on p. 297. It will be recalled that t was not employed with these data because the requirement of homogeneity of variance was not satisfied; since n was large a z deviate significance test was made. On the assumption that the *sampling distribution* of mean differences would be normally distributed, the z of 8.5 obtained (p. 297) with the significance test for mean differences is indicative of somewhat more power than is the median test by chi-square. Thus,

By the Parametric Method:

$$z = 8.5$$

By the Distribution-Free Method:

$$z = 5.3$$

since with one d.f., $\chi^2 = 28.4$, and $\sqrt{\chi^2} = z = 5.3$.

By an *alpha* criterion as small as .001 (often used with very large samples), the critical value of z for a two-tailed test is 3.3. Therefore the null hypothesis is rejectable by a considerable margin of z deviate difference beyond the critical value of z. Inasmuch as the size of the sample is large, the scale range of expected sampling variation for the null hypothesis is relatively small. Hence, at z deviate distances of 5.3 and 8.5 from a zero difference, the theoretical probability of rejecting false null hypotheses approaches 1.0 in both cases.

Versatility of the Median Test by Chi-Square

The median test by chi-square is one of the most versatile of the various distribution-free methods for significance testing. It can be used for significance tests of differences (in effect, *median differences*) between the results of:

1. Independent samples (as in the preceding example).
2. Related or matched samples.

Furthermore, the results of three or more samples may be tested for median differences among groups, as was done by analysis of variance for *mean* differences among groups in the single factor randomized group or randomized block designs. In the case of related or matched samples, where the results (pair by pair or block by block) are compared, the significance test is sometimes called a SIGN test for which exact binomial probabilities may be used (p. 168) when n/k for chi-square is not approximately 5 or more.

The median test by chi-square as a sign test for the results of three randomized samples is developed later for the data of Table 12.5.

Mann-Whitney U Test

$$H_0: U - \frac{n_1 n_2}{2} = 0 \tag{12.10}$$

This test is a more powerful distribution-free method than is the preceding one for evaluating the significance of differences between independent samples. Although it is essentially a median test, it takes into account *more* information from the sample results. Whereas the median test by chi-square takes into account only two positions of the distributions of independent samples, viz., above and below the median, the Mann-Whitney test takes into account all ordinal positions of the two groups.

The use of the method will be described with two small random samples of birth weights drawn randomly from the original birth weight measurements of the 249 premature infants of Table 6.8. A sample of 8 cases was drawn from the 67 who expired, and a sample of 22 cases was drawn from the 182 who survived, these n's being in the same ratio as the original divisions of the two groups. The results are presented in Table 12.2.

The measures of each group are arrayed separately in order of size from highest to lowest. They are then ranked *as if* they comprised a single group, with the lowest measure receiving a rank of 1. (Note that when there are negative as well as positive values in two sets of sample data, the largest negative number is taken as the least in the series and assigned a rank of 1.) Cases of tied ranks are treated in the way described earlier for rank order correlation (p. 146). Ties may occur within groups without affecting the value of U, as at 11.5 for the survival group of Table 12.2. Ties occurring between the two groups, as at 6.5 and again at 15.5 (the latter value being the median rank of the 30 measures of the combined groups), do affect the value of U, but if there are not too many such ties, the result should not be seriously affected.

The ranks received by each group are summed to give $\sum R_1$ and $\sum R_2$ for the respective groups, $\sum R_1$ usually being taken as the lower of the two sums. For the expired group, $\sum R_1 = 52$; for the survival group, $\sum R_2 = 413$. The sum of these sums should equal the sum of all integer ranks from 1 to $(n_1 + n_2)$, or 30 for these data. (See Formula 2.3.):

$$\sum R = \frac{n(n + 1)}{2} = \frac{30(31)}{2} = 465 \qquad \text{(Check)} \qquad 52 + 413 = 465$$

Expected Sum of Ranks

If the null hypothesis were true and therefore the two groups were from the same population, their expected sum of ranks would be as follows:

$$E(\sum R_1) = \frac{n_1(n_1 + n_2 + 1)}{2} \tag{12.11}$$

$$= \frac{8(8 + 22 + 1)}{2} = 124$$

and

$$E(\sum R_2) = \frac{n_2(n_1 + n_2 + 1)}{2} \tag{12.12}$$

$$= \frac{22(8 + 22 + 1)}{2} = 341$$

The sums of their expected sum of ranks should, of course, equal $\sum R$.

$$124 + 341 = 465 \qquad \text{(Check)}$$

Needed for significance testing is a method to measure the sampling variation expected around either one of these expected sum of rank values (they are complementary). When samples are small (either n less than 8), tables of exact probabilities for the U statistic by Mann and Whitney (1947) are available in Table J of the Appendix. When both n_1 and n_2 are equal to or larger than 8, the normal z deviate may be used.

The U Statistic

This statistic is calculated as follows:

$$U_1 = n_1 n_2 + \frac{n_1(n_1 + 1)}{2} - \sum R_1 \tag{12.13}$$

where $\sum R_1$ is the sum of ranks of the n_1 group. It is equal to 52 for the data of Table 12.2.

For Data of Table 12.2:

$$U_1 = 8(22) + \frac{8(9)}{2} - 52 = 176 + 36 - 52 = 160$$

The alternative (by subtraction):

$$U_2 = n_1 n_2 - U_1 = 8(22) - 160 = 176 - 160 = 16$$

This result can be checked with $\sum R_2$ of the n_2 group for U_2:

By Calculation:

$$U_2 = n_1 n_2 + \frac{n_2(n_2 + 1)}{2} - \sum R_2 \tag{12.14}$$

$$= 8(22) + \frac{22(23)}{2} - 413 = 176 + 253 - 413 = 16 \quad \text{(Check)}$$

The smaller of the two values found for U_1 and U_2 is taken as the value of the U statistic for the exact probabilities of the Mann-Whitney tables. For a z deviate test of significance, it of course makes no difference whether U_1 or U_2 is used, since both will be equidistant from the hypothesized mean of the sampling distribution of the U statistic.

z Deviate Test of Significance for U

When both n_1 and n_2 are equal to or greater than 8, the expected sampling variation of the U statistic for the null hypothesis of $N_1 N_2/2$ is approximately normal. Hence a z deviate test of significance may be made. The standard error of U is as follows:

$$\sigma_U = \sqrt{\frac{(n_1)(n_2)(n_1 + n_2 + 1)}{12}} \tag{12.15}$$

The lower value of U is found to deviate -3.4σ from the null hypothesis as follows:

For H_0: $U - \dfrac{n_1 n_2}{2} = 0$

$$z = \frac{U - \dfrac{n_1 n_2}{2}}{\sigma_U} \tag{12.16}$$

$$= \frac{16 - \dfrac{176}{2}}{\sqrt{\dfrac{8(22)(8 + 22 + 1)}{12}}} = \frac{-72}{21.3} = -3.4$$

The null hypothesis is thus rejected with confidence, since the critical value of z in a two-tailed test (as this one is) is 3.3 for an alpha of .001. Therefore the median difference in the birth weights of these two groups is significantly greater than a chance difference for a common population median. Even with the small samples, prematures who expire have a significantly lower median birth weight than those who survive.

Table 12.2. Small Random Samples of Birth Weights of Premature Infants

Those Who Expired		Those Who Survived	
Weight in Grams ($n_1 = 8$)	Rank	Weight in Grams ($n_2 = 22$)	Rank
		2041	30
		1950	29
		1928	28
		1850	27
		1786	26
		1775	25
		1760	24
		1680	23
		1630	22
		1616	21
		1446	20
		1417	19
		1380	18
		1361	17
1332	15.5	1332	15.5
		1304	14
		1240	13
		1162	11.5
		1162	11.5
1160	10		
		1134	9
1049	8		
1020	6.5	1020	6.5
940	5		
935	4		
		907	3
794	2		
530	1		
$\sum R_1 = 52$		$\sum R_2 = 413$	

SOURCE: Same as Table 6.8.

Parametric Methods

Parametric methods for assessing the significance of differences between the measurements of independent samples were developed in Chapter 10 for hypotheses such as the following:

$$H_0: \mu_2 - \mu_1 = 0 \qquad \text{(p. 288)}$$
$$H_\Delta: \mu_2 - \mu_1 \leq 0 \qquad \text{(p. 288)}$$
$$H_0: \sigma_1{}^2 - \sigma_2{}^2 = 0 \qquad \text{(p. 291)}$$

Generally the use of these methods is based on the assumption that the sample data are derived from populations of measures that are normally distributed.

SIGNIFICANCE TESTS FOR DIFFERENCES BETWEEN PAIRED RESULTS OF TWO MATCHED OR RELATED SAMPLES

When the experimental method of the matched group design is employed and the sampling units (persons) are paired on a matching variable, the data of measurables may be converted either to counts (of $+$ and $-$ signs) or to ranks, 1 to n. Distribution-free tests of significance may then be applied to the data, as given below.

Sign Test for Countables

This test, based on the sign of differences between the measures of matched pairs of related samples, has already been described on p. 168 as an exact test. The binomial probability model was used in testing the hypothesis that the frequency of $+$ signs is equal to the frequency of $-$ signs:

$$H_0: \mathbf{F}(+\text{'s}) = \mathbf{F}(-\text{'s}) \qquad \text{or} \qquad \mathbf{F}(+\text{'s}) - \mathbf{F}(-\text{'s}) = 0 \qquad (12.17)$$

Median Test by Chi-Square

The same hypothesis tested in the preceding section for results of independent samples is tested for related samples by the method described in Table 12.1:

$$H_0: MDN_1 - MDN_2 = 0 \qquad [12.7]$$

Chi-Square for Differences Between Proportions of Related Samples

The following hypothesis is tested:

$$H_0: P_1 - P_2 = 0 \qquad \text{or} \qquad P_1 = P_2 = P \qquad (12.18)$$

The technique for testing this hypothesis was developed on pp. 267 ff. for the results of repeated interviews of the same family units with the interpolation of an educational campaign to influence attitudes after the first interview.

Wilcoxon Test of Signed-Ranks for Differences Between Matched Pairs

The following hypothesis is tested:

$$H_0: \sum R(+) = \sum R(-) \quad \text{or} \quad \sum R(+) - \sum R(-) = 0 \quad (12.19)$$

where $\sum R(+)$ is the sum of positive ranks and $\sum R(-)$ is the sum of negative ranks.

As in the case of the Mann-Whitney test for independent samples, the Wilcoxon test for related samples uses more information and hence can be generally expected to be a more valuable significance test than is the sign test or the median test. The Wilcoxon test was the forerunner of the Mann-Whitney, having been developed by Wilcoxon (1949) for speedy assessment of differences of matched or related samples.

As indicated in Table 12.3, the *magnitude* of the difference between the measures of each pair of subjects of a control and experimental group is indicated in column 4 with the *sign* (+ or −) of the difference. These differences, D, are then ranked in column 5, *without regard to their sign*, the smallest difference receiving a rank of 1. Ties are given average ranks, as heretofore (p. 146). Zero differences are eliminated with corresponding reduction in n' pairs of measures from 10 to 9.

Table 12.3. Computations for the Wilcoxon Test of Significance of Signed Ranks for Matched Pairs

Sampling Units (1)	Control Group (2)	Experimental Group (3)	Difference, D (4)	Rank $R\|D\|$ (5)	$R(+)$ (6)	$R(-)$ (7)
A	162	168	6	8	8	
B	154	155	1	1	1	
C	153	160	7	9	9	
D	151	148	−3	4.0		4.0
E	149	153	4	6	6	
F	147	150	3	4.0	4.0	
G	140	137	−3	4.0		4.0
H	139	139	0			
I	137	135	−2	2		2
J	130	135	5	7	7	
					35	10
					$\sum R(+)$	$\sum R(-)$

$P(T \leq 10) > .05$ (Table K of Appendix, for $n' = 9$, and T (nondirectional test) being the lesser of the two $\sum R$'s)

The ranks of column 5 are then summed in columns 6 and 7 according to the signs of their differences in column 4; hence the name of *signed ranks* for this method. The smaller of the two signed-rank sums yields Wilcoxon's T statistic. For the data of Table 12.3, T is 10.

Reference to Table K of the Appendix indicates that $T_{.95}$ is 6 for a nondirectional significance test. The *larger* the magnitude of T (being the smaller of the two signed-ranked sums), the less significant will be the differences between the matched groups. And since the critical value for n' is a T of 6, the null hypothesis for the data of Table 12.3 with a T of 10 cannot be rejected.

Wilcoxon's table of critical values for T, reproduced in Table K, carries the argument through $n' = 25$. When n' is more than 25, the sampling distribution of T will be approximately normal, with mean equal to the following:

$$\overline{T} = \frac{n'(n' + 1)}{4} \tag{12.20}$$

Hence a z significance test can be made for T as follows:

When $n' > 25$:

$$z = \frac{T - \overline{T}}{\sigma_T} = \frac{T - \dfrac{n'(n' + 1)}{4}}{\sqrt{\dfrac{n'(n' + 1)(2n' + 1)}{24}}} \tag{12.21}$$

As in the case of the U statistic, T or T' (where T' would be the larger of the signed-rank sum) may be used in the evaluation of a result, since the sampling distribution of T statistics is now assumed to be a bilaterally symmetrical approximation of the normal probability model.

Comparison of Sign Test with Signed-Rank Test

Earlier it was pointed out that a weakness of the *sign* test for assessing the significance of matched group differences lies in the fact that differences of little magnitude have the same weight as differences of great magnitude. From the foregoing account of the Wilcoxon test, the greater usefulness of the signed-rank test over the sign test may be apparent.

A comparison of the results of the two methods for the data of the ten husband-wife pairs (p. 168 ff.) is presented in Table 12.4. The sign test was found to yield a result by the *exact test* (p. 168), significant at *alpha* of .05, since **P** (9 or 10 | 's) = .011, and **P** (9 or 10 +'s or 9 or 10 's) = .022. A z deviate test for the same data, corrected for continuity, yields a **P** value of about the same magnitude, viz., .013 for 9 or 10 +'s, or .026 for a two-tailed, nondirectional test.

The Wilcoxon test, however, which takes into account the magnitude of the differences between the husbands' and wives' measures, yields a T of 10, and hence an insignificant result at *alpha* of .05. This is the case, since by Table K and $n' = 10$, $T_{.025}$ and $T_{.975}$ are — or $+8$ for a nondirectional test with *alpha* $= .05$.

Table 12.4. A Comparison of Sign Test Results with Signed-Rank Test Results
(Data of Ten Related Pairs of Measures; p. 168)

Sampling Unit	Husbands	Wives	Sign Test (+)	Sign Test (—)	D	$R\|D\|$	R(+)	R(—)
J	36	15	+		21	10	10	
I	34	36		—	— 2	5		5
H	31	32		—	— 1	2.5		2.5
G	30	35		—	— 5	6		6
F	21	40		—	—19	9		9
E	18	19		—	— 1	2.5		2.5
D	16	17		—	— 1	2.5		2.5
C	13	24		—	—11	8		8
B	12	13		—	— 1	2.5		2.5
A	10	16		—	— 6	7		7
			$\Sigma = 1$	9			10	45
							T	T'

Sign Test: Exact probabilities from binomial (p. 168): **P** (9 or 10—) $= .011$. As a normal z deviate corrected for continuity: $z = 2.22$; **P** $= .0132$. (These are both directional values; **P** is doubled for nondirectional.)

Signed-Rank Test: **P** $(T \leq 10) > .05$ (nondirectional); $> .025$ (directional)

Parametric Methods

Parametric methods for significance testing of differences between measurements of related samples were developed in Chapter 10 for the following null hypothesis:

$$H_0: \mu_1 - \mu_2 = 0 \qquad (p. 298)$$

SIGNIFICANCE OF DIFFERENCES FOR RESULTS OF MORE THAN TWO SAMPLES

Several distribution-free methods are available as alternatives to the method of analysis of variance for the evaluation of the significance of differences among more than two sets of results. The three methods to be described here are the following:

1. The median test by chi-square either for independent samples of the randomized group design or for related samples of the matched block design.

2. The Kruskal-Wallis test of the H statistic for results from independent, randomized groups (also a chi-square test).
3. The Friedman chi-square test for related groups of the matched block design.

Median Test by Chi-Square for k Groups

Median test by chi-square is again used as a significance test of the distribution of plus and minus differences of the measures of each subsample from the median of the total distribution. If all the measures of one group were below the overall median, if all those of another group were above the median, and if those of a third group were about evenly distributed above and below the median of all the measures, then the rejectability of the following null hypothesis would be mainly a question of the size of the several samples:

$$H_0: \text{MDN}_1 = \text{MDN}_2 = \cdots = \text{MDN}_k = \text{MDN} \qquad (12.22)$$

Fictional data for three subsamples of reaction time measures are presented in Table 12.5. Populations of such measures are more likely to be skewed than normally distributed; hence a distribution-free method for the analysis of the significance of differences over k groups may be preferred to analysis of variance. The overall median is found to be 135.1 milliseconds. The hypothesized frequencies for each of the six cells of the contingency table are in parentheses next to the obtained frequencies of each, as obtained from the crosstabulation of the original data into the 2 by 3 correlation chart.

Chi-square is found to be 22.1, as follows:

$$\chi^2 = \frac{(11 - 5.3)^2}{5.3} + \frac{(5 - 5.3)^2}{5.3} + \cdots + \frac{(11 - 5.7)^2}{5.7} = 22.1$$

By Table C, $\chi^2_{.999} = 13.82$ for 2 d.f.'s; hence the null hypothesis of equal population medians is rejected with confidence.

Kruskal-Wallis H Test of Ranks for k Independent Samples

This test for the significance of differences among three or more groups is developed on the same principles underlying the Mann-Whitney test. The null hypothesis tested is that the sum of ranks (ranked overall) for *each* of the k subsamples is *relatively* the same. When the size of each subsample is the same (as is recommended both here and in analysis of variance), then the null hypothesis tested is the following:

$$H_0: \Sigma R_1 = \Sigma R_2 = \cdots = \Sigma R_k = \Sigma R$$

or (in effect),

$$H_0: \overline{R}_1 = \overline{R}_2 = \cdots = \overline{R}_k = \overline{R} \qquad (12.23)$$

Table 12.5. Median Test by Chi-Square for
Differences Among Three Groups

Measures of Experimental Groups: Reaction Times in Milliseconds; Experimental Variations			Distribution of All Measures of the Three Groups	
A_1	A_2	A_3	Milliseconds	f
147 +	120 −	110 −	160–164	1
140 +	156 +	115 −	155–159	1
154 +	148 +	118 −	150–154	2
142 +	130 −	125 −	145–149	5
162 +	125 −	122 −	140–144	4
137 +	146 +	105 −	135–139	4
151 +	132 −	130 −	130–134	4
149 +	141 +	120 −	125–129	3
138 +	135 −	112 −	120–124	4
139 +	140 +	128 −	115–119	2
145 +	130 −	121 −	110–114	2
n_j = 11	11	11	105–109	1

mdn$_j$ = 145 msec   135 msec   120 msec

$n = 33$

$mdn = 134.5 + (.5/4)5 = 135.1$

CONTINGENCY TABLE FOR CHI-SQUARE

	A_1	A_2	A_3	n_r
Above median:	11 (5.3) ^{a}	5 (5.3) ^{b}	0 (5.3) ^{c}	16
Below median:	0 (5.7) ^{d}	6 (5.7) ^{e}	11 (5.7) ^{f}	17
n_c	11	11	11	$n' = 33$

$F_a = (16/33)11 = 5.3$; $F_d = (17/33)11 = 5.7$ (Formula 6.17)

Note that if the sizes of the samples differ, then the respective sums of R_k will be *relative* to the size of each.

When the frequency of ranks for each of the k subsamples or groups is a minimum of 5, the following statistic, H, has sampling distributions satisfactorily approximated by the continuous distributions of chi-square of Table C:

$$H = \frac{12}{n(n+1)} \sum^k \frac{\sum R_j^2}{n_j} - 3(n+1) \qquad (12.24)$$

When $n_j \leq 5$, exact probabilities may be obtained from tables prepared by Kruskal and Wallis (1952).

The reaction time measures of Table 12.5 have been assigned ranks from 1 to n in Table 12.6, with the smallest measure having the rank of 1 (even though this is indicative of the speediest result), and the largest having the rank of n, which is 33. The few ties have been treated in the usual way, i.e., averaged over the ranks involved, and may be ignored. However, whenever many such ties occur relative to the size of the subsamples, the value of H may be corrected by the following factor:

H, corrected for ties:
$$H_c = \frac{H}{1 - \dfrac{\sum\limits_{t}(f_t^3 - f_t)}{n^3 - n}} \qquad (12.25)$$

where f_t is the frequency of ties in a set (at least two). Since there are three sets of ties of two each and one set of three, the correction factor for the data of Table 12.6 would be negligible, as follows:

$$c = 1 - \frac{(3)(2^3 - 2) + (3^3 - 3)}{33^3 - 33} = .998$$

Table 12.6.   Computations for the Kruskal-Wallis H Statistic for a Significance Test of Differences Among the Mean Ranks of Three or More Independent Samples

(Data of Table 12.5)

	Experimental Groups Ranks (Overall) of the Measures		
	A_1	A_2	A_3
	27	6.5	2
	21.5	32	4
	31	28	5
	24	14.0	10.5
	33	10.5	9
	18	26	1
	30	16	14.0
	29	23	6.5
	19	17	3
	20	21.5	12
	25	14	8
$\sum R_j$	277.5	208.5	75.0 $\sum R = 561$
n_j	11	11	11 $n = 33$

$R = 1$ for the smallest measures; $R = 33$ for the largest measure.
All tied ranks are signified by an entry after the decimal.
$\sum R = 33(34)/2 = 561$ (Check)

$$H = \frac{12}{33(34)}\left[\frac{(277.5)^2 + (208.5)^2 + (75.0)^2}{11}\right] - 3(34) = 10.6 \quad \text{(Formula 12.24)}$$

The computed value of the H statistic in Table 12.6 is 10.6. The number of d.f.'s $= k - 1 = 2$. Since $\chi^2_{.99} = 9.2$ for 2 d.f.'s, $P(\chi^2 \geq H$ of 10.6$) <$ .01, and the null hypothesis is rejected with confidence.

Note that the sensitivity of the Kruskal-Wallis test to the magnitude of the fictional data of Table 12.5 results in a value of chi-square of 10.6 as against the larger value of 22.1 for the median test. The method that takes into account the magnitude of the measures as rankables is usually preferred over a method that simply classifies them according to plus or minus directions from the overall median even though in this particular example the latter method with signs yields the larger value of chi-square.

Friedman's Rank Test by Chi-Square for k Related Samples

Just as the Wilcoxon test is a useful distribution-free method for a statistical appraisal of the significance of differences between two matched or related groups, Friedman's chi-square test (1937, 1940) for ranks is useful with the randomized block design where $k = 3$ or more related subsamples. A block may consist of a triad or more of different sampling units (persons) matched on a variable, or a block may consist of three or more measures obtained from the same person.

The measures of Table 12.5 have been repeated in Table 12.7, but this time *as if* they were measures of related samples. As on p. 344, the blocks of matched triads are set up row by row, numbered 1 through 11, and the variations of the experimental factor A are set up by columns. The null hypothesis to be tested is the same as for the Kruskal-Wallis test, viz.,

$$H_0: \Sigma R_1 = \Sigma R_2 = \cdots = \Sigma R_k = \Sigma R$$

which (in effect) is

$$H_0: \overline{R}_1 = \overline{R}_2 = \cdots = \overline{R}_k = \overline{R} \tag{12.26}$$

With Friedman's test, however, the consistency of ranks *within* blocks (rows) for each experimental variation (columns) will be taken into account. If the null hypothesis is tenable, the distribution of the ranks within each row should be at random, and therefore the sums of the ranks of the columns should be equal for random variation. The chi-square statistic developed by Friedman to measure the way in which the ranks distribute themselves over the rows and then sum up in the columns is as follows:

$$\chi_r{}^2 = \frac{12}{n_j k(k + 1)} \sum^k \left(\sum R_j \right)^2 - 3n_j(k + 1) \tag{12.27}$$

where the subscript r is used to indicate that this is a computation of chi-square based on ranks.

**Table 12.7. Computations for the Friedman Significance Test for
Differences Among Three or More Subsamples of the
Matched Block Design
(or with Repetition of Measurements over Same Subjects)**
(Data of Table 12.5)

Blocks (Triads)	Measures in Milliseconds for Three Experimental Groups			Ranks of Measures Within Blocks		
	A_1	A_2	A_3	A_1	A_2	A_3
1	147	120	110	3	2	1
2	140	156	115	2	3	1
3	154	148	118	3	2	1
4	142	130	125	3	2	1
5	162	125	122	3	2	1
6	137	146	105	2	3	1
7	151	132	130	3	2	1
8	149	141	120	3	2	1
9	138	135	112	3	2	1
10	139	140	128	2	3	1
11	145	130	121	3	2	1
			$\sum R_j =$	30	25	11 $\sum R = 66$

$$\sum R = 11 \left[\frac{3(4)}{2} \right] = 66 \quad \text{(Check)}$$

$$\chi_r^2 = \frac{12}{11(3)(3+1)} [(30)^2 + (25)^2 + (11)^2] - 3(11)(3+1) = 17.6$$

(Formula 12.27)

Chi-square is found in Table 12.7 to be 17.6. From Table C, with
$k - 1$ d.f.'s, i.e., 2 d.f.'s, $P(\chi^2 = 17.5) < .001$, and hence the null hypothesis that the subsample sums (or means) of ranks differ but randomly
is rejected. The differences are too great to be satisfactorily explained
in terms of random variation only. Therefore it would be concluded for
such data that the three variations of the independent experimental variable result in statistically significant differences.

Moses (1953) points out that when $k > 7$ and $n_j \geq 6$, the chi-square
approximations (of Table C) will be "quite adequate." When k or n_j,
or both, is less, then the computed value of the χ^2 statistic is likely to be
too large rather than too small. Thus a result may appear to be statistically
more significant than it really is. Friedman (1940) provides critical values
of chi-square for few k's and n_j's.

Relation of χ_r^2 to W

It will be observed that Kendall's concordance coefficient W, to be developed in the next section, is based on the same set of considerations as

Friedman's rank test by chi-square:

$$W = \frac{\chi_r{}^2}{n(k-1)} \qquad \text{and} \qquad \chi_r{}^2 = n(k-1)W \qquad (12.28)$$

Parametric Methods

Parametric methods for significance testing of differences among more than two samples are, of course, the analysis of variance methods of the preceding chapter. In general, two classes of hypotheses were tested:

$$H_0: \mu_1 = \mu_2 = \cdots = \mu_k = \mu \qquad \text{(p. 321)}$$
$$H_0: \sigma_1{}^2 = \sigma_2{}^2 = \cdots = \sigma_k{}^2 = \sigma^2 \qquad \text{(p. 330)}$$

The null hypothesis for zero interaction was also tested by analysis of variance. The superiority over distribution-free methods of the parametric methods of significance testing by analysis of variance stems especially from their greater versatility and usefulness with experimental designs. There are no satisfactory substitutes to be found in the distribution-free repertoire for analysis of variance for interaction effects, and for testing the experimental and interrelated effects characteristic of factorial designs. (See Anderson, 1961.)

CORRELATION OF BIVARIATES

Parametric and distribution-free methods of correlation were developed in Chapters 5 and 6. One additional distribution-free method of correlation for rankables will be presented in this final chapter, viz., Kendall's method (1948) for the concordance coefficient W.

For Measurables

The various methods for Pearson's r of Chapters 5 and 6 were for the correlation of measurable data. The *use and interpretation* of the various coefficients developed are generally based on the assumption of normal population distributions of the measurements correlated. *Eta* correlation was developed in Chapter 6 for bivariate distributions that are nonlinear.

For Countables

Two distribution-free methods were developed in Chapter 6 for the measurement of the correlation of bivariate distributions of countable data. Their coefficients are *phi* and C, the contingency coefficient by chi-square.

For Rankables

Spearman's rank difference method for the correlation of the rankables of a bivariate distribution was described in Chapter 6. It is a distribution-free method. It was seen to be useful not only for original data in the form of ranks but also for countables or measurables, or both, whose bivariate distributions might not be satisfactorily measured by r or *eta* (for nonlinear relations). The data of Table 6.7 were of this kind.

Kendall's Concordance Coefficient W

If all the possible intercorrelations of the bivariate relations of three or more variables were obtained by Spearman's rank difference method, and then averaged, the result would bear the following relation to W, the concordance coefficient:

$$\bar{r}_r = \frac{kW - 1}{k - 1} \tag{12.29}$$

The concordance coefficient W is equal to the following:

$$W = \frac{12S}{k^2 n(n^2 - 1)} \tag{12.30}$$

Its computation is carried out in Table 12.8, S being a sum of squares, k the number of judges (or classifications), and n the number of rankings per judge or classification.

The data of Table 12.8 were generated as follows: A class of 11 psychology students in a graduate course in statistics were asked toward the end of the term's work to *rank each other*, 1 to n, with respect to the success with which they judged each other to be adjusting to the demands of the course. One might have supposed that those judged by their peers to be adjusting best would have ranked more consistently than those judged to be making the poorest adjustment. (One could perhaps also have supposed the opposite, since the correlation between the insights of statisticians and of psychologists is not known.) To investigate this supposition, the results were used as indicated in Table 12.8. The four top-rated persons are judges A, B, C, and D, and the four lowest-rated persons are judges H, I, J, and K. (The judgments made by the three middle-rated persons are omitted.)

The ranks of each judge are spread across the rows. Thus each row is a *block* of 11 ranks made by one person. The sums of the ranks of the columns give the pooled results of the several judges. If there is little or no agreement among them, i.e., no concordance in their rankings, then the rank sums of the columns should be the same except for random variation. But the more the similarity of rank values within each column (and hence systematic differences in the sums of column ranks), the greater the concordance or agreement among the judges. (Note that such agreements would not necessarily form any particular order across the rows unless the sums of the ranks themselves were arranged in order. (This has not been done in Table 12.8.) The extent of agreement is thus measured by W, the concordance coefficient.

Table 12.8. Comparison of Results of Two Groups of Judges by Means of Kendall's Concordance Coefficient W

Rankings of the Class of 11 Students

GROUP I

Judges		(1)	(2)	(3)	(4)	(5)	(6)	(7)	(8)	(9)	(10)	(11)
A		1	4	5	3	10	11	7	9	6	2	8
B		1	7	2	8	3	10	9	11	4	5	6
C		1	5	3	7	8	9	10	4	6	2	11
D		1	11	5	6	2	7	8	6	7	3	10
$\sum R_j =$		4	27	15	24	23	37	34	30	23	12	35

$$\overset{n}{\sum}(\sum R_j) = 264$$

$(\sum R_j)^2 =$	16	729	225	576	529	1369	1156	900	529	144	1225

$$\overset{n}{\sum}(\sum R_j)^2 = 7398$$

$$S = 7398 - \frac{(264)^2}{11} = 1062; \qquad W = \frac{12(1062)}{16(11)(120)} = .60$$

(Formula 12.32) (Formula 12.33)

GROUP II

H		1	10	2	11	4	6	9	8	3	5	7
I		1	6	5	9	2	10	7	11	4	3	8
J		1	11	5	9	2	4	8	6	7	3	10
K		1	2	5	4	6	7	9	11	3	8	10
$\sum R_j =$		4	29	17	33	14	27	33	36	17	19	35

$$\overset{n}{\sum}(\sum R_j) = 264$$

$(\sum R_j)^2 =$	16	841	289	1089	196	729	1089	1296	289	361	1225

$$\overset{n}{\sum}(\sum R_j)^2 = 7420$$

$$S = 7420 - \frac{(264)^2}{11} = 1084; \qquad W = \frac{12(1084)}{16(11)(120)} = .62$$

For the calculation of W, the sums of each column of ranks of Table 12.8 are summed and checked for accuracy against the following:

Check Sum:
$$\sum R = k \frac{n(n+1)}{2} \tag{12.31}$$

When k is 4 and n (the number of ranks per set) is 11, $\sum R$ equals 264.

The rank sums of each column are squared and summed to obtain S of Formula 12.30 for W. S is obtained by the now familiar method for sum of squares:

$$S = \overset{n}{\sum}\left(\sum R_j\right)^2 - \frac{[\overset{n}{\sum}(\sum R_j)]^2}{n} \tag{12.32}$$

The idea originally suggested, that the top-rated judges would be more consistent in their rankings than the low-rated judges, is not borne out by the results. In fact a hypothesis favoring the top-rated judges is perhaps not quite so plausible as one favoring the consistency of the rankings of the low-rated judges. Their concordance coefficient W is slightly (but insignificantly) larger than the W for the former four judges: .62 as against .60.

Significance of W

Are these two values of W sufficiently large to indicate that concordance among the rankings made by the judges is greater than may be expected by chance? Kendall (1943, vol. 1) gives exact probabilities of S when k and n are small. They need to be used when $n < 6$ and $k < 4$. For larger series of n ranks and k judges (or classifications), the following F test may be employed to test the null hypothesis for $W = 0$. (Note that W cannot take negative values but may range from 0 to 1.)

For H_0: $W = 0$: $$F = \frac{W(k - 1)}{1 - W} \tag{12.33}$$

with numerator d.f.$_1$

$$= n - 1 - \left(\frac{2}{k}\right) \tag{12.34}$$

with denominator d.f.$_2$

$$= (k - 1)\left(n - 1 - \frac{2}{k}\right) \tag{12.35}$$

For the smaller W coefficient of Table 12.8:

$$F = \frac{.60(4 - 1)}{1 - .60} = 4.5$$

with d.f.$_1$ $= 11 - 1 - (\tfrac{2}{4}) = 9.5$

with d.f.$_2$ $= (4 - 1)(11 - 1 - \tfrac{2}{4}) = 28.5$

By Table F of the Appendix, $\mathbf{P}(F \geq 4.5) < .001$ for 9.5 and 28.5 d.f.'s, since for 9 and 28 d.f.'s, $F_{.999} = 4.5$. Hence the null hypothesis of $W = 0$ can be rejected for both W coefficients.

Relation of W to r_r

It will be noted that a W coefficient of the order of .60 is equivalent to a mean value of .47 for the six Spearman rank difference r_r's that would have had to be computed if the sets of ranks of the four judges had been correlated two sets at a time:

$$\bar{r}_r = \frac{4(.60) - 1}{4 - 1} = .47 \qquad [12.29]$$

That there is also considerable concordance or agreement between the two sets of results by the two groups of judges is indicated in Table 12.9. Spearman's rank difference correlation between the two sets of pooled sums of ranks is found to be .74.

Table 12.9. Correlation of the Rankings of the Two Groups of Judges by Spearman's Rank Difference Method
(Data of Table 12.8)

	(1)	(2)	(3)	(4)	(5)	(6)	(7)	(8)	(9)	(10)	(11)
Ranks of Group I Results:	1	7	3	6	4.5	11	9	8	4.5	2	10
Ranks of Group II Results:	1	7	3.5	8.5	2	6	8.5	11	3.5	5	10
D:	0	0	−.5	−2.5	2.5	5	.5	−3	1	−3	0
D^2:	0	0	.25	6.25	6.25	25	.25	9	1	9	0
										Σ	= 57

$$r_r = 1 - \frac{6(57)}{11(120)} = .74 \qquad \text{(Formula 6.20)}$$

Parametric Methods

Parametric methods for significance testing of r correlations and their differences were developed in Chapter 10. In general the classes of hypotheses tested were as follows:

$$H_0: \rho = 0 \qquad \text{(p. 302)}$$
$$H_A: \rho \leq 0 \qquad \text{(p. 302)}$$
$$H_0: \rho_{12} - \rho_{34} = 0 \qquad \text{(p. 306)}$$
$$H_0: \rho_{12} - \rho_{13} = 0 \qquad \text{(p. 307)}$$

F significance tests for *eta* correlation and for the linearity of the regression of bivariate distributions were presented in the preceding chapter (p. 342 ff.).

IN CONCLUSION

In concluding this introduction to applied statistics, the author wishes to emphasize that the standard tools for significance testing are generally those to be found in Chapters 9, 10 and 11. Additional methods developed in this final chapter have been presented mainly as useful alternatives when the parametric methods for t and F are inappropriate.

How is a researcher to know what state of affairs prevails? How is he to know when a parametric method is to be preferred over a distribution-free method, or vice versa? Some may think that distribution-free methods are better to use with results from small samples. However, a distribution-free method should not be chosen over t or F just because samples are small (n_j's of 5, for example). It is usually unlikely that the data of small samples will warrant the rejection of the null hypothesis of homogeneity of variance or of normally distributed populations of measures. And, as pointed out in Chapter 11, the requirement of normality is for populations of measures rather than for the data of samples.

Because significance tests by analysis of variance have greater *versatility* than the distribution-free methods, the former are the standard methods ordinarily to be employed in the small-sample designs of experimental research. When there is a choice between the use of t or of a distribution-free method such as the Mann-Whitney or Wilcoxon test, the parametric method is ordinarily preferred, especially with small samples, simply because it *uses more information*. If, on the other hand, sample sizes are large enough to make it appear likely by appropriate significance tests that either the requirement of homogeneity of variance or of normally distributed populations is untenable, then the distribution-free methods developed in this chapter may be employed as suitable techniques for significance testing. Some researchers also find them useful as *short-cut substitutes* for parametric methods, which at times they may very well be.

REFERENCES

Anderson, N. H. 1961. Scales and statistics: parametric and nonparametric. *Psychological Bulletin*, **58**, 305–316.

Anon. 1952. *Tables of the Binomial Probability Distribution*. Washington, D.C.: National Bureau of Standards. Applied Mathematics Series, No. 6.

Aube, D. 1953. Extended tables for the Mann-Whitney statistic. *Bulletin of the Institute of Educational Research at Indiana University*, **1**.

Bartlett, M. S. 1937. Some examples of statistical methods of research in agriculture and applied biology. *Journal of the Royal Statistical Society*, Supplement 4, **121**, 137–170.

Bingham, W. V. 1937. *Aptitudes and Aptitude Testing*. New York: Harper.

Box, C. E. P. 1953. Non-normality and tests on variances. *Biometrika*, **40**, 318–335.

Chapanis, Alphonse. 1962. An exact multinomial one-sample test of significance. *Psychological Bulletin*, **59**, 306-310.

Cheshire, L., Saffir, M., and Thurstone, L. L. 1933. *Computing Diagrams for the Tetrachoric Correlation Coefficient*. Chicago: University of Chicago Bookstore.

Clopper, C. J., and Pearson, E. S. 1934. The use of confidence or fiducial limits illustrated in the case of the binomial. *Biometrika*, **26**, 404–413.

Cochran, W. G. 1941. The distribution of the largest of a set of estimated variances as a fraction of their total. *Annals of Eugenics*, **11**, 47–52.

Cochran, W. G. 1950. The comparison of percentages in matched samples. *Biometrika*, **37**, 256–266.

Cochran, W. G. 1953. 1959, 2nd ed. *Sampling Techniques*. New York: Wiley.

Cochran, W. G., and Cox, G. M. 1957, 2nd ed. *Experimental Designs*. New York: Wiley.

Cohen, M. R., and Nagel, E. 1934. *Logic and Scientific Method*. New York: Harcourt Brace.

Cronbach, L. J. 1957. The two disciplines of scientific psychology. *American Psychologist*, **11**, 671–684.

Croxton, F. E., and Cowden, D. J. 1939. 1960, 3rd ed. *Practical Business Statistics*. New York: Prentice-Hall.

Cureton, E. E. 1939. The principal compulsions of factor-analysts. *Harvard Educational Review*, **9**, 287–295.

Davidoff, M. D., and Goheen, H. W. 1953. A table for the rapid determination of the tetrachoric correlation coefficient. *Psychometrika*, **18**, 115–121.

Deming, W. E. 1950. *Some Theory of Sampling*. New York: Wiley.

Deming, W. E. 1960. *Sample Design in Business Research*. New York: Wiley.

DuBois, P. H. 1957. *Multivariate Correlational Analysis*. New York: Harper.

Duncan, D. B. 1955. Multiple range and multiple *F* tests. *Biometrics*, **11**, 1–42.

Dunlap, J. W. 1936. Note on computation of biserial correlations in item evaluation. *Psychometrika*, **1**, 51–60.

Dunnette, C. W. 1955. A multiple comparison procedure for comparing several treatments with a control. *Journal of American Statistical Association*, **50**, 1096–1121.

Edwards, A. L. 1950. 1960, rev. *Experimental Design in Psychological Research*. New York: Rinehart.

Edwards, A. L. 1954. *Statistical Methods for the Behavioral Sciences*. New York: Rinehart.

Festinger, Leon. 1953. Laboratory experiments. Ch. 4, *Research Methods in the Behavioral Sciences*. Leon Festinger and Daniel Katz, eds. New York: Dryden.

Field, H. A. 1934. The limits of learning ability in rhesus monkeys. *Genetic Psychology Monograph*, **15**, 369–537.

Fisher, R. A. 1925. 1948, 10th ed. *Statistical Methods for Research Workers*. Edinburgh: Oliver & Boyd.

Fisher, R. A. 1935. 1949, 5th ed. *The Design of Experiments*. London: Oliver & Boyd.

Fisher, R. A. 1950. 1959, rev. *Statistical Methods & Scientific Inference*. New York: Hafner.

Fisher, R. A., and Yates, F. 1938. *Statistical Tables for Biological, Agricultural, and Medical Research*. Edinburgh: Oliver & Boyd.

Friedman, Milton. 1937. The use of ranks to avoid the assumption of normality implicit in the analysis of variance. *Journal of American Statistical Association*, **32**, 675–701.

Fruchter, Benjamin. 1959. *Introduction to Factor Analysis*. New York: Van Nostrand.

Galton, Francis (Sir). 1869. 1952, reprinted. *Hereditary Genius: An Inquiry into Its Laws and Consequences*. New York: Horizon Press.

Galton, Francis (Sir). 1886. *Hereditary Stature*. Royal Society Proceedings, XL.

Gardner, Martin. 1959. *Mathematical Puzzles and Diversions*. New York: Simon and Schuster.

Goedicke, Victor. 1953. *Introduction to the Theory of Statistics*. New York: Harper.

Gossett, W. S. 1908. See "Student."

Guilford, J. P. 1954, 2nd ed. *Psychometric Methods*. New York: McGraw-Hill.

Hartley, H. O. 1950. The maximum *F*-ratio as a short-cut test for homogeneity of variance. *Biometrika*, **37**, 308–19.

Hoel, P. G. 1960. *Elementary Statistics*. New York: Wiley.

Hogben, Lancelot. 1957. *Statistical Theory: The Relationship of Probability, Credibility and Error*. London: Allen & Unwin.

Hotelling, Harold. 1940. The selection of variates for use in prediction, with some comments on the general problem of nuisance parameters. *Annals of Math. Statistics*, **11**, 271–283.

Hudgins, C. V. 1933. Conditioning and the voluntary control of the pupillary light reflex. *Journal of General Psychology*, **8**, 3–51.

Hull, Clark. 1928. *Aptitude Testing*. Yonkers, N.Y.: World.

Jaspen, Nathan. 1946. Serial correlation. *Psychometrika*, **11**, 23–30.

Jenkins, W. L. 1956. Triserial *r*—a neglected statistic. *Journal of Applied Psychology*, **40**, 63–64.

Kelley, T. L. 1947. *Fundamentals of Statistics*. Cambridge, Mass.: Harvard University Press.

Kendall, M. G. 1943. *The Advanced Theory of Statistics.* Philadelphia: Lippincott.

Kendall, M. G. 1948. 1955, 2nd ed. *Rank Correlation Methods.* London: Griffin.

Kendall, M. G., and Smith, B. B. 1938. Randomness and random sampling numbers. *Journal of the Royal Statistical Society,* **101,** 147–166.

Kendall, M. G., and Smith, B. B. 1951. *Tracts for Computers, No. 24.* Tables of random sampling numbers. London: Cambridge University Press.

Koch, A. M. 1935. The limits of learning—cebus monkeys. *Genetic Psychology Monograph,* **17,** 165–234.

Kruskal, W. H., and Wallis, W. A. 1952. Use of ranks in one-criterion variance analysis. *Journal of the American Statistical Association,* **47,** 584–621.

Laplace, Pierre Simon, the Marquis de Laplace. 1951 ed. *The Application of the Calculus of Probabilities to Natural Philosophy.* New York: Dover.

Lerner, Daniel, ed. 1958. *Evidence & Inference.* Glencoe, Illinois: Free Press.

Lewinsohn, Richard. 1961. *Science, Prophecy and Prediction.* New York: Harper.

McNemar, Quinn. 1955, 2nd ed. *Psychological Statistics.* New York: Wiley.

McNemar, Quinn. 1960. At random: sense and nonsense. *American Journal of Psychology,* **15,** 295–300.

Mahalanobis, P. C. 1946a. On large-scale sample surveys. *Philosophical Transactions of the Royal Society,* B (Biological Series), **231,** 329–451.

Mahalanobis, P. C. 1946b. Recent experiments in statistical sampling in the Indian Statistical Institute. *Journal of the Royal Statistical Society,* **109,** 325–370.

Mann, H. B., and Whitney, D. R. 1947. On a test of whether one of two random variables is stochastically larger than the other. *Annals of Math. Statistics,* **18,** 50–60.

Mantel, Nathan. 1951. On a rapid estimation of standard errors for the means of small samples. *American Statistician,* **5,** 26–27.

Moses, L. E. 1952. Nonparametric statistics for psychological research. *Psychological Bulletin,* **49,** 122–143.

Moses, L. E. 1953. Non-parametric methods. Chapter 18 of *Statistical Inference* by Walker and Lev. New York: Holt.

Murphy, Gardner. 1961. *Challenge of Psychical Research; a Primer of Parasychology.* New York: Harper.

Neyman, Jerzy. 1960. Indeterminism in science and new demands on statisticians. *Journal of American Statistical Association,* **55,** 625–639.

Pearson, E. S., and Wishart, J. 1942. 1958, 3rd ed. *"Student's" Collected Papers.* London: Cambridge University Press.

Pearson, E. S., and Hartley, H. O. 1954. 1958, 2nd ed. *Biometrika Tables for Statisticians.* London: Cambridge University Press.

Pearson, Karl. 1892. 1911, 3rd ed. 1937, 4th ed. *The Grammar of Science.* London: Dent.

Pearson, Karl. 1901. On the correlation of characters not quantitatively measurable. *Philosophical Transactions.* A Series, **195,** 1–47.

Pearson, Karl. 1914. *Tables for Statisticians & Biometricians.* London: Cambridge University Press.

Peatman, J. G. 1947. *Descriptive and Sampling Statistics.* New York: Harper.

Peatman, J. G. 1948–1949. DK's for Truman. *International Journal of Opinion & Attitude Research,* **2,** 537–542.

Peatman, J. G., and Schafer, R. 1942. A table of random numbers from selective service numbers. *Journal of Psychology,* **14,** 295–305.

Peters, C. C., and Van Voorhis, W. R. 1940. *Statistical Procedures and Their Mathematical Bases.* New York: McGraw-Hill.

Rand Corporation. 1955. *A Million Random Digits with 100,000 Normal Deviates.* Glencoe, Illinois: Free Press.

Salzer, H. E. 1951. *Tables of n!* $\cdots$ *For the First Thousand Values of n.* Washington, D.C.: National Bureau of Standards. Applied Mathematics Series, No. 16.

Savage, I. R. 1957. Nonparametric statistics [a review of S. Siegel's book of this title]. *Journal of American Statistical Association,* **52,** 331–344.

Scheffé, Henry. 1953. A method for judging all contrasts in the analysis of variance. *Biometrika,* **40,** 87–104.

Sheldon, W. H. 1940. *The Varieties of Human Physique.* New York: Harper.

Sheldon, W. H. 1942. *The Varieties of Temperament.* New York: Harper.

Siegel, Sidney. 1956. *Nonparametric Statistics.* New York: McGraw-Hill.

Sindlinger & Co. 1960. Great debates on radio and television. *Broadcasting Magazine.* **59,** 19, 27–29.

Smith, J. G., and Duncan, A. J. 1945. *Sampling Statistics and Applications.* New York: McGraw-Hill.

Snedecor, G. W. 1956, 5th ed. *Statistical Methods.* Ames, Iowa: Iowa State College Press.

Spearman, Charles. 1904. The proof and measurement of association between two things. *American Journal of Psychology,* **15,** 72–101.

"Student" (W. S. Gossett). 1908. The probable error of a mean. *Biometrika,* **6.** Also in: "*Student's Collected Papers,* 1958, Pearson & Wishart, eds. London: Cambridge University Press.

Thorndike, E. L. 1905. Measurement of twins. *Journal of Philosophy, Psychology, & Science Method,* **2,** 547–553.

Thorndike, R. L., and Gallup, G. H. 1941. Verbal Intelligence of the American adult. *Journal of General Psychology,* **30,** 75–85.

Thorndike, R. L., and Hagen, E. 1961, 2nd ed. *Measurement and Evaluation in Psychology and Education.* New York: Wiley.

Tukey, J. W. 1949. One degree of freedom for non-additivity. *Biometrics,* **5,** 232–242.

Tukey, J. W. 1949. Comparing individual means in the analysis of variance. *Biometrics,* **5,** 99–114.

U. S. Bureau of the Census. 1962. *Statistical Abstract of the United States: 1962.* (Eighty-third edition.) Washington, D.C.

Walker, H. M. 1929. *Studies in the History of Statistical Method.* Baltimore: Williams and Wilkins.

Walker, H. M. 1952. *Mathematics Essential for Elementary Statistics.* New York: Holt.

Walker, H. M., and Lev, J. 1953. *Statistical Inference.* New York: Holt.

Wilcoxon, Frank. 1949. *Some Rapid Approximate Statistical Procedures.* New York: American Cyanamid Co.

Yates, Frank. 1949. *Sampling Methods for Censuses & Surveys.* London: Griffin.

Yule, G. U. 1912. 1940, 12th ed. *An Introduction to the Theory of Statistics.* London: Griffin.

APPENDIX

APPENDIX

Table A. Areas and Ordinates of the Laplace-Gaussian Normal Distribution in Terms of x/σ
(z Deviates)

(1) z $\left(\dfrac{x}{\sigma}\right)$	(2) A Area from Mean to $\dfrac{x}{\sigma}$	(3) B Area in Larger Portion	(4) C Area in Smaller Portion	(5) y Ordinate at $\dfrac{x}{\sigma}$
.00	.0000	.5000	.5000	.3989
.01	.0040	.5040	.4960	.3989
.02	.0080	.5080	.4920	.3989
.03	.0120	.5120	.4880	.3988
.04	.0160	.5160	.4840	.3986
.05	.0199	.5199	.4801	.3984
.06	.0239	.5239	.4761	.3982
.07	.0279	.5279	.4721	.3980
.08	.0319	.5319	.4681	.3977
.09	.0359	.5359	.4641	.3973
.10	.0398	.5398	.4602	.3970
.11	.0438	.5438	.4562	.3965
.12	.0478	.5478	.4522	.3961
.13	.0517	.5517	.4483	.3956
.14	.0557	.5557	.4443	.3951
.15	.0596	.5596	.4404	.3945
.16	.0636	.5636	.4364	.3939
.17	.0675	.5675	.4325	.3932
.18	.0714	.5714	.4286	.3925
.19	.0753	.5753	.4247	.3918
.20	.0793	.5793	.4207	.3910
.21	.0832	.5832	.4168	.3902
.22	.0871	.5871	.4129	.3894
.23	.0910	.5910	.4090	.3885
.24	.0948	.5948	.4052	.3876
.25	.0987	.5987	.4013	.3867
.26	.1026	.6026	.3974	.3857
.27	.1064	.6064	.3936	.3847
.28	.1103	.6103	.3897	.3836
.29	.1141	.6141	.3859	.3825
.30	.1179	.6179	.3821	.3814
.31	.1217	.6217	.3783	.3802
.32	.1255	.6255	.3745	.3790
.33	.1293	.6293	.3707	.3778
.34	.1331	.6331	.3669	.3765
.35	.1368	.6368	.3632	.3752
.36	.1406	.6406	.3594	.3739
.37	.1443	.6443	.3557	.3725
.38	.1480	.6480	.3520	.3712
.39	.1517	.6517	.3483	.3697
.40	.1554	.6554	.3446	.3683
.41	.1591	.6591	.3409	.3668
.42	.1628	.6628	.3372	.3653
.43	.1664	.6664	.3336	.3637
.44	.1700	.6700	.3300	.3621
.45	.1736	.6736	.3264	.3605
.46	.1772	.6772	.3228	.3589
.47	.1808	.6808	.3192	.3572
.48	.1844	.6844	.3156	.3555
.49	.1879	.6879	.3121	.3538

(1) z $\left(\frac{x}{\sigma}\right)$	(2) A Area from Mean to $\frac{x}{\sigma}$	(3) B Area in Larger Portion	(4) C Area in Smaller Portion	(5) y Ordinate at $\frac{x}{\sigma}$
.50	.1915	.6915	.3085	.3521
.51	.1950	.6950	.3050	.3503
.52	.1985	.6985	.3015	.3485
.53	.2019	.7019	.2981	.3467
.54	.2054	.7054	.2946	.3448
.55	.2088	.7088	.2912	.3429
.56	.2123	.7123	.2877	.3410
.57	.2157	.7157	.2843	.3391
.58	.2190	.7190	.2810	.3372
.59	.2224	.7224	.2776	.3352
.60	.2257	.7257	.2743	.3332
.61	.2291	.7291	.2709	.3312
.62	.2324	.7324	.2676	.3292
.63	.2357	.7357	.2643	.3271
.64	.2389	.7389	.2611	.3251
.65	.2422	.7422	.2578	.3230
.66	.2454	.7454	.2546	.3209
.67	.2486	.7486	.2514	.3187
.68	.2517	.7517	.2483	.3166
.69	.2549	.7549	.2451	.3144
.70	.2580	.7580	.2420	.3123
.71	.2611	.7611	.2389	.3101
.72	.2642	.7642	.2358	.3079
.73	.2673	.7673	.2327	.3056
.74	.2704	.7704	.2296	.3034
.75	.2734	.7734	.2266	.3011
.76	.2764	.7764	.2236	.2989
.77	.2794	.7794	.2206	.2966
.78	.2823	.7823	.2177	.2943
.79	.2852	.7852	.2148	.2920
.80	.2881	.7881	.2119	.2897
.81	.2910	.7910	.2090	.2874
.82	.2939	.7939	.2061	.2850
.83	.2967	.7967	.2033	.2827
.84	.2995	.7995	.2005	.2803
.85	.3023	.8023	.1977	.2780
.86	.3051	.8051	.1949	.2756
.87	.3078	.8078	.1922	.2732
.88	.3106	.8106	.1894	.2709
.89	.3133	.8133	.1867	.2685
.90	.3159	.8159	.1841	.2661
.91	.3186	.8186	.1814	.2637
.92	.3212	.8212	.1788	.2613
.93	.3238	.8238	.1762	.2589
.94	.3264	.8264	.1736	.2565
.95	.3289	.8289	.1711	.2541
.96	.3315	.8315	.1685	.2516
.97	.3340	.8340	.1660	.2492
.98	.3365	.8365	.1635	.2468
.99	.3389	.8389	.1611	.2444

(1) z $\left(\dfrac{x}{\sigma}\right)$	(2) A Area from Mean to $\dfrac{x}{\sigma}$	(3) B Area in Larger Portion	(4) C Area in Smaller Portion	(5) y Ordinate at $\dfrac{x}{\sigma}$
1.00	.3413	.8413	.1587	.2420
1.01	.3438	.8438	.1562	.2396
1.02	.3461	.8461	.1539	.2371
1.03	.3485	.8485	.1515	.2347
1.04	.3508	.8508	.1492	.2323
1.05	.3531	.8531	.1469	.2299
1.06	.3554	.8554	.1446	.2275
1.07	.3577	.8577	.1423	.2251
1.08	.3599	.8599	.1401	.2227
1.09	.3621	.8621	.1379	.2203
1.10	.3643	.8643	.1357	.2179
1.11	.3665	.8665	.1335	.2155
1.12	.3686	.8686	.1314	.2131
1.13	.3708	.8708	.1292	.2107
1.14	.3729	.8729	.1271	.2083
1.15	.3749	.8749	.1251	.2059
1.16	.3770	.8770	.1230	.2036
1.17	.3790	.8790	.1210	.2012
1.18	.3810	.8810	.1190	.1989
1.19	.3830	.8830	.1170	.1965
1.20	.3849	.8849	.1151	.1942
1.21	.3869	.8869	.1131	.1919
1.22	.3888	.8888	.1112	.1895
1.23	.3907	.8907	.1093	.1872
1.24	.3925	.8925	.1075	.1849
1.25	.3944	.8944	.1056	.1826
1.26	.3962	.8962	.1038	.1804
1.27	.3980	.8980	.1020	.1781
1.28	.3997	.8997	.1003	.1758
1.29	.4015	.9015	.0985	.1736
1.30	.4032	.9032	.0968	.1714
1.31	.4049	.9049	.0951	.1691
1.32	.4066	.9066	.0934	.1669
1.33	.4082	.9082	.0918	.1647
1.34	.4099	.9099	.0901	.1626
1.35	.4115	.9115	.0885	.1604
1.36	.4131	.9131	.0869	.1582
1.37	.4147	.9147	.0853	.1561
1.38	.4162	.9162	.0838	.1539
1.39	.4177	.9177	.0823	.1518
1.40	.4192	.9192	.0808	.1497
1.41	.4207	.9207	.0793	.1476
1.42	.4222	.9222	.0778	.1456
1.43	.4236	.9236	.0764	.1435
1.44	.4251	.9251	.0749	.1415
1.45	.4265	.9265	.0735	.1394
1.46	.4279	.9279	.0721	.1374
1.47	.4292	.9292	.0708	.1354
1.48	.4306	.9306	.0694	.1334
1.49	.4319	.9319	.0681	.1315

Table A. (continued)

(1) z $\left(\dfrac{x}{\sigma}\right)$	(2) A Area from Mean to $\dfrac{x}{\sigma}$	(3) B Area in Larger Portion	(4) C Area in Smaller Portion	(5) y Ordinate at $\dfrac{x}{\sigma}$
1.50	.4332	.9332	.0668	.1295
1.51	.4345	.9345	.0655	.1276
1.52	.4357	.9357	.0643	.1257
1.53	.4370	.9370	.0630	.1238
1.54	.4382	.9382	.0618	.1219
1.55	.4394	.9394	.0606	.1200
1.56	.4406	.9406	.0594	.1182
1.57	.4418	.9418	.0582	.1163
1.58	.4429	.9429	.0571	.1145
1.59	.4441	.9441	.0559	.1127
1.60	.4452	.9452	.0548	.1109
1.61	.4463	.9463	.0537	.1092
1.62	.4474	.9474	.0526	.1074
1.63	.4484	.9484	.0516	.1057
1.64	.4495	.9495	.0505	.1040
1.65	.4505	.9505	.0495	.1023
1.66	.4515	.9515	.0485	.1006
1.67	.4525	.9525	.0475	.0989
1.68	.4535	.9535	.0465	.0973
1.69	.4545	.9545	.0455	.0957
1.70	.4554	.9554	.0446	.0940
1.71	.4564	.9564	.0436	.0925
1.72	.4573	.9573	.0427	.0909
1.73	.4582	.9582	.0418	.0893
1.74	.4591	.9591	.0409	.0878
1.75	.4599	.9599	.0401	.0863
1.76	.4608	.9608	.0392	.0848
1.77	.4616	.9616	.0384	.0833
1.78	.4625	.9625	.0375	.0818
1.79	.4633	.9633	.0367	.0804
1.80	.4641	.9641	.0359	.0790
1.81	.4649	.9649	.0351	.0775
1.82	.4656	.9656	.0344	.0761
1.83	.4664	.9664	.0336	.0748
1.84	.4671	.9671	.0329	.0734
1.85	.4648	.9678	.0322	.0721
1.86	.4686	.9686	.0314	.0707
1.87	.4693	.9693	.0307	.0694
1.88	.4699	.9699	.0301	.0681
1.89	.4706	.9706	.0294	.0669
1.90	.4713	.9713	.0287	.0656
1.91	.4719	.9719	.0281	.0644
1.92	.4726	.9726	.0274	.0632
1.93	.4732	.9732	.0268	.0620
1.94	.4738	.9738	.0202	.0608
1.95	.4744	.9744	.0256	.0596
1.96	.4750	.9750	.0250	.0584
1.97	.4756	.9756	.0244	.0573
1.98	.4761	.9761	.0239	.0562
1.99	.4767	.9767	.0233	.0551

(1) z $\left(\dfrac{x}{\sigma}\right)$	(2) A Area from Mean to $\dfrac{x}{\sigma}$	(3) B Area in Larger Portion	(4) C Area in Smaller Portion	(5) y Ordinate at $\dfrac{x}{\sigma}$
2.00	.4772	.9772	.0228	.0540
2.01	.4778	.9778	.0222	.0529
2.02	.4783	.9783	.0217	.0519
2.03	.4788	.9788	.0212	.0508
2.04	.4793	.9793	.0207	.0498
2.05	.4798	.9798	.0202	.0488
2.06	.4803	.9803	.0197	.0478
2.07	.4808	.9808	.0192	.0468
2.08	.4812	.9812	.0188	.0459
2.09	.4817	.9817	.0183	.0449
2.10	.4821	.9821	.0179	.0440
2.11	.4826	.9826	.0174	.0431
2.12	.4830	.9830	.0170	.0422
2.13	.4834	.9834	.0166	.0413
2.14	.4838	.9838	.0162	.0404
2.15	.4842	.9842	.0158	.0396
2.16	.4846	.9846	.0154	.0387
2.17	.4850	.9850	.0150	.0379
2.18	.4854	.9854	.0146	.0371
2.19	.4857	.9857	.0143	.0363
2.20	.4861	.9861	.0139	.0355
2.21	.4864	.9864	.0136	.0347
2.22	.4868	.9868	.0132	.0339
2.23	.4871	.9871	.0129	.0332
2.24	.4875	.9875	.0125	.0325
2.25	.4878	.9878	.0122	.0317
2.26	.4881	.9881	.0119	.0310
2.27	.4884	.9884	.0116	.0303
2.28	.4887	.9887	.0113	.0297
2.29	.4890	.9890	.0110	.0290
2.30	.4893	.9893	.0107	.0283
2.31	.4896	.9896	.0104	.0277
2.32	.4898	.9898	.0102	.0270
2.33	.4901	.9901	.0099	.0264
2.34	.4904	.9904	.0096	.0258
2.35	.4906	.9906	.0094	.0252
2.36	.4909	.9909	.0091	.0246
2.37	.4911	.9911	.0089	.0241
2.38	.4913	.9913	.0087	.0235
2.39	.4916	.9916	.0084	.0229
2.40	.4918	.9918	.0082	.0224
2.41	.4920	.9920	.0080	.0219
2.42	.4922	.9922	.0078	.0213
2.43	.4925	.9925	.0075	.0208
2.44	.4927	.9927	.0073	.0203
2.45	.4929	.9929	.0071	.0198
2.46	.4931	.9931	.0069	.0194
2.47	.4932	.9932	.0068	.0189
2.48	.4934	.9934	.0066	.0184
2.49	.4936	.9936	.0064	.0180

(1) z $\left(\frac{x}{\sigma}\right)$	(2) A Area from Mean to $\frac{x}{\sigma}$	(3) B Area in Larger Portion	(4) C Area in Smaller Portion	(5) y Ordinate at $\frac{x}{\sigma}$
2.50	.4938	.9938	.0062	.0175
2.51	.4940	.9940	.0060	.0171
2.52	.4941	.9941	.0059	.0167
2.53	.4943	.9943	.0057	.0163
2.54	.4945	.9945	.0055	.0158
2.55	.4946	.9946	.0054	.0154
2.56	.4948	.9948	.0052	.0151
2.57	.4949	.9949	.0051	.0147
2.58	.4951	.9951	.0049	.0143
2.59	.4952	.9952	.0048	.0139
2.60	.4953	.9953	.0047	.0136
2.61	.4955	.9955	.0045	.0132
2.62	.4956	.9956	.0044	.0129
2.63	.4957	.9957	.0043	.0126
2.64	.4959	.9959	.0041	.0122
2.65	.4960	.9960	.0040	.0119
2.66	.4961	.9961	.0039	.0116
2.67	.4962	.9962	.0038	.0113
2.68	.4963	.9963	.0037	.0110
2.69	.4964	.9964	.0036	.0107
2.70	.4965	.9965	.0035	.0104
2.71	.4966	.9966	.0034	.0101
2.72	.4967	.9967	.0033	.0099
2.73	.4968	.9968	.0032	.0096
2.74	.4969	.9969	.0031	.0093
2.75	.4970	.9970	.0030	.0091
2.76	.4971	.9971	.0029	.0088
2.77	.4972	.9972	.0028	.0086
2.78	.4973	.9973	.0027	.0084
2.79	.4974	.9974	.0026	.0081
2.80	.4974	.9974	.0026	.0079
2.81	.4975	.9975	.0025	.0077
2.82	.4976	.9976	.0024	.0075
2.83	.4977	.9977	.0023	.0073
2.84	.4977	.9977	.0023	.0071
2.85	.4978	.9978	.0022	.0069
2.86	.4979	.9979	.0021	.0067
2.87	.4979	.9979	.0021	.0065
2.88	.4980	.9980	.0020	.0063
2.89	.4981	.9981	.0019	.0061
2.90	.4981	.9981	.0019	.0060
2.91	.4982	.9982	.0018	.0058
2.92	.4982	.9982	.0018	.0056
2.93	.4983	.9983	.0017	.0055
2.94	.4984	.9984	.0016	.0053
2.95	.4984	.9984	.0016	.0051
2.96	.4985	.9985	.0015	.0050
2.97	.4985	.9985	.0015	.0048
2.98	.4986	.9986	.0014	.0047
2.99	.4986	.9986	.0014	.0046

(1)	(2)	(3)	(4)	(5)
z	A	B	C	y
$\left(\dfrac{x}{\sigma}\right)$	Area from Mean to $\dfrac{x}{\sigma}$	Area in Larger Portion	Area in Smaller Portion	Ordinate at $\dfrac{x}{\sigma}$
3.00	.4987	.9987	.0013	.0044
3.01	.4987	.9987	.0013	.0043
3.02	.4987	.9987	.0013	.0042
3.03	.4988	.9988	.0012	.0040
3.04	.4988	.9988	.0012	.0039
3.05	.4989	.9989	.0011	.0038
3.06	.4989	.9989	.0011	.0037
3.07	.4989	.9989	.0011	.0036
3.08	.4990	.9990	.0010	.0035
3.09	.4990	.9990	.0010	.0034
3.10	.4990	.9990	.0010	.0033
3.11	.4991	.9991	.0009	.0032
3.12	.4991	.9991	.0009	.0031
3.13	.4991	.9991	.0009	.0030
3.14	.4992	.9992	.0008	.0029
3.15	.4992	.9992	.0008	.0028
3.16	.4992	.9992	.0008	.0027
3.17	.4992	.9992	.0008	.0026
3.18	.4993	.9993	.0007	.0025
3.19	.4993	.9993	.0007	.0025
3.20	.4993	.9993	.0007	.0024
3.21	.4993	.9993	.0007	.0023
3.22	.4994	.9994	.0006	.0022
3.23	.4994	.9994	.0006	.0022
3.24	.4994	.9994	.0006	.0021
3.30	.4995	.9995	.0005	.0017
3.40	.4997	.9997	.0003	.0012
3.50	.4998	.9998	.0002	.0009
3.60	.4998	.9998	.0002	.0006
3.70	.4999	.9999	.0001	.0004

SOURCE: *Statistical Methods for the Behavioral Sciences*, A. L. Edwards. Copyright © 1954 by Allen L. Edwards. Reprinted by permission of the publisher, Holt, Rinehart and Winston, Inc.

Table AA. Ordinate Values of the Normal Distribution
Expressed as Proportions of the Ordinate at the Mean*

$\frac{x}{\sigma}$	0	1	2	3	4	5	6	7	8	9
0.0	1.000	.999+	.999+	.999+	.999+	.999	.998	.998	.997	.996
0.1	.995	.994	.993	.992	.990	.989	.987	.986	.984	.982
0.2	.980	.978	.976	.974	.972	.969	.967	.964	.962	.959
0.3	.956	.953	.950	.947	.944	.941	.937	.934	.930	.927
0.4	.923	.918	.916	.912	.908	.904	.900	.895	.891	.887
0.5	.882	.878	.874	.869	.864	.860	.855	.850	.845	.841
0.6	.835	.830	.825	.820	.815	.810	.804	.799	.794	.788
0.7	.783	.777	.772	.766	.760	.755	.749	.743	.738	.732
0.8	.726	.720	.714	.709	.703	.697	.691	.685	.679	.673
0.9	.667	.661	.655	.649	.643	.637	.631	.625	.619	.613
1.0	.607	.600	.594	.588	.582	.576	.570	.564	.558	.552
1.1	.546	.540	.534	.528	.522	.516	.510	.504	.498	.493
1.2	.487	.481	.475	.469	.464	.458	.452	.446	.441	.435
1.3	.430	.424	.418	.413	.407	.402	.397	.391	.386	.381
1.4	.375	.370	.365	.360	.355	.350	.344	.339	.334	.330
1.5	.325	.320	.315	.310	.306	.301	.296	.292	.287	.283
1.6	.278	.274	.269	.265	.261	.256	.252	.248	.244	.240
1.7	.236	.232	.228	.224	.220	.216	.213	.209	.205	.201
1.8	.198	.194	.191	.187	.184	.181	.177	.174	.171	.168
1.9	.164	.161	.158	.155	.152	.149	.146	.144	.141	.138
2.0	.135	.133	.130	.127	.125	.122	.120	.117	.115	.113
2.1	.110	.108	.106	.103	.101	.099	.097	.095	.093	.091
2.2	.089	.087	.085	.083	.081	.080	.078	.076	.074	.073
2.3	.071	.069	.068	.066	.065	.063	.062	.060	.059	.058
2.4	.056	.055	.054	.052	.051	.050	.049	.047	.046	.045
2.5	.044	.043	.042	.041	.040	.039	.038	.037	.036	.035
2.6	.034	.033	.032	.031	.031	.030	.029	.028	.028	.027
2.7	.026	.025	.025	.024	.023	.023	.022	.022	.021	.020
2.8	.020	.019	.019	.018	.018	.017	.017	.016	.016	.015
2.9	.015	.014	.014	.014	.013	.013	.013	.012	.012	.011
3.0	.011									
4.0	.0003									
5.0	.00000									

SOURCE: J. G. Peatman, *Descriptive and Sampling Statistics*. New York: Harper, 1947.
* The height of the mean ordinate is taken as 1.000. The proportion of frequencies at the mean for a finite distribution size N is equal to $N/2.51\sigma'$, where σ' is a point estimate from s', the standard deviation in unit intervals: $s' = s/i$, i being the size of the interval on which s was calculated.

Example: When the size of a sample is 100 cases and $s = 15$ and $i = 10$, then

$$F_{\bar{x}} = \frac{100}{2.51(15/10)} = 26.6, \text{ and } F_{z=.25} = .969 (26.6) = 25.8, \text{ etc.}$$

Table B. Critical Values of "Student's" *t* Statistic

	Alpha Level of Significance for Directional Tests					
	.10	.05	.025	.01	.005	.0005
	Alpha Level of Significance for Nondirectional Tests					
d.f.	.20	.10	.05	.02	.01	.001
1	1.000	6.314	12.706	31.821	63.657	636.619
2	.816	2.920	4.303	6.965	9.925	31.598
3	.765	2.353	3.182	4.541	5.841	12.941
4	.741	2.132	2.776	3.747	4.604	8.610
5	.727	2.015	2.571	3.365	4.032	6.859
6	.718	1.943	2.447	3.143	3.707	5.959
7	.711	1.895	2.365	2.998	3.499	5.405
8	.706	1.860	2.306	2.896	3.355	5.041
9	.703	1.833	2.262	2.821	3.250	4.781
10	.700	1.812	2.228	2.764	3.169	4.587
11	.697	1.796	2.201	2.718	3.106	4.437
12	.695	1.782	2.179	2.681	3.055	4.318
13	.694	1.771	2.160	2.650	3.012	4.221
14	.692	1.761	2.145	2.624	2.977	4.140
15	.691	1.753	2.131	2.602	2.947	4.073
16	.690	1.746	2.120	2.583	2.921	4.015
17	.689	1.740	2.110	2.567	2.898	3.965
18	.688	1.734	2.101	2.552	2.878	3.922
19	.688	1.729	2.093	2.539	2.861	3.883
20	.687	1.725	2.086	2.528	2.845	3.850
21	.686	1.721	2.080	2.518	2.831	3.819
22	.686	1.717	2.074	2.508	2.819	3.792
23	.685	1.714	2.069	2.500	2.807	3.767
24	.685	1.711	2.064	2.492	2.797	3.745
25	.684	1.708	2.060	2.485	2.787	3.725
26	.684	1.706	2.056	2.479	2.779	3.707
27	.684	1.703	2.052	2.473	2.771	3.690
28	.683	1.701	2.048	2.467	2.763	3.674
29	.683	1.699	2.045	2.462	2.756	3.659
30	.683	1.697	2.042	2.457	2.750	3.646
40	.681	1.684	2.021	2.423	2.704	3.551
60	.679	1.671	2.000	2.390	2.660	3.460
120	.677	1.658	1.980	2.358	2.617	3.373
∞	.674	1.645	1.960	2.326	2.576	3.291

SOURCE: Abridged from Table III of R. A. Fisher and F. Yates, *Statistical Tables for Biological, Agricultural, and Medical Research*, published by Oliver & Boyd, Ltd., Edinburgh, 1938; reproduced by permission of the authors and publishers.

Table C. Centile Values

d.f.	$\chi^2_{.005}$	$\chi^2_{.01}$	$\chi^2_{.025}$	$\chi^2_{.05}$	$\chi^2_{.10}$	$\chi^2_{.25}$	$\chi^2_{.50}$
1	. .	. .	. .	. .	.02	.10	.45
2	.01	.02	.05	.10	.21	.58	1.4
3	.07	.11	.22	.35	.58	1.21	2.4
4	.21	.30	.48	.71	1.1	1.92	3.4
5	.41	.55	.83	1.1	1.6	2.7	4.4
6	.68	.87	1.2	1.6	2.2	3.5	5.4
7	.99	1.24	1.7	2.2	2.8	4.3	6.4
8	1.3	1.65	2.2	2.7	3.5	5.1	7.3
9	1.7	2.09	2.7	3.3	4.2	5.9	8.3
10	2.2	2.56	3.2	3.9	4.9	6.7	9.3
11	2.6	3.05	3.8	4.6	5.6	7.6	10.3
12	3.1	3.57	4.4	5.2	6.3	8.4	11.3
13	3.6	4.11	5.0	5.9	7.0	9.3	12.3
14	4.1	4.66	5.6	6.6	7.8	10.2	13.3
15	4.6	5.23	6.3	7.3	8.5	11.0	14.3
16	5.1	5.81	6.9	8.0	9.3	11.9	15.3
17	5.7	6.41	7.6	8.7	10.1	12.8	16.3
18	6.3	7.01	8.2	9.4	10.9	13.7	17.3
19	6.8	7.63	8.9	10.1	11.7	14.6	18.3
20	7.4	8.26	9.6	10.9	12.4	15.5	19.3
21	8.0	8.9	10.3	11.6	13.2	16.3	20.3
22	8.6	9.5	11.0	12.3	14.0	17.2	21.3
23	9.3	10.2	11.7	13.1	14.8	18.1	22.3
24	9.9	10.9	12.4	13.8	15.7	19.0	23.3
25	10.5	11.5	13.1	14.6	16.5	19.9	24.3
26	11.2	12.2	13.8	15.4	17.3	20.8	25.3
27	11.8	12.9	14.6	16.2	18.1	21.7	26.3
28	12.5	13.6	15.3	16.9	18.9	22.7	27.3
29	13.1	14.3	16.0	17.7	19.8	23.6	28.3
30	13.8	15.0	16.8	18.5	20.6	24.5	29.3

SOURCE: Abridged from Table 8 of E. S. Pearson and H. O. Hartley, *Biometrika Tables for Statisticians*, vol. 1, 2nd ed., 1958, published by the Syndics of the Cambridge University Press, London; reproduced by permission of the authors and publishers.

of the Chi-Square Statistic

d.f.	$\chi^2_{.75}$	$\chi^2_{.90}$	$\chi^2_{.95}$	$\chi^2_{.975}$	$\chi^2_{.99}$	$\chi^2_{.995}$	$\chi^2_{.999}$
1	1.3	2.7	3.8	5.0	6.6	7.9	10.8
2	2.8	4.6	6.0	7.4	9.2	10.6	13.8
3	4.1	6.3	7.8	9.4	11.3	12.8	16.3
4	5.4	7.8	9.5	11.1	13.3	14.9	18.5
5	6.6	9.2	11.1	12.8	15.1	16.7	20.5
6	7.8	10.6	12.6	14.4	16.8	18.5	22.5
7	9.0	12.0	14.1	16.0	18.5	20.3	24.3
8	10.2	13.4	15.5	17.5	20.1	22.0	26.1
9	11.4	14.7	16.9	19.0	21.7	23.6	27.9
10	12.5	16.0	18.3	20.5	23.2	25.2	29.6
11	13.7	17.3	19.7	21.9	24.7	26.8	31.3
12	14.8	18.5	21.0	23.3	26.2	28.3	32.9
13	16.0	19.8	22.4	24.7	27.7	29.8	34.5
14	17.1	21.1	23.7	26.1	29.1	31.3	36.1
15	18.2	22.3	25.0	27.5	30.6	32.8	37.7
16	19.4	23.5	26.3	28.8	32.0	34.3	39.3
17	20.5	24.8	27.6	30.2	33.4	35.7	40.8
18	21.6	26.0	28.9	31.5	34.8	37.2	42.3
19	22.7	27.2	30.1	32.9	36.2	38.6	43.8
20	23.8	28.4	31.4	34.2	37.6	40.0	45.3
21	24.9	29.6	32.7	35.5	38.9	41.4	46.8
22	26.0	30.8	33.9	36.8	40.3	42.8	48.3
23	27.1	32.0	35.2	38.1	41.6	44.2	49.7
24	28.2	33.2	36.4	39.4	43.0	45.6	51.2
25	29.3	34.4	37.7	40.6	44.3	46.9	52.6
26	30.4	35.6	38.9	41.9	45.6	48.3	54.0
27	31.5	36.7	40.1	43.2	47.0	49.6	55.5
28	32.6	37.9	41.3	44.5	48.3	51.0	56.9
29	33.7	39.1	42.6	45.7	49.6	52.3	58.3
30	34.8	40.3	43.8	47.0	50.9	53.3	59.7

Note that median values of chi-square are in $\chi^2_{.50}$ column.

Table D.   Davidoff-Goheen Table for Estimating Tetrachoric r from ad/bc Ratios

r_t	ad/bc	r_t	ad/bc	r_t	ad/bc
.00	0–1.00	.35	2.49–2.55	.70	8.50–8.90
.01	1.01–1.03	.36	2.56–2.63	.71	8.91–9.35
.02	1.04–1.06	.37	2.64–2.71	.72	9.36–9.82
.03	1.07–1.08	.38	2.72–2.79	.73	9.83–10.33
.04	1.09–1.11	.39	2.80–2.87	.74	10.34–10.90
.05	1.12–1.14	.40	2.88–2.96	.75	10.91–11.51
.06	1.15–1.17	.41	2.97–3.05	.76	11.52–12.16
.07	1.18–1.20	.42	3.06–3.14	.77	12.17–12.89
.08	1.21–1.23	.43	3.15–3.24	.78	12.90–13.70
.09	1.24–1.27	.44	3.25–3.34	.79	13.71–14.58
.10	1.28–1.30	.45	3.35–3.45	.80	14.59–15.57
.11	1.31–1.33	.46	3.46–3.56	.81	15.58–16.65
.12	1.34–1.37	.47	3.57–3.68	.82	16.66–17.88
.13	1.38–1.40	.48	3.69–3.80	.83	17.89–19.28
.14	1.41–1.44	.49	3.81–3.92	.84	19.29–20.85
.15	1.45–1.48	.50	3.93–4.06	.85	20.86–22.68
.16	1.49–1.52	.51	4.07–4.20	.86	22.69–24.76
.17	1.53–1.56	.52	4.21–4.34	.87	24.77–27.22
.18	1.57–1.60	.53	4.35–4.49	.88	27.23–30.09
.19	1.61–1.64	.54	4.50–4.66	.89	30.10–33.60
.20	1.65–1.69	.55	4.67–4.82	.90	33.61–37.79
.21	1.70–1.73	.56	4.83–4.99	.91	37.80–43.06
.22	1.74–1.78	.57	5.00–518	.92	43.07–49.83
.23	1.79–1.83	.58	5.19–5.38	.93	49.84–58.79
.24	1.84–1.88	.59	5.39–5.59	.94	58.80–70.95
.25	1.89–1.93	.60	5.60–5.80	.95	70.96–89.01
.26	1.94–1.98	.61	5.81–6.03	.96	89.02–117.54
.27	1.99–2.04	.62	6.04–6.28	.97	117.55–169.67
.28	2.05–2.10	.63	6.29–6.54	.98	169.68–293.12
.29	2.11–2.15	.64	6.55–6.81	.99	293.13–923.97
.30	2.16–2.22	.65	6.82–7.10	1.00	923.98 . . .
.31	2.23–2.28	.66	7.11–7.42		
.32	2.29–2.34	.67	7.43–7.75		
.33	2.35–2.41	.68	7.76–8.11		
.34	2.42–2.48	.69	8.12–8.49		

SOURCE: M. D. Davidoff and H. W. Goheen. A table for the rapid determination of the tetrachoric correlation coefficient. *Psychometrika*, 1953, **18**, 115–121. Reprinted with the permission of the authors and publisher

Table E. Fisher's Z Transformation Function for Pearson's r Correlation Coefficient

$$Z = \tfrac{1}{2}\left[\log_e (1 + r) - \log_e (1 - r)\right]$$

r	Z	r	Z	r	Z	r	Z	r	Z
.000	.000	.200	.203	.400	.424	.600	.693	.800	1.099
.005	.005	.205	.208	.405	.430	.605	.701	.805	1.113
.010	.010	.210	.213	.410	.436	.610	.709	.810	1.127
.015	.015	.215	.218	.415	.442	.615	.717	.815	1.142
.020	.020	.220	.224	.420	.448	.620	.725	.820	1.157
.025	.025	.225	.229	.425	.454	.625	.733	.825	1.172
.030	.030	.230	.234	.430	.460	.630	.741	.830	1.188
.035	.035	.235	.239	.435	.466	.635	.750	.835	1.204
.040	.040	.240	.245	.440	.472	.640	.758	.840	1.221
.045	.045	.245	.250	.445	.478	.645	.767	.845	1.238
.050	.050	.250	.255	.450	.485	.650	.775	.850	1.256
.055	.055	.255	.261	.455	.491	.655	.784	.855	1.274
.060	.060	.260	.266	.460	.497	.660	.793	.860	1.293
.065	.065	.265	.271	.465	.504	.665	.802	.865	1.313
.070	.070	.270	.277	.470	.510	.670	.811	.870	1.333
.075	.075	.275	.282	.475	.517	.675	.820	.875	1.354
.080	.080	.280	.288	.480	.523	.680	.829	.880	1.376
.085	.085	.285	.293	.485	.530	.685	.838	.885	1.398
.090	.090	.290	.299	.490	.536	.690	.848	.890	1.422
.095	.095	.295	.304	.495	.543	.695	.858	.895	1.447
.100	.100	.300	.310	.500	.549	.700	.867	.900	1.472
.105	.105	.305	.315	.505	.556	.705	.877	.905	1.499
.110	.110	.310	.321	.510	.563	.710	.887	.910	1.528
.115	.116	.315	.326	.515	.570	.715	.897	.915	1.557
.120	.121	.320	.332	.520	.576	.720	.908	.920	1.589
.125	.126	.325	.337	.525	.583	.725	.918	.925	1.623
.130	.131	.330	.343	.530	.590	.730	.929	.930	1.658
.135	.136	.335	.348	.535	.597	.735	.940	.935	1.697
.140	.141	.340	.354	.540	.604	.740	.950	.940	1.738
.145	.146	.345	.360	.545	.611	.745	.962	.945	1,783
.150	.151	.350	.365	.550	.618	.750	.973	.950	1.832
.155	.156	.355	.371	.555	.626	.755	.984	.955	1.886
.160	.161	.360	.377	.560	.633	.760	.996	.960	1.946
.165	.167	.365	.383	.565	.640	.765	1.008	.965	2.014
.170	.172	.370	.388	.570	.648	.770	1.020	.970	2.092
.175	.177	.375	.394	.575	.655	.775	1.033	.975	2.185
.180	.182	.380	.400	.580	.662	.780	1.045	.980	2.298
.185	.187	.385	.406	.585	.670	.785	1.058	.985	2.443
.190	.192	.390	.412	.590	.678	.790	1.071	.990	2.647
.195	.198	.395	.418	.595	.685	.795	1.085	.995	2.994

SOURCE: *Statistical Methods for the Behavioral Sciences*, A. L. Edwards. Copyright © 1954 by Allen L. Edwards. The table was constructed by F. P. Kilpatrick and D. A. Buchanan, using Fisher's formula, as above. Reprinted by permission of the publishers, Holt, Rinehart and Winston, Inc.

Table EE. Critical Values of Pearson's *r* Correlation Coefficient for Five *Alpha* Significance Levels

$n' - 2$	.10	.05	.02	.01	.001
1	.98769	.99692	.999507	.999877	.9999988
2	.90000	.95000	.98000	.990000	.99900
3	.8054	.8783	.93433	.95873	.99116
4	.7293	.8114	.8822	.91720	.97406
5	.6694	.7545	.8329	.8745	.95074
6	.6215	.7067	.7887	.8343	.92493
7	.5822	.6664	.7498	.7977	.8982
8	.5494	.6319	.7155	.7646	.8721
9	.5214	.6021	.6851	.7348	.8471
10	.4973	.5760	.6581	.7079	.8233
11	.4762	.5529	.6339	.6835	.8010
12	.4575	.5324	.6120	.6614	.7800
13	.4409	.5139	.5923	.6411	.7603
14	.4259	.4973	.5742	.6226	.7420
15	.4124	.4821	.5577	.6055	.7246
16	.4000	.4683	.5425	.5897	.7084
17	.3887	.4555	.5285	.5751	.6932
18	.3783	.4438	.5155	.5614	.6787
19	.3687	.4329	.5034	.5487	.6652
20	.3598	.4227	.4921	.5368	.6524
25	.3233	.3809	.4451	.4869	.5974
30	.2960	.3494	.4093	.4487	.5541
35	.2746	.3246	.3810	.4182	.5189
40	.2573	.3044	.3578	.3932	.4896
45	.2428	.2875	.3384	.3721	.4648
50	.2306	.2732	.3218	.3541	.4433
60	.2108	.2500	.2948	.3248	.4078
70	.1954	.2319	.2737	.3017	.3799
80	.1829	.2172	.2565	.2830	.3568
90	.1726	.2050	.2422	.2673	.3375
100	.1638	.1946	.2301	.2540	.3211

SOURCE: Reprinted from Table VI of R. A. Fisher and F. Yates, *Statistical Tables for Biological, Agricultural, and Medical Research*, published by Oliver and Boyd, Ltd., Edinburgh, 1938; reproduced by permission of the authors and publishers.

Table EEE. Factorials for Integers 0 to 20

n	$n!$
0	1
1	1
2	2
3	6
4	24
5	120
6	720
7	5040
8	40320
9	362880
10	3628800
11	39916800
12	479001600
13	6227020800
14	87178291200
15	1307674368000
16	20922789888000
17	355687428096000
18	6402373705728000
19	121645100408832000
20	2432902008176640000

SOURCE: Salzer, H. E. 1951. Tables of $n!$ and $\Gamma(n + \frac{1}{2})$ for the First Thousand Values of n. National Bureau of Standards, Applied Mathematics Series No. 16. U.S. Government Printing Office, Washington, D.C.

d.f.$_1$ \ d.f.$_2$	1	2	3	4	5	6	7	8	9	10
1	161.4	199.5	215.7	224.6	230.2	234.0	236.8	238.9	240.5	241.9
	4052.	*4999.5*	*5403.*	*5625.*	*5764.*	*5859.*	*5928.*	*5982.*	*6022.*	*6056.*
	4053*	5000*	5404*	5625*	5764*	5859*	5929*	5981*	6023*	6056*
2	18.51	19.00	19.16	19.25	19.30	19.33	19.35	19.37	19.38	19.40
	98.49	*99.01*	*99.17*	*99.25*	*99.30*	*99.33*	*99.36*	*99.37*	*99.39*	*99.40*
	998.5	999.0	999.2	999.2	999.3	999.3	999.4	999.4	999.4	999.4
3	10.13	9.55	9.28	9.12	9.01	8.94	8.89	8.85	8.81	8.79
	34.12	*30.82*	*29.46*	*28.71*	*28.24*	*27.91*	*27.67*	*27.49*	*27.35*	*27.23*
	167.5	148.5	141.1	137.1	134.6	132.8	131.6	130.6	129.9	129.2
4	7.71	6.94	6.59	6.39	6.26	6.16	6.09	6.04	6.00	5.96
	21.20	*18.00*	*16.69*	*15.98*	*15.52*	*15.21*	*14.98*	*14.80*	*14.66*	*14.55*
	74.14	61.25	56.18	53.44	51.71	50.53	49.66	49.00	48.47	48.05
5	6.61	5.79	5.41	5.19	5.05	4.95	4.88	4.82	4.77	4.74
	16.26	*13.27*	*12.06*	*11.39*	*10.97*	*10.67*	*10.46*	*10.29*	*10.16*	*10.05*
	47.18	37.12	33.20	31.09	29.75	28.84	28.16	27.64	27.24	26.92
6	5.99	5.14	4.76	4.53	4.39	4.28	4.21	4.15	4.10	4.06
	13.75	*10.92*	*9.78*	*9.15*	*8.75*	*8.47*	*8.26*	*8.10*	*7.98*	*7.87*
	35.51	27.00	23.70	21.92	20.81	20.03	19.46	19.03	18.69	18.41
7	5.59	4.74	4.35	4.12	3.97	3.87	3.79	3.73	3.68	3.64
	12.25	*9.55*	*8.45*	*7.85*	*7.46*	*7.19*	*6.99*	*6.84*	*6.72*	*6.62*
	29.25	21.69	18.77	17.19	16.21	15.52	15.02	14.63	14.33	14.08
8	5.32	4.46	4.07	3.84	3.69	3.58	3.50	3.44	3.39	3.35
	11.26	*8.65*	*7.59*	*7.01*	*6.63*	*6.37*	*6.18*	*6.03*	*5.91*	*5.81*
	25.42	18.49	15.83	14.39	13.49	12.86	12.40	12.04	11.77	11.54
9	5.12	4.26	3.86	3.63	3.48	3.37	3.29	3.23	3.18	3.14
	10.56	*8.02*	*6.99*	*6.42*	*6.06*	*5.80*	*5.61*	*5.47*	*5.35*	*5.26*
	22.86	16.39	13.90	12.56	11.71	11.13	10.70	10.37	10.11	9.89
10	4.96	4.10	3.71	3.48	3.33	3.22	3.14	3.07	3.02	2.98
	10.04	*7.56*	*6.55*	*5.99*	*5.64*	*5.39*	*5.20*	*5.06*	*4.94*	*4.85*
	21.04	14.91	12.55	11.28	10.48	9.92	9.52	9.20	8.96	8.75
11	4.84	3.98	3.59	3.36	3.20	3.09	3.01	2.95	2.90	2.85
	9.65	*7.21*	*6.22*	*5.67*	*5.32*	*5.07*	*4.89*	*4.74*	*4.63*	*4.54*
	19.69	13.81	11.56	10.35	9.58	9.05	8.66	8.35	8.12	7.92
12	4.75	3.89	3.49	3.26	3.11	3.00	2.91	2.85	2.80	2.75
	9.33	*6.93*	*5.95*	*5.41*	*5.06*	*4.82*	*4.64*	*4.50*	*4.39*	*4.30*
	18.64	12.97	10.80	9.63	8.89	8.38	8.00	7.71	7.48	7.29
13	4.67	3.81	3.41	3.18	3.03	2.92	2.83	2.77	2.71	2.67
	9.07	*6.70*	*5.74*	*5.21*	*4.86*	*4.62*	*4.44*	*4.30*	*4.19*	*4.10*
	17.81	12.31	10.21	9.07	8.35	7.86	7.49	7.21	6.98	6.80
14	4.60	3.74	3.34	3.11	2.96	2.85	2.76	2.70	2.65	2.60
	8.86	*6.51*	*5.56*	*5.04*	*4.69*	*4.46*	*4.28*	*4.14*	*4.03*	*3.94*
	17.14	11.78	9.73	8.62	7.92	7.43	7.08	6.80	6.58	6.40
15	4.54	3.68	3.29	3.06	2.90	2.79	2.71	2.64	2.59	2.54
	8.68	*6.36*	*5.42*	*4.89*	*4.56*	*4.32*	*4.14*	*4.00*	*3.89*	*3.80*
	16.59	11.34	9.34	8.25	7.57	7.09	6.74	6.47	6.26	6.08

* Multiply these entries by 100.

408

12	15	20	24	30	40	60	120	∞	d.f.₁ / d.f.₂
243.9	245.9	248.0	249.1	250.1	251.1	252.2	253.3	254.3	
6106.	*6157.*	*6209.*	*6235.*	*6261.*	*6287.*	*6313.*	*6339.*	*6366.*	1
6107*	6158*	6209*	6235*	6261*	6287*	6313*	6340*	6366*	
19.41	19.43	19.45	19.45	19.46	19.47	19.48	19.49	19.50	
99.42	*99.43*	*99.45*	*99.46*	*99.47*	*99.47*	*99.48*	*99.49*	*99.50*	2
999.4	999.4	999.4	999.5	999.5	999.5	999.5	999.5	999.5	
8.74	8.70	8.66	8.64	8.62	8.59	8.57	8.55	8.53	
27.05	*26.87*	*26.69*	*26.60*	*26.50*	*26.41*	*26.32*	*26.22*	*26.13*	3
128.3	127.4	126.4	125.9	125.4	125.0	124.5	124.0	123.5	
5.91	5.86	5.80	5.77	5.75	5.72	5.69	5.66	5.63	
14.37	*14.20*	*14.02*	*13.93*	*13.84*	*13.75*	*13.65*	*13.56*	*13.46*	4
47.41	46.76	46.10	45.77	45.43	45.09	44.75	44.40	44.05	
4.68	4.62	4.56	4.53	4.50	4.46	4.43	4.40	4.36	
9.89	*9.72*	*9.55*	*9.47*	*9.38*	*9.29*	*9.20*	*9.11*	*9.02*	5
26.42	25.91	25.39	25.14	24.87	24.60	24.33	24.06	23.79	
4.00	3.94	3.87	3.84	3.81	3.77	3.74	3.70	3.67	
7.72	*7.56*	*7.40*	*7.31*	*7.23*	*7.14*	*7.06*	*6.97*	*6.88*	6
17.99	17.56	17.12	16.89	16.67	16.44	16.21	15.99	15.75	
3.57	3.51	3.44	3.41	3.38	3.34	3.30	3.27	3.23	
6.47	*6.31*	*6.16*	*6.07*	*5.99*	*5.91*	*5.82*	*5.74*	*5.65*	7
13.71	13.32	12.93	12.73	12.53	12.33	12.12	11.91	11.70	
3.28	3.22	3.15	3.12	3.08	3.04	3.01	2.97	2.93	
5.67	*5.52*	*5.36*	*5.28*	*5.20*	*5.12*	*5.03*	*4.95*	*4.86*	8
11.19	10.84	10.48	10.30	10.11	9.92	9.73	9.53	9.33	
3.07	3.01	2.94	2.90	2.86	2.83	2.79	2.75	2.71	
5.11	*4.96*	*4.81*	*4.73*	*4.65*	*4.57*	*4.48*	*4.40*	*4.31*	9
9.57	9.24	8.90	8.72	8.55	8.37	8.19	8.00	7.81	
2.91	2.85	2.77	2.74	2.70	2.66	2.62	2.58	2.54	
4.71	*4.56*	*4.41*	*4.33*	*4.25*	*4.17*	*4.08*	*4.00*	*3.91*	10
8.45	8.13	7.80	7.64	7.47	7.30	7.12	6.94	6.76	
2.79	2.72	2.65	2.61	2.57	2.53	2.49	2.45	2.40	
4.40	*4.25*	*4.10*	*4.02*	*3.94*	*3.86*	*3.78*	*3.69*	*3.60*	11
7.63	7.32	7.01	6.85	6.68	6.52	6.35	6.17	6.00	
2.69	2.62	2.54	2.51	2.47	2.43	2.38	2.34	2.30	
4.16	*4.01*	*3.86*	*3.78*	*3.70*	*3.62*	*3.54*	*3.45*	*3.36*	12
7.00	6.71	6.40	6.25	6.09	5.93	5.76	5.59	5.42	
2.60	2.53	2.46	2.42	2.38	2.34	2.30	2.25	2.21	
3.96	*3.82*	*3.66*	*3.59*	*3.51*	*3.43*	*3.34*	*3.25*	*3.17*	13
6.52	6.23	5.93	5.78	5.63	5.47	5.30	5.14	4.97	
2.53	2.46	2.39	2.35	2.31	2.27	2.22	2.18	2.13	
3.80	*3.66*	*3.51*	*3.43*	*3.35*	*3.27*	*3.18*	*3.09*	*3.00*	14
6.13	5.85	5.56	5.41	5.25	5.10	4.94	4.77	4.60	
2.48	2.40	2.33	2.29	2.25	2.20	2.16	2.11	2.07	
3.67	*3.52*	*3.37*	*3.29*	*3.21*	*3.13*	*3.05*	*2.96*	*2.87*	15
5.81	5.54	5.25	5.10	4.95	4.80	4.64	4.47	4.31	

Table F. (continued)

d.f.$_2$ \ d.f.$_1$	1	2	3	4	5	6	7	8	9	10
16	4.49 / *8.53* / **16.12**	3.63 / *6.23* / **10.97**	3.24 / *5.29* / **9.00**	3.01 / *4.77* / **7.94**	2.85 / *4.44* / **7.27**	2.74 / *4.20* / **6.81**	2.66 / *4.03* / **6.46**	2.59 / *3.89* / **6.19**	2.54 / *3.78* / **5.98**	2.49 / *3.69* / **5.81**
17	4.45 / *8.40* / **15.72**	3.59 / *6.11* / **10.66**	3.20 / *5.18* / **8.73**	2.96 / *4.67* / **7.68**	2.81 / *4.34* / **7.02**	2.70 / *4.10* / **6.56**	2.61 / *3.93* / **6.22**	2.55 / *3.79* / **5.96**	2.49 / *3.68* / **5.75**	2.45 / *3.59* / **5.58**
18	4.41 / *8.29* / **15.38**	3.55 / *6.01* / **10.39**	3.16 / *5.09* / **8.49**	2.93 / *4.58* / **7.46**	2.77 / *4.25* / **6.81**	2.66 / *4.01* / **6.35**	2.58 / *3.84* / **6.02**	2.51 / *3.71* / **5.76**	2.46 / *3.60* / **5.56**	2.41 / *3.51* / **5.39**
19	4.38 / *8.18* / **15.08**	3.52 / *5.93* / **10.16**	3.13 / *5.01* / **8.28**	2.90 / *4.50* / **7.26**	2.74 / *4.17* / **6.62**	2.63 / *3.94* / **6.18**	2.54 / *3.77* / **5.85**	2.48 / *3.63* / **5.59**	2.42 / *3.52* / **5.39**	2.38 / *3.43* / **5.22**
20	4.35 / *8.10* / **14.82**	3.49 / *5.85* / **9.95**	3.10 / *4.94* / **8.10**	2.87 / *4.43* / **7.10**	2.71 / *4.10* / **6.46**	2.60 / *3.87* / **6.02**	2.51 / *3.70* / **5.69**	2.45 / *3.56* / **5.44**	2.39 / *3.46* / **5.24**	2.35 / *3.37* / **5.08**
21	4.32 / *8.02* / **14.59**	3.47 / *5.78* / **9.77**	3.07 / *4.87* / **7.94**	2.84 / *4.37* / **6.95**	2.68 / *4.04* / **6.32**	2.57 / *3.81* / **5.88**	2.49 / *3.64* / **5.56**	2.42 / *3.51* / **5.31**	2.37 / *3.40* / **5.11**	2.32 / *3.31* / **4.95**
22	4.30 / *7.95* / **14.38**	3.44 / *5.72* / **9.61**	3.05 / *4.82* / **7.80**	2.82 / *4.31* / **6.81**	2.66 / *3.99* / **6.19**	2.55 / *3.76* / **5.76**	2.46 / *3.59* / **5.44**	2.40 / *3.45* / **5.19**	2.34 / *3.35* / **4.99**	2.30 / *3.26* / **4.83**
23	4.28 / *7.88* / **14.19**	3.42 / *5.66* / **9.47**	3.03 / *4.76* / **7.67**	2.80 / *4.26* / **6.69**	2.64 / *3.94* / **6.08**	2.53 / *3.71* / **5.65**	2.44 / *3.54* / **5.33**	2.37 / *3.41* / **5.09**	2.32 / *3.30* / **4.89**	2.27 / *3.21* / **4.73**
24	4.26 / *7.82* / **14.03**	3.40 / *5.61* / **9.34**	3.01 / *4.72* / **7.55**	2.78 / *4.22* / **6.59**	2.62 / *3.90* / **5.98**	2.51 / *3.67* / **5.55**	2.42 / *3.50* / **5.23**	2.36 / *3.36* / **4.99**	2.30 / *3.26* / **4.80**	2.25 / *3.17* / **4.64**
25	4.24 / *7.77* / **13.88**	3.39 / *5.57* / **9.22**	2.99 / *4.68* / **7.45**	2.76 / *4.18* / **6.49**	2.60 / *3.85* / **5.88**	2.49 / *3.63* / **5.46**	2.40 / *3.46* / **5.15**	2.34 / *3.32* / **4.91**	2.28 / *3.22* / **4.71**	2.24 / *3.13* / **4.56**
26	4.23 / *7.72* / **13.74**	3.37 / *5.53* / **9.12**	2.98 / *4.64* / **7.36**	2.74 / *4.14* / **6.41**	2.59 / *3.82* / **5.80**	2.47 / *3.59* / **5.38**	2.39 / *3.42* / **5.07**	2.32 / *3.29* / **4.83**	2.27 / *3.18* / **4.64**	2.22 / *3.09* / **4.48**
27	4.21 / *7.68* / **13.61**	3.35 / *5.49* / **9.02**	2.96 / *4.60* / **7.27**	2.73 / *4.11* / **6.33**	2.57 / *3.78* / **5.73**	2.46 / *3.56* / **5.31**	2.37 / *3.39* / **5.00**	2.31 / *3.26* / **4.76**	2.25 / *3.15* / **4.57**	2.20 / *3.06* / **4.41**
28	4.20 / *7.64* / **13.50**	3.34 / *5.45* / **8.93**	2.95 / *4.57* / **7.19**	2.71 / *4.07* / **6.25**	2.56 / *3.75* / **5.66**	2.45 / *3.53* / **5.24**	2.36 / *3.36* / **4.93**	2.29 / *3.23* / **4.69**	2.24 / *3.12* / **4.50**	2.19 / *3.03* / **4.35**
29	4.18 / *7.60* / **13.39**	3.33 / *5.42* / **8.85**	2.93 / *4.54* / **7.12**	2.70 / *4.04* / **6.19**	2.55 / *3.73* / **5.59**	2.43 / *3.50* / **5.18**	2.35 / *3.33* / **4.87**	2.28 / *3.20* / **4.64**	2.22 / *3.09* / **4.45**	2.18 / *3.00* / **4.29**
30	4.17 / *7.56* / **13.29**	3.32 / *5.39* / **8.77**	2.92 / *4.51* / **7.05**	2.69 / *4.02* / **6.12**	2.53 / *3.70* / **5.53**	2.42 / *3.47* / **5.12**	2.33 / *3.30* / **4.82**	2.27 / *3.17* / **4.58**	2.21 / *3.07* / **4.39**	2.16 / *2.98* / **4.24**

12	15	20	24	30	40	60	120	∞	d.f.₁ / d.f.₂
2.42	2.35	2.28	2.24	2.19	2.15	2.11	2.06	2.01	
3.55	*3.41*	*3.26*	*3.18*	*3.10*	*3.02*	*2.93*	*2.84*	*2.75*	**16**
5.55	**5.27**	**4.99**	**4.85**	**4.70**	**4.54**	**4.39**	**4.23**	**4.06**	
2.38	2.31	2.23	2.19	2.15	2.10	2.06	2.01	1.96	
3.46	*3.31*	*3.16*	*3.08*	*3.00*	*2.92*	*2.83*	*2.75*	*2.65*	**17**
5.32	**5.05**	**4.78**	**4.63**	**4.48**	**4.33**	**4.18**	**4.02**	**3.85**	
2.34	2.27	2.19	2.15	2.11	2.06	2.02	1.97	1.92	
3.37	*3.23*	*3.08*	*3.00*	*2.92*	*2.84*	*2.75*	*2.66*	*2.57*	**18**
5.13	**4.87**	**4.59**	**4.45**	**4.30**	**4.15**	**4.00**	**3.84**	**3.67**	
2.31	2.23	2.16	2.11	2.07	2.03	1.98	1.93	1.88	
3.30	*3.15*	*3.00*	*2.92*	*2.84*	*2.76*	*2.67*	*2.58*	*2.49*	**19**
4.97	**4.70**	**4.43**	**4.29**	**4.14**	**3.99**	**3.84**	**3.68**	**3.51**	
2.28	2.20	2.12	2.08	2.04	1.99	1.95	1.90	1.84	
3.23	*3.09*	*2.94*	*2.86*	*2.78*	*2.69*	*2.61*	*2.52*	*2.42*	**20**
4.82	**4.56**	**4.29**	**4.15**	**4.00**	**3.86**	**3.70**	**3.54**	**3.38**	
2.25	2.18	2.10	2.05	2.01	1.96	1.92	1.87	1.81	
3.17	*3.03*	*2.88*	*2.80*	*2.72*	*2.64*	*2.55*	*2.46*	*2.36*	**21**
4.70	**4.44**	**4.17**	**4.03**	**3.88**	**3.74**	**3.58**	**3.42**	**3.26**	
2.23	2.15	2.07	2.03	1.98	1.94	1.89	1.84	1.78	
3.12	*2.98*	*2.83*	*2.75*	*2.67*	*2.58*	*2.50*	*2.40*	*2.31*	**22**
4.58	**4.33**	**4.06**	**3.92**	**3.78**	**3.63**	**3.48**	**3.32**	**3.15**	
2.20	2.13	2.05	2.01	1.96	1.91	1.86	1.81	1.76	
3.07	*2.93*	*2.78*	*2.70*	*2.62*	*2.54*	*2.45*	*2.35*	*2.26*	**23**
4.48	**4.23**	**3.96**	**3.82**	**3.68**	**3.53**	**3.38**	**3.22**	**3.05**	
2.18	2.11	2.03	1.98	1.94	1.89	1.84	1.79	1.73	
3 03	*2.89*	*2.74*	*2.66*	*2.58*	*2.49*	*2.40*	*2.31*	*2.21*	**24**
4.39	**4.14**	**3.87**	**3.74**	**3.59**	**3.45**	**3.29**	**3.14**	**2.97**	
2.16	2.09	2.01	1.96	1.92	1.87	1.82	1.77	1.71	
2.99	*2.85*	*2.70*	*2.62*	*2.54*	*2.45*	*2.36*	*2.27*	*2.17*	**25**
4.31	**4.06**	**3.79**	**3.66**	**3.52**	**3.37**	**3.22**	**3.06**	**2.89**	
2.15	2.07	1.99	1.95	1.90	1.85	1.80	1.75	1.69	
2.96	*2.81*	*2.66*	*2.58*	*2.50*	*2.42*	*2.33*	*2.23*	*2.13*	**26**
4.24	**3.99**	**3.72**	**3.59**	**3.44**	**3.30**	**3.15**	**2.99**	**2.82**	
2.13	2.06	1.97	1.93	1.88	1.84	1.79	1.73	1.67	
2.93	*2.78*	*2.63*	*2.55*	*2.47*	*2.38*	*2.29*	*2.20*	*2.10*	**27**
4.17	**3.92**	**3.66**	**3.52**	**3.38**	**3.23**	**3.08**	**2.92**	**2.75**	
2.12	2.04	1.96	1.91	1.87	1.82	1.77	1.71	1.65	
2.90	*2.75*	*2.60*	*2.52*	*2.44*	*2.35*	*2.26*	*2.17*	*2.06*	**28**
4.11	**3.86**	**3.60**	**3.46**	**3.32**	**3.18**	**3.02**	**2.86**	**2.69**	
2.10	2.03	1.94	1.90	1.85	1.81	1.75	1.70	1.64	
2.87	*2.73*	*2.57*	*2.49*	*2.41*	*2.33*	*2.23*	*2.14*	*2.03*	**29**
4.05	**3.80**	**3.54**	**3.41**	**3.27**	**3.12**	**2.97**	**2.81**	**2.64**	
2.09	2.01	1.93	1.89	1.84	1.79	1.74	1.68	1.62	
2.84	*2.70*	*2.55*	*2.47*	*2.39*	*2.30*	*2.21*	*2.11*	*2.01*	**30**
4.00	**3.75**	**3.49**	**3.36**	**3.22**	**3.07**	**2.92**	**2.76**	**2.59**	

Table F. (continued)

d.f.₂ \ d.f.₁	1	2	3	4	5	6	7	8	9	10
40	4.08	3.23	2.84	2.61	2.45	2.34	2.25	2.18	2.12	2.08
	7.31	*5.18*	*4.31*	*3.83*	*3.51*	*3.29*	*3.12*	*2.99*	*2.89*	*2.80*
	12.61	**8.25**	**6.60**	**5.70**	**5.13**	**4.73**	**4.44**	**4.21**	**4.02**	**3.87**
60	4.00	3.15	2.76	2.52	2.37	2.25	2.17	2.10	2.04	1.99
	7.08	*4.98*	*4.13*	*3.65*	*3.34*	*3.12*	*2.95*	*2.82*	*2.72*	*2.63*
	11.97	**7.76**	**6.17**	**5.31**	**4.76**	**4.37**	**4.09**	**3.87**	**3.69**	**3.54**
120	3.92	3.07	2.68	2.45	2.29	2.17	2.09	2.02	1.96	1.91
	6.85	*4.79*	*3.95*	*3.48*	*3.17*	*2.96*	*2.79*	*2.66*	*2.56*	*2.47*
	11.38	**7.32**	**5.79**	**4.95**	**4.42**	**4.04**	**3.77**	**3.55**	**3.38**	**3.24**
∞	3.84	3.00	2.60	2.37	2.21	2.10	2.01	1.94	1.88	1.83
	6.63	*4.61*	*3.78*	*3.32*	*3.02*	*2.80*	*2.64*	*2.51*	*2.41*	*2.32*
	10.83	**6.91**	**5.42**	**4.62**	**4.10**	**3.74**	**3.47**	**3.27**	**3.10**	**2.96**

SOURCE: Rearranged from Table 18 of E. S. Pearson and H. O. Hartley, *Biometrika Tables for Statisticians*, vol. 1, 2nd ed., 1958, published by the Syndics of the Cambridge University Press, London; reproduced by permission of the authors and publishers.

12	15	20	24	30	40	60	120	∞	d.f.₁/d.f.₂
2.00	1.92	1.84	1.79	1.74	1.69	1.64	1.58	1.51	
2.66	*2.52*	*2.37*	*2.29*	*2.20*	*2.11*	*2.02*	*1.92*	*1.80*	**40**
3.64	**3.40**	**3.15**	**3.01**	**2.87**	**2.73**	**2.57**	**2.41**	**2.23**	
1.92	1.84	1.75	1.70	1.65	1.59	1.53	1.47	1.39	
2.50	*2.35*	*2.20*	*2.12*	*2.03*	*1.94*	*1.84*	*1.73*	*1.60*	**60**
3.31	**3.08**	**2.83**	**2.69**	**2.55**	**2.41**	**2.25**	**2.08**	**1.89**	
1.83	1.75	1.66	1.61	1.55	1.50	1.43	1.35	1.25	
2.34	*2.19*	*2.03*	*1.95*	*1.86*	*1.76*	*1.66*	*1.53*	*1.38*	**120**
3.02	**2.78**	**2.53**	**2.40**	**2.26**	**2.11**	**1.95**	**1.76**	**1.54**	
1.75	1.67	1.57	1.52	1.46	1.39	1.32	1.22	1.00	
2.18	*2.04*	*1.88*	*1.79*	*1.70*	*1.59*	*1.47*	*1.32*	*1.00*	∞
2.74	**2.51**	**2.27**	**2.13**	**1.99**	**1.84**	**1.66**	**1.45**	**1.00**	

Critical values of $F_{.95}$ are in regular Roman type.
Critical values of $F_{.99}$ are in italics.
Critical values of $F_{.999}$ are in bold face type.

Table G. Various Functions of Pearson's r Correlation Coefficient

r	$\sqrt{r}$	r^2	$\sqrt{r - r^2}$	$\sqrt{1 - r}$	$1 - r^2$ k^2	$\sqrt{1 - r^2}$ k	$100(1 - k)$ E	r
1.00	1.0000	1.0000	0.0000	0.0000	0.0000	0.0000	100.00	1.00
.99	.9950	.9801	.0995	.1000	.0199	.1411	85.89	.99
.98	.9899	.9604	.1400	.1414	.0396	.1990	80.10	.98
.97	.9849	.9409	.1706	.1732	.0591	.2431	75.69	.97
.96	.9798	.9216	.1960	.2000	.0784	.2800	72.00	.96
.95	.9747	.9025	.2179	.2236	.0975	.3122	68.78	.95
.94	.9695	.8836	.2375	.2449	.1164	.3412	65.88	.94
.93	.9644	.8649	.2551	.2646	.1351	.3676	63.24	.93
.92	.9592	.8464	.2713	.2828	.1536	.3919	60.81	.92
.91	.9539	.8281	.2862	.3000	.1719	.4146	58.54	.91
.90	.9487	.8100	.3000	.3162	.1900	.4359	56.41	.90
.89	.9434	.7921	.3129	.3317	.2079	.4560	54.40	.89
.88	.9381	.7744	.3250	.3464	.2256	.4750	52.50	.88
.87	.9327	.7569	.3363	.3606	.2431	.4931	50.69	.87
.86	.9274	.7396	.3470	.3742	.2604	.5103	48.97	.86
.85	.9220	.7225	.3571	.3873	.2775	.5268	47.32	.85
.84	.9165	.7056	.3666	.4000	.2944	.5426	45.74	.84
.83	.9110	.6889	.3756	.4123	.3111	.5578	44.22	.83
.82	.9055	.6724	.3842	.4243	.3276	.5724	42.76	.82
.81	.9000	.6561	.3923	.4359	.3439	.5864	41.36	.81
.80	.8944	.6400	.4000	.4472	.3600	.6000	40.00	.80
.79	.8888	.6241	.4073	.4583	.3759	.6131	38.69	.79
.78	.8832	.6084	.4142	.4690	.3916	.6258	37.42	.78
.77	.8775	.5929	.4208	.4796	.4071	.6380	36.20	.77
.76	.8718	.5776	.4271	.4899	.4224	.6499	35.01	.76
.75	.8660	.5625	.4330	.5000	.4375	.6614	33.86	.75
.74	.8602	.5476	.4386	.5099	.4524	.6726	32.74	.74
.73	.8544	.5329	.4440	.5196	.4671	.6834	31.66	.73
.72	.8485	.5184	.4490	.5292	.4816	.6940	30.60	.72
.71	.8426	.5041	.4538	.5385	.4959	.7042	29.58	.71
.70	.8367	.4900	.4583	.5477	.5100	.7141	28.59	.70
.69	.8307	.4761	.4625	.5568	.5239	.7238	27.62	.69
.68	.8246	.4624	.4665	.5657	.5376	.7332	26.68	.68
.67	.8185	.4489	.4702	.5745	.5511	.7424	25.76	.67
.66	.8124	.4356	.4737	.5831	.5644	.7513	24.87	.66
.65	.8062	.4225	.4770	.5916	.5775	.7599	24.01	.65
.64	.8000	.4096	.4800	.6000	.5904	.7684	23.16	.64
.63	.7937	.3969	.4828	.6083	.6031	.7766	22.34	.63
.62	.7874	.3844	.4854	.6164	.6156	.7846	21.54	.62
.61	.7810	.3721	.4877	.6245	.6279	.7924	20.76	.61
.60	.7746	.3600	.4899	.6325	.6400	.8000	20.00	.60
.59	.7681	.3481	.4918	.6403	.6519	.8074	19.26	.59
.58	.7616	.3364	.4936	.6481	.6636	.8146	18.54	.58
.57	.7550	.3249	.4951	.6557	.6751	.8216	17.84	.57
.56	.7483	.3136	.4964	.6633	.6864	.8285	17.15	.56
.55	.7416	.3025	.4975	.6708	.6975	.8352	16.48	.55
.54	.7348	.2916	.4984	.6782	.7084	.8417	15.83	.54
.53	.7280	.2809	.4991	.6856	.7191	.8480	15.20	.53
.52	.7211	.2704	.4996	.6928	.7296	.8542	14.58	.52
.51	.7141	.2601	.4999	.7000	.7399	.8602	13.98	.51
.50	.7071	.2500	.5000	.7071	.7500	.8660	13.40	.50

Table G. (continued)

r	$\sqrt{r}$	r^2	$\sqrt{r - r^2}$	$\sqrt{1 - r}$	$1 - r^2$ k^2	$\sqrt{1 - r^2}$ k	$100(1 - k)$ E	r
.50	.7071	.2500	.5000	.7071	.7500	.8660	13.40	.50
.49	.7000	.2401	.4999	.7141	.7599	.8717	12.83	.49
.48	.6928	.2304	.4996	.7211	.7696	.8773	12.27	.48
.47	.6856	.2209	.4991	.7280	.7791	.8827	11.73	.47
.46	.6782	.2116	.4984	.7348	.7884	.8879	11.21	.46
.45	.6708	.2025	.4975	.7416	.7975	.8930	10.70	.45
.44	.6633	.1936	.4964	.7483	.8064	.8980	10.20	.44
.43	.6557	.1849	.4951	.7550	.8151	.9028	9.72	.43
.42	.6481	.1764	.4936	.7616	.8236	.9075	9.25	.42
.41	.6403	.1681	.4918	.7681	.8319	.9121	8.79	.41
.40	.6325	.1600	.4899	.7746	.8400	.9165	8.35	.40
.39	.6245	.1521	.4877	.7810	.8479	.9208	7.92	.39
.38	.6164	.1444	.4854	.7874	.8556	.9250	7.50	.38
.37	.6083	.1369	.4828	.7937	.8631	.9290	7.10	.37
.36	.6000	.1296	.4800	.8000	.8704	.9330	6.70	.36
.35	.5916	.1225	.4770	.8062	.8775	.9367	6.33	.35
.34	.5831	.1156	.4737	.8124	.8844	.9404	5.96	.34
.33	.5745	.1089	.4702	.8185	.8911	.9440	5.60	.33
.32	.5657	.1024	.4665	.8246	.8976	.9474	5.25	.32
.31	.5568	.0961	.4625	.8307	.9039	.9507	4.93	.31
.30	.5477	.0900	.4583	.8367	.9100	.9539	4.61	.30
.29	.5385	.0841	.4538	.8426	.9159	.9570	4.30	.29
.28	.5292	.0784	.4490	.8485	.9216	.9600	4.00	.28
.27	.5196	.0729	.4440	.8544	.9271	.9629	3.71	.27
.26	.5099	.0676	.4386	.8602	.9324	.9656	3.44	.26
.25	.5000	.0625	.4330	.8660	.9375	.9682	3.18	.25
.24	.4899	.0576	.4271	.8718	.9424	.9708	2.92	.24
.23	.4796	.0529	.4208	.8775	.9471	.9732	2.68	.23
.22	.4690	.0484	.4142	.8832	.9516	.9755	2.45	.22
.21	.4583	.0441	.4073	.8888	.9559	.9777	2.23	.21
.20	.4472	.0400	.4000	.8944	.9600	.9798	2.02	.20
.19	.4359	.0361	.3923	.9000	.9639	.9818	1.82	.19
.18	.4243	.0324	.3842	.9055	.9676	.9837	1.63	.18
.17	.4123	.0289	.3756	.9110	.9711	.9854	1.46	.17
.16	.4000	.0256	.3666	.9165	.9744	.9871	1.29	.16
.15	.3873	.0225	.3571	.9220	.9775	.9887	1.13	.15
.14	.3742	.0196	.3470	.9274	.9804	.9902	.98	.14
.13	.3606	.0169	.3363	.9327	.9831	.9915	.85	.13
.12	.3464	.0144	.3250	.9381	.9856	.9928	.72	.12
.11	.3317	.0121	.3129	.9434	.9879	.9939	.61	.11
.10	.3162	.0100	.3000	.9487	.9900	.9950	.50	.10
.09	.3000	.0081	.2862	.9539	.9919	.9959	.41	.09
.08	.2828	.0064	.2713	.9592	.9936	.9968	.32	.08
.07	.2646	.0049	.2551	.9644	.9951	.9975	.25	.07
.06	.2449	.0036	.2375	.9695	.9964	.9982	.18	.06
.05	.2236	.0025	.2179	.9747	.9975	.9987	.13	.05
.04	.2000	.0016	.1960	.9798	.9984	.9992	.08	.04
.03	.1732	.0009	.1706	.9849	.9991	.9995	.05	.03
.02	.1414	.0004	.1400	.9899	.9996	.9998	.02	.02
.01	.1000	.0001	.0995	.9950	.9999	.9999	.01	.01
.00	.0000	.0000	.0000	1.0000	1.0000	1.0000	.00	.00

SOURCE: Reprinted from Table XVIII of W. V. Bingham, *Aptitudes and Aptitude Testing*, 1937, Harper, New York.

Table H. Critical Values for Hartley's Maximum *F*-Ratio Significance Test for Homogeneity of Variance

[*Alpha* = .05 and .01 (in italics)]

d.f. \ k	2	3	4	5	6	7	8	9	10	11	12
2	39.0 / *199.*	87.5 / *448.*	142. / *729.*	202. / *1036.*	266. / *1362.*	333. / *1705.*	403. / *2063.*	475. / *2432.*	550. / *2813.*	626. / *3204.*	704. / *3605.*
3	15.4 / *47.5*	27.8 / *85.*	39.2 / *120.*	50.7 / *151.*	62.0 / *184.*	72.9 / *216.**	83.5 / *249.**	93.9 / *281.**	104. / *310.**	114. / *337.**	124. / *361.**
4	9.60 / *23.2*	15.5 / *37.*	20.6 / *49.*	25.2 / *59.*	29.5 / *69.*	33.6 / *79.*	37.5 / *89.*	41.1 / *97.*	44.6 / *106.*	48.0 / *113.*	51.4 / *120.*
5	7.15 / *14.9*	10.8 / *22.*	13.7 / *28.*	16.3 / *33.*	18.7 / *38.*	20.8 / *42.*	22.9 / *46.*	24.7 / *50.*	26.5 / *54.*	28.2 / *57.*	29.9 / *60.*
6	5.82 / *11.1*	8.38 / *15.5*	10.4 / *19.1*	12.1 / *22.*	13.7 / *25.*	15.0 / *27.*	16.3 / *30.*	17.5 / *32.*	18.6 / *34.*	19.7 / *36.*	20.7 / *37.*
7	4.99 / *8.89*	6.94 / *12.1*	8.44 / *14.5*	9.70 / *16.5*	10.8 / *18.4*	11.8 / *20.*	12.7 / *22.*	13.5 / *23.*	14.3 / *24.*	15.1 / *26.*	15.8 / *27.*
8	4.43 / *7.50*	6.00 / *9.9*	7.18 / *11.7*	8.12 / *13.2*	9.03 / *14.5*	9.78 / *15.8*	10.5 / *16.9*	11.1 / *17.9*	11.7 / *18.9*	12.2 / *19.8*	12.7 / *21.*
9	4.03 / *6.54*	5.34 / *8.5*	6.31 / *9.9*	7.11 / *11.1*	7.80 / *12.1*	8.41 / *13.1*	8.95 / *13.9*	9.45 / *14.7*	9.91 / *15.3*	10.3 / *16.0*	10.7 / *16.6*

Table H. (continued)

d.f. \ k	2	3	4	5	6	7	8	9	10	11	12	k / d.f.
10	3.72 / *5.85*	4.85 / *7.4*	5.67 / *8.6*	6.34 / *9.6*	6.92 / *10.4*	7.42 / *11.1*	7.87 / *11.8*	8.28 / *12.4*	8.66 / *12.9*	9.01 / *13.4*	9.34 / *13.9*	10
12	3.28 / *4.91*	4.16 / *6.1*	4.79 / *6.9*	5.30 / *7.6*	5.72 / *8.2*	6.09 / *8.7*	6.42 / *9.1*	6.72 / *9.5*	7.00 / *9.9*	7.25 / *10.2*	7.48 / *10.6*	12
15	2.86 / *4.07*	3.54 / *4.9*	4.01 / *5.5*	4.37 / *6.0*	4.68 / *6.4*	4.95 / *6.7*	5.19 / *7.1*	5.40 / *7.3*	5.59 / *7.5*	5.77 / *7.8*	5.93 / *8.0*	15
20	2.46 / *3.32*	2.95 / *3.8*	3.29 / *4.3*	3.54 / *4.6*	3.76 / *4.9*	3.94 / *5.1*	4.10 / *5.3*	4.24 / *5.5*	4.37 / *5.6*	4.49 / *5.8*	4.59 / *5.9*	20
30	2.07 / *2.63*	2.40 / *3.0*	2.61 / *3.3*	2.78 / *3.4*	2.91 / *3.6*	3.02 / *3.7*	3.12 / *3.8*	3.21 / *3.9*	3.29 / *4.0*	3.36 / *4.1*	3.39 / *4.2*	30
60	1.67 / *1.96*	1.85 / *2.2*	1.96 / *2.3*	2.04 / *2.4*	2.11 / *2.4*	2.17 / *2.5*	2.22 / *2.5*	2.26 / *2.6*	2.30 / *2.6*	2.33 / *2.7*	2.36 / *2.7*	60
∞	1.00 / *1.00*	1.00 / *1.00*	1.00 / *1.00*	1.00 / *1.00*	1.00 / *1.00*	1.00 / *1.00*	1.00 / *1.00*	1.00 / *1.00*	1.00 / *1.00*	1.00 / *1.00*	1.00 / *1.00*	∞

SOURCE: Reprinted from Table 31 of E. S. Pearson and H. O. Hartley, *Biometrika Tables for Statisticians*, vol. 1, 2nd ed., 1958, published by the Syndics of the Cambridge University Press, London; reproduced by permission of the authors and publishers.

* Values in the column $k = 2$ and in the rows d.f. $= 2$ and ∞ are exact. Elsewhere the third digit may be in error by a few units for $F_{.95}$ and several units for $F_{.99}$. The third digit figures of values marked by an asterisk are the most uncertain.

417

Table I. Confidence Limits for *P* in Binomial Sampling, Given a Sample Statistic *p*

1. Alpha Level of Significance of .05

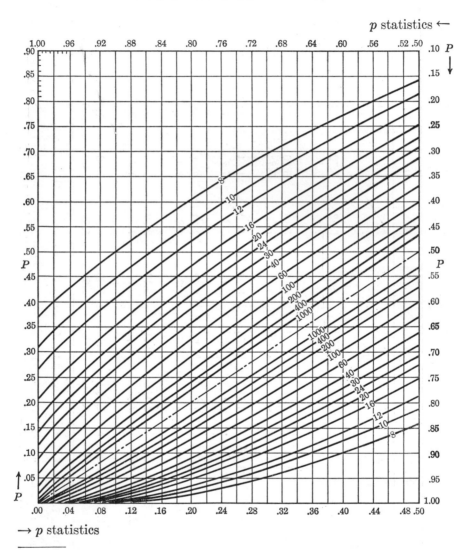

The numbers printed along the curves indicate the sample size *n*.

SOURCE: Table 41 of E. S. Pearson and H. O. Hartley, *Biometrika Tables for Statisticians*, vol. 1, 2nd ed., 1958, published by The Syndics of the Cambridge University Press, London; reproduced by permission of the authors and publishers.

Table I. (continued)
2. Alpha Level of Significance of .01

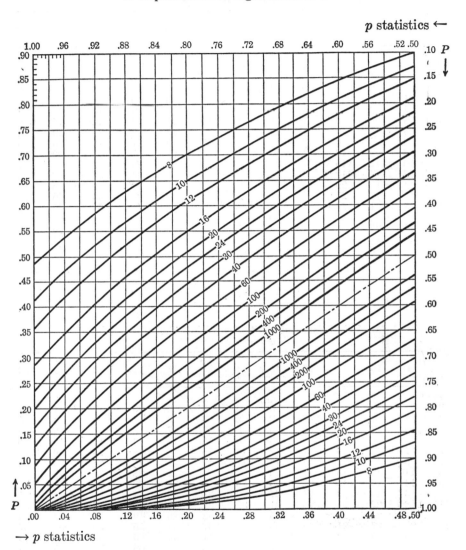

p statistics ←

→ *p* statistics

NOTE: The process of reading from the curves can be simplified with the help of the right-angled corner of a loose sheet of paper or thin card, along the edges of which are marked off the scales shown in the top left-hand corner of each chart.

Table J. Critical Values of the U Statistic of the Mann-Whitney Test

(a) Critical Values of U for a One-Tailed Test at .001 or for a Two-Tailed Test at .002

n_1 \ n_2	9	10	11	12	13	14	15	16	17	18	19	20
1												
2												
3									0	0	0	0
4		0	0	0	1	1	1	2	2	3	3	3
5	1	1	2	2	3	3	4	5	5	6	7	7
6	2	3	4	4	5	6	7	8	9	10	11	12
7	3	5	6	7	8	9	10	11	13	14	15	16
8	5	6	8	9	11	12	14	15	17	18	20	21
9	7	8	10	12	14	15	17	19	21	23	25	26
10	8	10	12	14	17	19	21	23	25	27	29	32
11	10	12	15	17	20	22	24	27	29	32	34	37
12	12	14	17	20	23	25	28	31	34	37	40	42
13	14	17	20	23	26	29	32	35	38	42	45	48
14	15	19	22	25	29	32	36	39	43	46	50	54
15	17	21	24	28	32	36	40	43	47	51	55	59
16	19	23	27	31	35	39	43	48	52	56	60	65
17	21	25	29	34	38	43	47	52	57	61	66	70
18	23	27	32	37	42	46	51	56	61	66	71	76
19	25	29	34	40	45	50	55	60	66	71	77	82
20	26	32	37	42	48	54	59	65	70	76	82	88

(b) Critical Values of U for a One-Tailed Test at .01 or for a Two-Tailed Test at .02

n_1 \ n_2	9	10	11	12	13	14	15	16	17	18	19	20
1												
2					0	0	0	0	0	0	1	1
3	1	1	1	2	2	2	3	3	4	4	4	5
4	3	3	4	5	5	6	7	7	8	9	9	10
5	5	6	7	8	9	10	11	12	13	14	15	16
6	7	8	9	11	12	13	15	16	18	19	20	22
7	9	11	12	14	16	17	19	21	23	24	26	28
8	11	13	15	17	20	22	24	26	28	30	32	34
9	14	16	18	21	23	26	28	31	33	36	38	40
10	16	19	22	24	27	30	33	36	38	41	44	47
11	18	22	25	28	31	34	37	41	44	47	50	53
12	21	24	28	31	35	38	42	46	49	53	56	60
13	23	27	31	35	39	43	47	51	55	59	63	67
14	26	30	34	38	43	47	51	56	60	65	69	73
15	28	33	37	42	47	51	56	61	66	70	75	80
16	31	36	41	46	51	56	61	66	71	76	82	87
17	33	38	44	49	55	60	66	71	77	82	88	93
18	36	41	47	53	59	65	70	76	82	88	94	100
19	38	44	50	56	63	60	75	82	88	94	101	107
20	40	47	53	60	67	73	80	87	93	100	107	114

SOURCE: Adapted and abridged from Tables 1, 3, 5, and 7 of D. Aube. Extended tables for the Mann-Whitney statistic. *Bulletin of the Institute of Educational Research at Indiana University*, 1953, **1**, No. 2. Reproduced from S. Siegel. *Nonparametric Statistics for the Behavioral Sciences*. New York: McGraw-Hill, 1956. Reprinted by permission of the Institute of Educational Research and McGraw-Hill Book Co.

Table J. (continued)

(c) Critical Values of U for a One-Tailed Test at .025 or for a Two-Tailed Test at .05

n_1 \ n_2	9	10	11	12	13	14	15	16	17	18	19	20
1												
2	0	0	1	1	1	1	1	1	2	2	2	2
3	2	3	3	4	4	5	5	6	6	7	7	8
4	4	5	6	7	8	9	10	11	11	12	13	13
5	7	8	9	11	12	13	14	15	17	18	19	20
6	10	11	13	14	16	17	19	21	22	24	25	27
7	12	14	16	18	20	22	24	26	28	30	32	34
8	15	17	19	22	24	26	29	31	34	36	38	41
9	17	20	23	26	28	31	34	37	39	42	45	48
10	20	23	26	29	33	36	39	42	45	48	52	55
11	23	26	30	33	37	40	44	47	51	55	58	62
12	26	29	33	37	41	45	49	53	57	61	65	69
13	28	33	37	41	45	50	54	59	63	67	72	76
14	31	36	40	45	50	55	59	64	67	74	78	83
15	34	39	44	49	54	59	64	70	75	80	85	90
16	37	42	47	53	59	64	70	75	81	86	92	98
17	39	45	51	57	63	67	75	81	87	93	99	105
18	42	48	55	61	67	74	80	86	93	99	106	112
19	45	52	58	65	72	78	85	92	99	106	113	119
20	48	55	62	69	76	83	90	98	105	112	119	127

(d) Critical Values of U for a One-Tailed Test at .05 or for a Two-Tailed Test at .10

n_1 \ n_2	9	10	11	12	13	14	15	16	17	18	19	20
1											0	0
2	1	1	1	2	2	2	3	3	3	4	4	4
3	3	4	5	5	6	7	7	8	9	9	10	11
4	6	7	8	9	10	11	12	14	15	16	17	18
5	9	11	12	13	15	16	18	19	20	22	23	25
6	12	14	16	17	19	21	23	25	26	28	30	32
7	15	17	19	21	24	26	28	30	33	35	37	39
8	18	20	23	26	28	31	33	36	39	41	44	47
9	21	24	27	30	33	36	39	42	45	48	51	54
10	24	27	31	34	37	41	44	48	51	55	58	62
11	27	31	34	38	42	46	50	54	57	61	65	69
12	30	34	38	42	47	51	55	60	64	68	72	77
13	33	37	42	47	51	56	61	65	70	75	80	84
14	36	41	46	51	56	61	66	71	77	82	87	92
15	39	44	50	55	61	66	72	77	83	88	94	100
16	42	48	54	60	65	71	77	83	89	95	101	107
17	45	51	57	64	70	77	83	89	96	102	109	115
18	48	55	61	68	75	82	88	95	102	109	116	123
19	51	58	65	72	80	87	94	101	109	116	123	130
20	54	62	69	77	84	92	100	107	115	123	130	138

Table K. Critical Values of Wilcoxon's T Statistic for the Matched-Pairs Signed-Ranks Test

| | Level of Significance for One-Tailed Test | | |
	.025	.01	.005
	Level of Significance for Two-Tailed Test		
n'	.05	.02	.01
6	0	—	—
7	2	0	—
8	4	2	0
9	6	3	2
10	8	5	3
11	11	7	5
12	14	10	7
13	17	13	10
14	21	16	13
15	25	20	16
16	30	24	20
17	35	28	23
18	40	33	28
19	46	38	32
20	52	43	38
21	59	49	43
22	66	56	49
23	73	62	55
24	81	69	61
25	89	77	68

SOURCE: Adapted from Table I of F. Wilcoxon. *Some Rapid Approximate Statistical Procedures.* New York: American Cyanamid Company, 1949, p. 13. Reproduced from S. Siegel. *Nonparametric Statistics for the Behavioral Sciences.* New York: McGraw-Hill, 1956. Reprinted by permission of the American Cyanamid Co. and McGraw-Hill Book Co.
Note that n' is the number of matched pairs.

Table KK. Coefficients and Sums of Coefficients of the Binomial

$$(Q + P)^n$$

n	0	1	2	3	4	5	6	7	8	9	10	SUM
0	1											1
1	1	1										2
2	1	2	1									4
3	1	3	3	1								8
4	1	4	6	4	1							16
5	1	5	10	10	5	1						32
6	1	6	15	20	15	6	1					64
7	1	7	21	35	35	21	7	1				128
8	1	8	28	56	70	56	28	8	1			256
9	1	9	36	84	126	126	84	36	9	1		512
10	1	10	45	120	210	252	210	120	45	10	1	1024

[For the following, half of the coefficients are given (plus the middle coefficient when n is even).]

n	0	1	2	3	4	5	6	7	8	9	10	SUM
11	1	11	55	165	330	462						2048
12	1	12	66	220	495	792	924					4096
13	1	13	78	286	715	1287	1716					8192
14	1	14	91	364	1001	2002	3003	3432				16384
15	1	15	105	455	1365	3003	5005	6435				32768
16	1	16	120	560	1820	4368	8008	11440	12870			65536
17	1	17	136	680	2380	6188	12376	19448	24310			131072
18	1	18	153	816	3060	8568	18564	31824	43758	48620		262144
19	1	19	171	969	3876	11628	27132	50388	75582	92378		524288
20	1	20	190	1140	4845	15504	38760	77520	125970	167960	184756	1048576

Table L.

Row						Column Number										
	1	2	3	4	5	6	7	8	9	10	11	12	13	14	15	16
1	2	7	8	9	4	0	7	2	3	2	5	4	2	6	7	1
2	2	2	6	0	4	1	7	7	3	8	7	3	6	7	9	4
3	9	1	6	6	3	9	4	9	1	0	5	1	5	2	2	7
4	7	0	5	5	9	2	7	5	7	8	0	8	8	5	0	6
5	4	7	3	6	6	3	9	8	2	1	7	9	7	6	4	2
6	8	2	0	2	8	7	7	6	0	2	2	3	1	1	1	6
7	0	8	7	5	3	3	6	4	2	6	8	3	1	6	5	0
8	9	4	1	9	0	8	4	6	6	8	6	3	3	2	2	3
9	5	0	0	6	7	4	0	0	0	1	9	5	9	9	1	8
10	1	9	5	4	1	5	2	6	2	9	4	1	1	5	8	4
11	5	6	4	4	1	8	7	2	8	3	6	1	5	9	8	6
12	7	9	2	5	1	9	7	9	3	1	8	6	8	7	7	6
13	3	3	3	5	9	5	1	4	0	8	2	5	6	3	5	4
14	1	9	0	4	0	0	9	9	5	7	4	1	5	9	4	7
15	5	4	4	7	2	0	3	7	9	1	0	9	6	2	9	7
16	2	9	8	2	5	5	9	3	2	0	4	9	0	6	4	4
17	9	7	6	2	6	7	7	3	3	3	1	7	5	0	9	6
18	5	8	2	4	3	3	0	8	5	3	5	7	5	8	3	5
19	4	3	4	9	5	0	3	6	2	9	7	4	6	2	5	6
20	1	1	9	8	4	8	0	6	7	0	9	7	9	6	9	9
21	6	9	1	8	3	3	7	5	9	6	6	7	7	6	0	4
22	7	0	0	3	8	1	3	4	7	9	5	2	6	9	9	7
23	3	7	2	0	8	1	5	6	9	0	1	7	8	9	6	6
24	2	7	0	0	0	6	5	0	6	5	6	0	3	2	9	3
25	3	0	7	0	7	8	4	9	4	2	8	2	4	7	4	9
26	6	2	9	3	3	1	7	7	5	2	2	3	4	6	4	2
27	5	4	9	2	1	4	8	5	7	0	9	6	4	7	2	1
28	0	3	7	0	1	7	3	8	0	3	6	2	3	1	0	9
29	9	3	6	6	2	2	0	9	7	2	3	9	2	8	7	3
30	2	9	5	6	9	9	5	6	9	8	2	8	0	0	4	4
31	8	5	7	2	9	2	6	5	9	3	9	7	1	8	3	5
32	8	4	5	7	7	9	9	5	1	4	5	5	0	9	5	3
33	8	7	9	8	1	8	4	1	4	3	7	7	0	9	1	9
34	7	3	2	5	1	8	6	3	2	8	5	8	6	9	3	4
35	8	9	9	0	1	8	8	8	9	5	7	5	0	4	1	1
36	0	2	9	7	8	8	1	7	6	1	6	7	6	4	2	5
37	0	5	2	3	2	3	8	1	8	8	1	6	2	3	0	7
38	2	2	6	8	1	6	9	6	2	6	7	9	1	7	8	0
39	0	7	8	4	9	5	8	8	0	7	2	1	8	1	7	5
40	4	8	0	7	0	5	9	9	4	9	6	9	8	2	0	6
41	9	2	0	1	6	7	2	8	3	9	8	8	3	4	7	8
42	0	8	8	3	4	0	9	2	2	8	1	5	0	4	8	2
43	2	0	6	9	7	5	2	8	2	5	5	4	0	7	7	1
44	3	1	8	6	8	3	5	6	3	2	7	4	1	8	9	4
45	0	0	8	6	1	7	5	0	8	5	6	5	0	8	2	7
46	3	3	2	9	4	2	5	3	3	8	2	4	2	6	2	5
47	8	4	7	4	0	4	5	1	2	1	0	4	2	5	7	7
48	0	2	4	3	0	2	0	7	2	8	8	0	8	4	1	6
49	4	6	5	6	3	0	4	5	2	0	1	5	2	7	9	5
50	3	4	8	3	4	5	8	7	5	9	7	1	6	3	9	9

Source: "A Table of random numbers from selective service numbers," by J. G. Peatman and Roy Schafer, *Journal of Psychology*, **14**, 295–305, 1942.

Random Numbers

17	18	19	20	21	22	23	24	25	26	27	28	29	30	31	32	Row
6	8	5	9	1	3	5	4	0	3	6	6	7	6	5	1	1
2	1	3	8	9	0	3	4	9	0	2	6	3	0	9	8	2
5	2	5	3	4	1	3	9	5	8	1	3	8	2	9	2	3
0	5	9	0	5	7	4	5	2	0	6	1	6	4	2	0	4
4	9	6	0	3	6	3	5	3	9	9	1	8	5	1	3	5
4	8	5	2	2	3	4	2	2	6	5	2	2	4	9	6	6
0	5	5	7	8	1	0	1	2	9	1	4	3	4	7	6	7
7	4	7	5	1	5	7	6	3	7	9	4	5	5	3	5	8
1	4	7	4	9	8	7	2	4	3	0	8	6	4	2	7	9
4	4	6	1	8	7	8	6	4	8	7	4	4	0	5	8	10
2	2	9	1	9	0	4	8	1	0	1	3	5	3	4	4	11
6	5	0	3	8	1	1	2	4	7	8	9	1	7	5	2	12
6	5	7	2	6	7	8	9	9	9	8	0	9	1	5	3	13
6	4	8	2	6	4	4	1	8	8	1	5	4	3	8	0	14
4	7	6	1	1	6	1	2	2	9	5	8	4	4	8	6	15
2	1	5	7	3	6	5	5	4	5	7	9	6	6	4	0	16
1	1	3	9	2	1	1	0	0	1	3	7	7	3	7	3	17
9	3	4	5	4	6	3	9	2	7	1	1	4	9	1	3	18
9	8	3	6	1	4	0	3	5	9	7	1	8	0	6	9	19
4	0	6	0	0	5	9	6	5	1	4	2	0	4	1	9	20
5	3	4	5	7	3	0	6	1	0	3	0	0	3	5	0	21
3	2	5	0	2	3	5	3	9	7	4	8	9	4	1	5	22
6	0	7	8	1	9	6	7	4	8	9	6	3	6	5	1	23
1	7	2	2	8	4	9	0	4	3	2	4	5	5	1	2	24
6	0	4	3	8	1	7	7	0	9	8	4	6	3	1	2	25
2	4	7	5	4	4	4	1	7	1	6	7	1	2	6	8	26
8	9	7	6	1	3	3	4	6	6	5	9	0	7	0	3	27
5	5	2	5	9	2	0	2	8	7	7	2	0	2	7	2	28
1	0	7	0	8	9	3	8	8	5	3	1	3	1	0	9	29
8	8	5	7	2	1	3	4	9	5	2	6	8	3	6	6	30
6	6	1	2	1	5	5	5	6	1	7	1	5	7	5	9	31
1	3	9	3	7	8	1	4	0	5	4	1	5	4	4	0	32
4	6	1	3	8	6	5	9	2	2	8	1	6	9	0	1	33
5	2	6	1	9	0	6	9	0	5	4	6	8	0	3	2	34
6	0	3	1	3	0	3	5	8	9	2	7	8	8	7	1	35
0	5	8	3	2	4	7	7	2	2	6	2	6	8	6	0	36
3	0	1	2	6	2	6	8	3	7	4	4	3	8	9	9	37
2	4	8	0	4	7	3	3	8	4	4	8	4	3	3	8	38
3	0	7	4	1	0	3	2	0	1	2	8	6	5	9	4	39
4	0	7	8	1	1	4	2	1	6	7	0	7	3	1	2	40
4	0	5	1	6	8	7	8	3	5	4	5	0	4	0	6	41
6	2	9	2	1	9	8	5	3	1	0	7	8	5	3	9	42
7	8	6	8	5	1	3	7	8	2	7	1	9	3	6	3	43
5	6	8	0	6	4	6	4	1	0	9	1	9	8	1	4	44
1	1	6	3	4	6	0	0	9	4	7	9	2	4	8	7	45
2	9	0	1	3	7	6	5	9	1	4	6	0	1	0	0	46
9	4	6	5	8	3	3	8	1	0	3	7	7	7	8	6	47
0	2	3	5	9	7	5	1	3	6	3	2	8	7	5	8	48
3	0	2	2	1	6	1	1	0	0	9	1	6	1	7	7	49
0	9	4	2	5	8	9	5	3	3	3	6	4	5	2	0	50

Table M. Squares, Square Roots and Reciprocals of Integers from 1 to 1000

n	n^2	$\sqrt{n}$	$\dfrac{1}{n}$	$\dfrac{1}{\sqrt{n}}$
1	1	1.0000	1.000000	1.0000
2	4	1.4142	.500000	.7071
3	9	1.7321	.333333	.5774
4	16	2.0000	.250000	.5000
5	25	2.2361	.200000	.4472
6	36	2.4495	.166667	.4082
7	49	2.6458	.142857	.3780
8	64	2.8284	.125000	.3536
9	81	3.0000	.111111	.3333
10	100	3.1623	.100000	.3162
11	121	3.3166	.090909	.3015
12	144	3.4641	.083333	.2887
13	169	3.6056	.076923	.2774
14	196	3.7417	.071429	.2673
15	225	3.8730	.066667	.2582
16	256	4.0000	.062500	.2500
17	289	4.1231	.058824	.2425
18	324	4.2426	.055556	.2357
19	361	4.3589	.052632	.2294
20	400	4.4721	.050000	.2236
21	441	4.5826	.047619	.2182
22	484	4.6904	.045455	.2132
23	529	4.7958	.043478	.2085
24	576	4.8990	.041667	.2041
25	625	5.0000	.040000	.2000
26	676	5.0990	.038462	.1961
27	729	5.1962	.037037	.1925
28	784	5.2915	.035714	.1890
29	841	5.3852	.034483	.1857
30	900	5.4772	.033333	.1826
31	961	5.5678	.032258	.1796
32	1024	5.6569	.031250	.1768
33	1089	5.7446	.030303	.1741
34	1156	5.8310	.029412	.1715
35	1225	5.9161	.028571	.1690
36	1296	6.0000	.027778	.1667
37	1369	6.0828	.027027	.1644
38	1444	6.1644	.026316	.1622
39	1521	6.2450	.025641	.1601
40	1600	6.3246	.025000	.1581
41	1681	6.4031	.024390	.1562
42	1764	6,4807	.023810	.1543
43	1849	6.5574	.023256	.1525
44	1936	6.6332	.022727	.1508
45	2025	6.7082	.022222	.1491
46	2116	6.7823	.021739	.1474
47	2209	6.8557	.021277	.1459
48	2304	6.9282	.020833	.1443
49	2401	7.0000	.020408	.1429
50	2500	7.0711	.020000	.1414

n	n^2	$\sqrt{n}$	$\dfrac{1}{n}$	$\dfrac{1}{\sqrt{n}}$
51	2601	7.1414	.019608	.1400
52	2704	7.2111	.019231	.1387
53	2809	7.2801	.018868	.1374
54	2916	7.3485	.018519	.1361
55	3025	7.4162	.018182	.1348
56	3136	7.4833	.017857	.1336
57	3249	7.5498	.017544	.1325
58	3364	7.6158	.017241	.1313
59	3481	7.6811	.016949	.1302
60	3600	7.7460	.016667	.1291
61	3721	7.8102	.016393	.1280
62	3844	7.8740	.016129	.1270
63	3969	7.9373	.015873	.1260
64	4096	8.0000	.015625	.1250
65	4225	8.0623	.015385	.1240
66	4356	8.1240	.015152	.1231
67	4489	8.1854	.014925	.1222
68	4624	8.2462	.014706	.1213
69	4761	8.3066	.014493	.1204
70	4900	8.3666	.014286	.1195
71	5041	8.4261	.014085	.1187
72	5184	8.4853	.013889	.1179
73	5329	8.5440	.013699	.1170
74	5476	8.6023	.013514	.1162
75	5625	8.6603	.013333	.1155
76	5776	8.7178	.013158	.1147
77	5929	8.7750	.018987	.1140
78	6084	8.8318	.012821	.1132
79	6241	8.8882	.012658	.1125
80	6400	8.9443	.012500	.1118
81	6561	9.0000	.012346	.1111
82	6724	9.0554	.012195	.1104
83	6889	9.1104	.012048	.1098
84	7056	9.1652	.011905	.1091
85	7225	9.2195	.011765	.1085
86	7396	9.2736	.011628	.1078
87	7569	9.3274	.011494	.1072
88	7744	9.3808	.011364	.1066
89	7921	9.4340	.011236	.1060
90	8100	9.4868	.011111	.1054
91	8281	9.5394	.010989	.1048
92	8464	9.5917	.010870	.1043
93	8649	9.6437	.010753	.1037
94	8836	9.6954	.010638	.1031
95	9025	9.7468	.010526	.1026
96	9216	9.7980	.010417	.1021
97	9409	9.8489	.010309	.1015
98	9604	9.8995	.010204	.1010
99	9801	9.9499	.010101	.1005
100	10000	10.0000	.010000	.1000

n	n^2	$\sqrt{n}$	$\dfrac{1}{n}$	$\dfrac{1}{\sqrt{n}}$
101	10201	10.0499	.009901	.0995
102	10404	10.0995	.009804	.0990
103	10609	10.1489	.009709	.0985
104	10816	10.1980	.009615	.0981
105	11025	10.2470	.009524	.0976
106	11236	10.2956	.009434	.0971
107	11449	10.3441	.009346	.0967
108	11664	10.3923	.009259	.0962
109	11881	10.4403	.009174	.0958
110	12100	10.4881	.009091	.0953
111	12321	10.5357	.009009	.0949
112	12544	10,5830	.008929	.0945
113	12769	10.6301	.008850	.0941
114	12996	10.6771	.008772	.0937
115	13225	10.7238	.008696	.0933
116	13456	10.7703	.008621	.0928
117	13689	10.8167	.008547	.0925
118	13924	10.8628	.008475	.0921
119	14161	10.9087	.008403	.0917
120	14400	10.9545	.008333	.0913
121	14641	11.0000	.008264	.0909
122	14884	11.0454	.008197	.0905
123	15129	11.0905	.008130	.0902
124	15376	11.1355	.008065	.0898
125	15625	11.1803	.008000	.0894
126	15876	11.2250	.007937	.0891
127	16129	11.2694	.007874	.0887
128	16384	11.3137	.007813	.0884
129	16641	11.3578	.007752	.0880
130	16900	11.4018	.007692	.0877
131	17161	11.4455	.007634	.0874
132	17424	11.4891	.007576	.0870
133	17689	11.5326	.007519	.0867
134	17956	11.5758	.007463	.0864
135	18225	11.6190	.007407	.0861
136	18496	11.6619	.007353	.0857
137	18769	11.7047	.007299	.0854
138	19044	11.7473	.007246	.0851
139	19321	11.7898	.007194	.0848
140	19600	11.8322	.007143	.0845
141	19881	11.8743	.007092	.0842
142	20164	11.9164	.007042	.0839
143	20449	11.9583	.006993	.0836
144	20736	12.0000	.006944	.0833
145	21025	12.0416	.006897	.0830
146	21316	12.0830	.006849	.0828
147	21609	12.1244	.006803	.0825
148	21904	12.1655	.006757	.0822
149	22201	12.2066	.006711	.0819
150	22500	12.2474	.006667	.0816

n	n^2	$\sqrt{n}$	$\dfrac{1}{n}$	$\dfrac{1}{\sqrt{n}}$
151	22801	12.2882	.006623	.0814
152	23104	12.3288	.006579	.0811
153	23409	12.3693	.006536	.0808
154	23716	12.4097	.006494	.0806
155	24025	12.4499	.006452	.0803
156	24336	12.4900	.006410	.0801
157	24649	12.5300	.006369	.0798
158	24964	12.5698	.006329	.0796
159	25281	12.6095	.006289	.0793
160	25600	12.6491	.006250	.0791
161	25921	12.6886	.006211	.0788
162	26244	12.7279	.006173	.0786
163	26569	12.7671	.006135	.0783
164	26896	12.8062	.006098	.0781
165	27225	12.8452	.006061	.0778
166	27556	12.8841	.006024	.0776
167	27889	12.9228	.005988	.0774
168	28224	12.9615	.005952	.0772
169	28561	13.0000	.005917	.0769
170	28900	13.0384	.005882	.0767
171	29241	13.0767	.005848	.0765
172	29584	13.1149	.005814	.0762
173	29929	13.1529	.005780	.0760
174	30276	13.1909	.005747	.0758
175	30625	13.2288	.005714	.0756
176	30976	13.2665	.005682	.0754
177	31329	13.3041	.005650	.0752
178	31684	13.3417	.005618	.0750
179	32041	13.3791	.005587	.0747
180	32400	13.4164	.005556	.0745
181	32761	13.4536	.005525	.0743
182	33124	13.4907	.005495	.0741
183	33489	13.5277	.005464	.0739
184	33856	13.5647	.005435	.0737
185	34225	13.6015	.005405	.0735
186	34596	13.6382	.005376	.0733
187	34969	13.6748	.005348	.0731
188	35344	13.7113	.005319	.0729
189	35721	13.7477	.005291	.0727
190	36100	13.7840	.005263	.0725
191	36481	13.8203	.005236	.0724
192	36864	13.8564	.005208	.0722
193	37249	13.8924	.005181	.0720
194	37636	13.9284	.005155	.0718
195	38025	13.9642	.005128	.0716
196	38416	14.0000	.005102	.0714
197	38809	14.0357	.005076	.0712
198	39204	14.0712	.005051	.0711
199	39601	14.1067	.005025	.0709
200	40000	14.1421	.005000	.0707

n	n^2	$\sqrt{n}$	$\dfrac{1}{n}$	$\dfrac{1}{\sqrt{n}}$
201	40401	14.1774	.004975	.0705
202	40804	14.2127	.004950	.0704
203	41209	14.2478	.004926	.0702
204	41616	14.2829	.004902	.0700
205	42025	14.3178	.004878	.0698
206	42436	14.3527	.004854	.0697
207	42849	14.3875	.004831	.0695
208	43264	14.4222	.004808	.0693
209	43681	14.4568	.004785	.0692
210	44100	14.4914	.004762	.0690
211	44521	14.5258	.004739	.0688
212	44944	14.5602	.004717	.0687
213	45369	14.5945	.004695	.0685
214	45796	14.6287	.004673	.0684
215	46225	14.6629	.004651	.0682
216	46656	14.6969	.004630	.0680
217	47089	14.7309	.004608	.0679
218	47524	14.7648	.004587	.0677
219	47961	14.7986	.004566	.0676
220	48400	14.8324	.004545	.0674
221	48841	14.8661	.004525	.0673
222	49284	14.8997	.004505	.0671
223	49729	14.9332	.004484	.0670
224	50176	14.9666	.004464	.0668
225	50625	15.0000	.004444	.0667
226	51076	15.0333	.004425	.0665
227	51529	15.0665	.004405	.0664
228	51984	15.0997	.004386	.0662
229	52441	15.1327	.004367	.0661
230	52900	15.1658	.004348	.0659
231	53361	15.1987	.004329	.0658
232	53824	15.2315	.004310	.0657
233	54289	15.2643	.004292	.0655
234	54756	15.2971	.004274	.0654
235	55225	15.3297	.004255	.0652
236	55696	15.3623	.004237	.0651
237	56169	15.3948	.004219	.0650
238	56644	15.4272	.004202	.0648
239	57121	15.4596	.004184	.0647
240	57600	15.4919	.004167	.0645
241	58081	15.5242	.004149	.0644
242	58564	15.5563	.004132	.0643
243	59049	15.5885	.004115	.0642
244	59536	15.6205	.004098	.0640
245	60025	15.6525	.004082	.0630
246	60516	15.6844	.004065	.0638
247	61009	15.7162	.004049	.0636
248	61504	15.7480	.004032	.0635
249	62001	15.7797	.004016	.0634
250	62500	15.8114	.004000	.0632

n	n^2	$\sqrt{n}$	$\dfrac{1}{n}$	$\dfrac{1}{\sqrt{n}}$
251	63001	15.8430	.003984	.0631
252	63504	15.8745	.003968	.0630
253	64009	15.9060	.003953	.0629
254	64516	15.9374	.003937	.0627
255	65025	15.9687	.003922	.0626
256	65536	16.0000	.003906	.0625
257	66049	16.0312	.003891	.0624
258	66564	16.0624	.003876	.0623
259	67081	16.0935	.003861	.0621
260	67600	16.1245	.003846	.0620
261	68121	16.1555	.003831	.0619
262	68644	16.1864	.003817	.0618
263	69169	16.2173	.003802	.0617
264	69696	16.2481	.003788	.0615
265	70225	16.2788	.003774	.0614
266	70756	16.3095	.003759	.0613
267	71289	16.3401	.003745	.0612
268	71824	16.3707	.003731	.0611
269	72361	16.4012	.003717	.0610
270	72900	16.4317	.003704	.0609
271	73441	16.4621	.003690	.0607
272	73984	16.4924	.003676	.0606
273	74529	16.5227	.003663	.0605
274	75076	16.5529	.003650	.0604
275	75625	16.5831	.003636	.0603
276	76176	16.6132	.003623	.0602
277	76729	16.6433	.003610	.0601
278	77284	16.6733	.003597	.0600
279	77841	16.7033	.003584	.0599
280	78400	16.7332	.003571	.0598
281	78961	16.7631	.003559	.0597
282	79524	16.7929	.003546	.0595
283	80089	16.8226	.003534	.0594
284	80656	16.8523	.003521	.0593
285	81225	16.8819	.003509	.0592
286	81796	16.9115	.003497	.0591
287	82369	16.9411	.003484	.0590
288	82944	16.9706	.003472	.0589
289	83521	17.0000	.003460	.0588
290	84100	17.0294	.003448	.0587
291	84681	17.0587	.003436	.0586
292	85264	17.0880	.003425	.0585
293	85849	17.1172	.003413	.0584
294	86436	17.1464	.003401	.0583
295	87025	17.1756	.003390	.0582
296	87616	17.2047	.003378	.0581
297	88209	17.2337	.003367	.0580
298	88804	17.2627	.003356	.0579
299	89401	17.2916	.003344	.0578
300	90000	17.3205	.003333	.0577

n	n^2	$\sqrt{n}$	$\dfrac{1}{n}$	$\dfrac{1}{\sqrt{n}}$
301	90601	17.3494	.003322	.0576
302	91204	17.3781	.003311	.0575
303	91809	17.4069	.003300	.0574
304	92416	17.4356	.003289	.0574
305	93025	17.4642	.003279	.0573
306	93636	17.4929	.003268	.0572
307	94249	17.5214	.003257	.0571
308	94864	17.5499	.003247	.0570
309	95481	17.5784	.003236	.0569
310	96100	17.6068	.003226	.0568
311	96721	17.6352	.003215	.0567
312	97344	17.6635	.003205	.0566
313	97969	17.6918	.003195	.0565
314	98596	17.7200	.003185	.0564
315	99225	17.7482	.003175	.0563
316	99856	17.7764	.003165	.0563
317	100489	17.8045	.003155	.0562
318	101124	17.8326	.003145	.0561
319	101761	17.8606	.003135	.0560
320	102400	17.8885	.003125	.0559
321	103041	17.9165	.003115	.0558
322	103684	17.9444	.003106	.0557
323	104329	17.9722	.003096	.0556
324	104976	18.0000	.003086	.0556
325	105625	18.0278	.003077	.0555
326	106276	18.0555	.003067	.0554
327	106929	18.0831	.003058	.0553
328	107584	18.1108	.003049	.0552
329	108241	18.1384	.003040	.0551
330	108900	18.1659	.003030	.0550
331	109561	18.1934	.003021	.0550
332	110224	18.2209	.003012	.0549
333	110889	18.2483	.003003	.0548
334	111556	18.2757	.002994	.0547
335	112225	18.3030	.002985	.0546
336	112896	18.3303	.002976	.0546
337	113569	18.3576	.002967	.0545
338	114244	18.3848	.002959	.0544
339	114921	18.4120	.002950	.0543
340	115600	18.4391	.002941	.0542
341	116281	18.4662	.002933	.0542
342	116964	18.4932	.002924	.0541
343	117649	18.5203	.002915	.0540
344	118336	18.5472	.002907	.0539
345	119025	18.5742	.002899	.0538
346	119716	18.6011	.002890	.0538
347	120409	18.6279	.002882	.0537
348	121104	18.6548	.002874	.0536
349	121801	18.6815	.002865	.0535
350	122500	18.7083	.002857	.0535

n	n^2	$\sqrt{n}$	$\dfrac{1}{n}$	$\dfrac{1}{\sqrt{n}}$
351	123201	18.7350	.002849	.0534
352	123904	18.7617	.002841	.0533
353	124609	18.7883	.002833	.0532
354	125316	18.8149	.002825	.0531
355	126025	18.8414	.002817	.0531
356	126736	18.8680	.002809	.0530
357	127449	18.8944	.002801	.0529
358	128164	18.9209	.002793	.0529
359	128881	18.9473	.002786	.0528
360	129600	18.9737	.002778	.0527
361	130321	19.0000	.002770	.0526
362	131044	19.0263	.002762	.0526
363	131769	19.0526	.002755	.0525
364	132496	19.0788	.002747	.0524
365	133225	19.1050	.002740	.0523
366	133956	19.1311	.002732	.0523
367	134689	19.1572	.002725	.0522
368	135424	19.1833	.002717	.0521
369	136161	19.2094	.002710	.0521
370	136900	19.2354	.002703	.0520
371	137641	19.2614	.002695	.0519
372	138384	19.2873	.002688	.0518
373	139129	19.3132	.002681	.0518
374	139876	19.3391	.002674	.0517
375	140625	19.3649	.002667	.0516
376	141376	19.3907	.002660	.0516
377	142129	19.4165	.002653	.0515
378	142884	19.4422	.002646	.0514
379	143641	19.4679	.002639	.0514
380	144400	19.4936	.002632	.0513
381	145161	19.5192	.002625	.0512
382	145924	19.5448	.002618	.0512
383	146689	19.5704	.002611	.0511
384	147456	19.5959	.002604	.0510
385	148225	19.6214	.002597	.0510
386	148996	19.6469	.002591	.0509
387	149769	19.6723	.002584	.0508
388	150544	19.6977	.002577	.0508
389	151321	19.7231	.002571	.0507
390	152100	19.7484	.002564	.0506
391	152881	19.7737	.002558	.0506
392	153664	19.7990	.002551	.0505
393	154449	19.8242	.002545	.0504
394	155236	19.8494	.002538	.0504
395	156025	19.8746	.002532	.0503
396	156816	19.8997	.002525	.0503
397	157609	19.9249	.002519	.0502
398	158404	19.9499	.002513	.0501
399	159210	19.9750	.002506	.0501
400	160000	20.0000	.002500	.0500

n	n^2	$\sqrt{n}$	$\dfrac{1}{n}$	$\dfrac{1}{\sqrt{n}}$
401	160801	20.0250	.002494	.0499
402	161604	20.0499	.002488	.0499
403	162409	20.0749	.002481	.0498
404	163216	20.0998	.002475	.0498
405	164025	20.1246	.002469	.0497
406	164836	20.1494	.002463	.0496
407	165649	20.1742	.002457	.0496
408	166464	20.1990	.002451	.0495
409	167281	20.2237	.002445	.0494
410	168100	20.2485	.002439	.0494
411	168921	20.2731	.002433	.0493
412	169744	20.2978	.002427	.0493
413	170569	20.3224	.002421	.0492
414	171396	20.3470	.002415	.0491
415	172225	20.3715	.002410	.0491
416	173056	20.3961	.002404	.0490
417	173889	20.4206	.002398	.0490
418	174724	20.4450	.002392	.0489
419	175561	20.4695	.002387	.0489
420	176400	20.4939	.002381	.0488
421	177241	20.5183	.002375	.0487
422	178084	20.5426	.002370	.0487
423	178929	20.5670	.002364	.0486
424	179776	20.5913	.002358	.0486
425	180625	20.6155	.002353	.0485
426	181476	20.6398	.002347	.0485
427	182329	20.6640	.002342	.0484
428	183184	20.6882	.002336	.0483
429	184041	20.7123	.002331	.0483
430	184900	20.7364	.002326	.0482
431	185761	20.7605	.002320	.0482
432	186624	20.7846	.002315	.0481
433	187489	20.8087	.002309	.0481
434	188356	20.8327	.002304	.0480
435	189225	20.8567	.002299	.0479
436	190096	20.8806	.002294	.0479
437	190969	20.9045	.002288	.0478
438	191844	20.9284	.002283	.0478
439	192721	20.9523	.002278	.0477
440	193600	20.9762	.002273	.0477
441	194481	21.0000	.002268	.0476
442	195364	21.0238	.002262	.0476
443	196249	21.0476	.002257	.0475
444	197136	21.0713	.002252	.0475
445	198025	21.0950	.002247	.0474
446	198916	21.1187	.002242	.0474
447	199809	21.1424	.002237	.0473
448	200704	21.1660	.002232	.0472
449	201601	21.1896	.002227	.0472
450	202500	21.2132	.002222	.0471

n	n^2	$\sqrt{n}$	$\dfrac{1}{n}$	$\dfrac{1}{\sqrt{n}}$
451	203401	21.2368	.002217	.0471
452	204304	21.2603	.002212	.0470
453	205209	21.2838	.002208	.0470
454	206116	21.3073	.002203	.0469
455	207025	21.3307	.002198	.0469
456	207936	21.3542	.002193	.0468
457	208849	21.3776	.002188	.0468
458	209764	21.4009	.002183	.0467
459	210681	21.4243	.002179	.0467
460	211600	21.4476	.002174	.0466
461	212521	21.4709	.002169	.0466
462	213444	21.4942	.002165	.0465
463	214369	21.5174	.002160	.0465
464	215296	21.5407	.002155	.0464
465	216225	21.5639	.002151	.0464
466	217156	21.5870	.002146	.0463
467	218089	21.6102	.002141	.0463
468	219024	21.6333	.002137	.0462
469	219961	21.6564	.002132	.0462
470	220900	21.6795	.002128	.0461
471	221841	21.7025	.002123	.0461
472	222784	21.7256	.002119	.0460
473	223729	21.7486	.002114	.0460
474	224676	21.7715	.002110	.0459
475	225625	21.7945	.002105	.0459
476	226576	21.8174	.002101	.0458
477	227529	21.8403	.002096	.0458
478	228484	21.8632	.002092	.0457
479	229441	21.8861	.002088	.0457
480	230400	21.9089	.002083	.0456
481	231361	21.9317	.002079	.0456
482	232324	21.9545	.002075	.0455
483	233289	21.9773	.002070	.0455
484	234256	22.0000	.002066	.0455
485	235225	22.0227	.002062	.0454
486	236196	22.0454	.002058	.0454
487	237169	22.0681	.002053	.0453
488	238144	22.0907	.002049	.0453
489	239121	22.1133	.002045	.0452
490	240100	22.1359	.002041	.0452
491	241081	22.1585	.002037	.0451
492	242064	22.1811	.002033	.0451
493	243049	22.2036	.002028	.0450
494	244036	22.2261	.002024	.0450
495	245025	22.2486	.002020	.0449
496	246016	22.2711	.002016	.0448
497	247009	22.2935	.002012	.0449
498	248004	22.3159	.002008	.0449
499	249001	22.3383	.002004	.0448
500	250000	22.3607	.002000	.0447

n	n^2	$\sqrt{n}$	$\dfrac{1}{n}$	$\dfrac{1}{\sqrt{n}}$
501	251001	22.3830	.001996	.0447
502	252004	22.4054	.001992	.0446
503	253009	22.4277	.001988	.0446
504	254016	22.4499	.001984	.0445
505	255025	22.4722	.001980	.0445
506	256036	22.4944	.001976	.0445
507	257049	22.5167	.001972	.0444
508	258064	22.5389	.001969	.0444
509	259081	22.5610	.001965	.0443
510	260100	22.5832	.001961	.0443
511	261121	22.6053	.001957	.0442
512	262144	22.6274	.001953	.0442
513	263169	22.6495	.001949	.0442
514	264196	22.6716	.001946	.0441
515	265225	22.6936	.001942	.0441
516	266256	22.7156	.001938	.0440
517	267289	22.7376	.001934	.0440
518	268324	22.7596	.001931	.0439
519	269361	22.7816	.001927	.0439
520	270400	22.8035	.001923	.0439
521	271441	22.8254	.001919	.0438
522	272484	22.8473	.001916	.0438
523	273529	22.8692	.001912	.0437
524	274576	22.8910	.001908	.0437
525	275625	22.9129	.001905	.0436
526	276676	22.9347	.001901	.0436
527	277729	22.9565	.001898	.0436
528	278784	22.9783	.001894	.0435
529	279841	23.0000	.001890	.0435
530	280900	23.0217	.001887	.0434
531	281961	23.0434	.001883	.0434
532	283024	23.0651	.001880	.0434
533	284089	23.0868	.001876	.0433
534	285156	23.1084	.001873	.0433
535	286225	23.1301	.001869	.0432
536	287296	23.1517	.001866	.0432
536	288369	23.1733	.001862	.0432
538	289444	23.1948	.001859	.0431
539	290521	23.2164	.001855	.0431
540	291600	23.2379	.001852	.0430
541	292681	23.2594	.001848	.0430
542	293764	23.2809	.001845	.0430
543	294849	23.3024	.001842	.0429
544	295936	23.3238	.001838	.0429
545	297025	23.3452	.001835	.0428
546	298116	23.3666	.001832	.0428
547	299209	23.3880	.001828	.0428
548	300304	23.4094	.001825	.0427
549	301401	23.4307	.001821	.0427
550	302500	23.4521	.001818	.0426

n	n^2	$\sqrt{n}$	$\dfrac{1}{n}$	$\dfrac{1}{\sqrt{n}}$
551	303601	23.4734	.001815	.0426
552	304704	23.4947	.001812	.0426
553	305809	23.5160	.001808	.0425
554	306916	23.5372	.001805	.0425
555	308025	23.5584	.001802	.0424
556	309136	23.5797	.001799	.0424
557	310249	23.6008	.001795	.0424
558	311364	23.6220	.001792	.0423
559	312481	23.6432	.001789	.0423
560	313600	23.6643	.001786	.0423
561	314721	23.6854	.001783	.0422
562	315844	23.7065	.001779	.0422
563	316969	23.7276	.001776	.0421
564	318096	23.7487	.001773	.0421
565	319225	23.7697	.001770	.0421
566	320356	23.7908	.001767	.0420
567	321489	23.8118	.001764	.0420
568	322624	23.8328	.001761	.0420
569	323761	23.8537	.001757	.0419
570	324900	23.8747	.001754	.0419
571	326041	23.8956	.001751	.0418
572	327184	23.9165	.001748	.0418
573	328329	23.9374	.001745	.0418
574	329476	23.9583	.001742	.0417
575	330625	23.9792	.001739	.0417
576	331776	24.0000	.001736	.0417
577	332929	24.0208	.001733	.0416
578	334084	24.0416	.001730	.0416
579	335241	24.0624	.001727	.0416
580	336400	24.0832	.001724	.0415
581	337561	24.1039	.001721	.0415
582	338724	24.1247	.001718	.0415
583	339889	24.1454	.001715	.0414
584	341056	24.1661	.001712	.0414
585	342225	24.1868	.001709	.0413
586	343396	24.2074	.001706	.0413
587	344569	24.2281	.001704	.0413
588	345744	24.2487	.001701	.0412
589	346921	24.2693	.001698	.0412
590	348100	24.2899	.001695	.0412
591	349281	24.3105	.001692	.0411
592	350464	24.3311	.001689	.0411
593	351649	24.3516	.001686	.0411
594	352836	24.3721	.001684	.0410
595	354025	24.3926	.001681	.0410
596	355216	24.4131	.001678	.0410
597	356409	24.4336	.001675	.0409
598	357604	24.4540	.001672	.0409
599	358801	24.4745	.001669	.0409
600	360000	24.4949	.001667	.0408

n	n^2	$\sqrt{n}$	$\dfrac{1}{n}$	$\dfrac{1}{\sqrt{n}}$
601	361201	24.5153	.001664	.0408
602	362404	24.5357	.001661	.0408
603	363609	24.5561	.001658	.0407
604	364816	24.5764	.001656	.0407
605	366025	24.5967	.001653	.0407
606	367236	24.6171	.001650	.0406
607	368449	24.6374	.001647	.0406
608	369664	24.6577	.001645	.0406
609	370881	24.6779	.001642	.0405
610	372100	24.6982	.001639	.0405
611	373321	24.7184	.001637	.0405
612	374544	24.7386	.001634	.0404
613	375769	24.7588	.001631	.0404
614	376996	24.7790	.001629	.0404
615	378225	24.7992	.001626	.0403
616	379456	24.8193	.001623	.0403
617	380689	24.8395	.001621	.0403
618	381924	24.8596	.001618	.0402
619	383161	24.8797	.001616	.0402
620	384400	24.8998	.001613	.0402
621	385641	24.9199	.001610	.0401
622	386884	24.9399	.001608	.0401
623	388129	24.9600	.001605	.0401
624	389376	24.9800	.001603	.0400
625	390625	25.0000	.001600	.0400
626	391876	25.0200	.001597	.0400
627	393129	25.0400	.001595	.0399
628	394384	25.0599	.001592	.0399
629	395641	25.0799	.001590	.0399
630	396900	25.0998	.001587	.0398
631	398161	25.1197	.001585	.0398
632	399424	25.1396	.001582	.0398
633	400689	25.1595	.001580	.0397
634	401956	25.1794	.001577	.0397
635	403225	25.1992	.001575	.0397
636	404496	25.2190	.001572	.0397
637	405769	25.2389	.001570	.0396
638	407044	25.2587	.001567	.0396
639	408321	25.2784	.001565	.0396
640	409600	25.2982	.001563	.0395
641	410881	25.3180	.001560	.0395
642	412164	25.3377	.001558	.0395
643	413449	25.3574	.001555	.0394
644	414736	25.3772	.001553	.0394
645	416025	25.3969	.001550	.0394
646	417316	25.4165	.001548	.0393
647	418609	25.4362	.001546	.0393
648	419904	25.4558	.001543	.0393
649	421201	25.4755	.001541	.0393
650	422500	25.4951	.001538	.0392

n	n^2	$\sqrt{n}$	$\dfrac{1}{n}$	$\dfrac{1}{\sqrt{n}}$
651	423801	25.5147	.001536	.0392
652	425104	25.5343	.001534	.0392
653	426409	25.5539	.001531	.0391
654	427716	25.5734	.001529	.0391
655	429025	25.5930	.001527	.0391
656	430336	25.6125	.001524	.0390
657	431649	25.6320	.001522	.0390
658	432964	25.6515	.001520	.0390
659	434281	25.6710	.001517	.0390
660	435600	25.6905	.001515	.0389
661	436921	25.7099	.001513	.0389
662	438244	25.7294	.001511	.0389
663	439569	25.7488	.001508	.0388
664	440896	25.7682	.001506	.0388
665	442225	25.7876	.001504	.0388
666	443556	25.8070	.001502	.0387
667	444889	25.8263	.001499	.0387
668	446224	25.8457	.001497	.0387
669	447561	25.8650	.001495	.0387
670	448900	25.8844	.001493	.0386
671	450241	25.9037	.001490	.0386
672	451584	25.9230	.001488	.0386
673	452929	25.9422	.001486	.0385
674	454276	25.9615	.001484	.0385
675	455625	25.9808	.001481	.0385
676	456976	26.0000	.001479	.0385
677	458329	26.0192	.001477	.0384
678	459684	26.0384	.001475	.0384
679	461041	26.0576	.001473	.0384
680	462400	26.0768	.001471	.0383
681	463761	26.0960	.001468	.0383
682	465124	26.1151	.001466	.0383
683	466489	26.1343	.001464	.0383
684	467856	26.1534	.001462	.0382
685	469225	26.1725	.001460	.0382
686	470596	26.1916	.001458	.0382
687	471969	26.2107	.001456	.0382
688	473344	26.2298	.001453	.0381
689	474721	26.2488	.001451	.0381
690	476100	26.2679	.001449	.0381
691	477481	26.2869	.001447	.0380
692	478864	26.3059	.001445	.0380
693	480249	26.3249	.001443	.0380
694	481636	26.3439	.001441	.0380
695	483025	26.3629	.001439	.0379
696	484416	26.3818	.001437	.0379
697	485809	26.4008	.001435	.0379
698	487204	26.4197	.001433	.0379
699	488601	26.4386	.001431	.0378
700	490000	26.4575	.001429	.0378

n	n^2	$\sqrt{n}$	$\dfrac{1}{n}$	$\dfrac{1}{\sqrt{n}}$
701	491401	26.4764	.001427	.0378
702	492804	26.4953	.001425	.0377
703	494209	26.5141	.001422	.0377
704	495616	26.5330	.001420	.0377
705	497025	26.5518	.001418	.0377
706	498436	26.5707	.001416	.0376
707	499849	26.5895	.001414	.0376
708	501264	26.6083	.001412	.0376
709	502681	26.6271	.001410	.0376
710	504100	26.6458	.001408	.0375
711	505521	26.6646	.001406	.0375
712	506944	26.6833	.001404	.0375
713	508369	26.7021	.001403	.0375
714	509796	26.7208	.001401	.0374
715	511225	26.7395	.001399	.0374
716	512656	26.7582	.001397	.0374
717	514089	26.7769	.001395	.0373
718	515524	26.7955	.001393	.0373
719	516961	26.8142	.001391	.0373
720	518400	26.8328	.001389	.0373
721	519841	26.8514	.001387	.0372
722	521284	26.8701	.001385	.0372
723	522729	26.8887	.001383	.0372
724	524176	26.9072	.001381	.0372
725	525625	26.9258	.001379	.0371
726	527076	26.9444	.001377	.0371
727	528529	26.9629	.001376	.0371
728	529984	26.9815	.001374	.0371
729	531441	27.0000	.001372	.0370
730	532900	27.0185	.001370	.0370
731	534361	27.0370	.001368	.0370
732	535824	27.0555	.001366	.0370
733	537289	27.0740	.001364	.0369
734	538756	27.0924	.001362	.0369
735	540225	27.1109	.001361	.0369
736	541696	26.1293	.001359	.0369
737	543169	27.1477	.001357	.0368
738	544644	27.1662	.001355	.0368
739	546121	27.1846	.001353	.0368
740	547600	27.2029	.001351	.0368
741	549081	27.2213	.001350	.0367
742	550564	27.2397	.001348	.0367
743	552049	27.2580	.001346	.0367
744	553536	27.2764	.001344	.0367
745	555025	27.2947	.001342	.0366
746	556516	27.3130	.001340	.0366
747	558009	27.3313	.001339	.0366
748	559504	27.3496	.001337	.0366
749	561001	27.3679	.001335	.0365
750	562500	27.3861	.001333	.0365

n	n^2	$\sqrt{n}$	$\dfrac{1}{n}$	$\dfrac{1}{\sqrt{n}}$
751	564001	27.4044	.001332	.0365
752	565504	27.4226	.001330	.0365
753	567009	27.4408	.001328	.0364
754	568516	27.4591	.001326	.0364
755	570025	27.4773	.001325	.0364
756	571536	27.4955	.001323	.0364
757	573049	27.5136	.001321	.0363
758	574564	27.5318	.001319	.0363
759	576081	27.5500	.001318	.0363
760	577600	27.5681	.001316	.0363
761	579121	27.5862	.001314	.0363
762	580644	27.6043	.001312	.0362
763	582169	27.6225	.001311	.0362
764	583696	27.6405	.001309	.0362
765	585225	27.6586	.001307	.0362
766	586756	27.6767	.001305	.0361
767	588289	27.6948	.001304	.0361
768	589824	27.7128	.001302	.0361
769	591361	27.7308	.001300	.0361
770	592900	27.7489	.001299	.0360
771	594441	27.7669	.001297	.0360
772	595984	27.7849	.001295	.0360
773	597529	27.8029	.001294	.0360
774	599076	27.8209	.001292	.0359
775	600625	27.8388	.001290	.0359
776	602176	27.8568	.001289	.0359
777	603729	27.8747	.001287	.0359
778	605284	27.8927	.001285	.0359
779	606841	27.9106	.001284	.0358
780	608400	27.9285	.001282	.0358
781	609961	27.9464	.001280	.0358
782	611524	27.9643	.001279	.0358
783	613089	27.9821	.001277	.0357
784	614656	28.0000	.001276	.0357
785	616225	28.0179	.001274	.0357
786	617796	28.0357	.001272	.0357
787	619369	28.0535	.001271	.0356
788	620944	28.0713	.001269	.0356
789	622521	28.0891	.001267	.0356
790	624100	28.1069	.001266	.0356
791	625681	28.1247	.001264	.0356
792	627264	28.1425	.001263	.0355
793	628849	28.1603	.001261	.0355
794	630436	28.1780	.001259	.0355
795	632025	28.1957	.001258	.0355
796	633616	28.2135	.001256	.0354
797	635209	28.2312	.001255	.0354
798	636804	28.2489	.001253	.0354
799	638401	28.2666	.001252	.0354
800	640000	28.2843	.001250	.0354

Table M. (continued)

n	n^2	$\sqrt{n}$	$\dfrac{1}{n}$	$\dfrac{1}{\sqrt{n}}$
801	641601	28.3019	.001248	.0353
802	643204	28.3196	.001247	.0353
803	644809	28.3373	.001245	.0353
804	646416	28.3549	.001244	.0353
805	648025	28.3725	.001242	.0352
806	649636	28.3901	.001241	.0352
807	651249	28.4077	.001239	.0352
808	652864	28.4253	.001248	.0352
809	654481	28.4429	.001236	.0352
810	656100	28.4605	.001235	.0351
811	657721	28.4781	.001233	.0351
812	659344	28.4956	.001232	.0351
813	660969	28.5132	.001230	.0351
814	662596	28.5307	.001229	.0351
815	664225	28.5482	.001227	.0350
816	665856	28.5657	.001225	.0350
817	667489	28.5832	.001224	.0350
818	669124	28.6007	.001222	.0350
819	670761	28.6182	.001221	.0349
820	672400	28.6356	.001220	.0349
821	674041	28.6531	.001218	.0349
822	675684	28.6705	.001217	.0349
823	677329	28.6880	.001215	.0349
824	678976	28.7054	.001214	.0348
825	680625	28.7228	.001212	.0348
826	682276	28.7402	.001211	.0348
827	683929	28.7576	.001209	.0348
828	685584	28.7750	.001208	.0348
829	687241	28.7924	.001206	.0347
830	688900	28.8097	.001205	.0347
831	690561	28.8271	.001203	.0347
832	692224	28.8444	.001202	.0347
833	693889	28.8617	.001200	.0346
834	695556	28.8791	.001199	.0346
835	697225	28.8964	.001198	.0346
836	698896	28.9137	.001196	.0346
837	700569	28.9310	.001195	.0346
838	702244	28.9482	.001193	.0345
839	703921	28.9655	.001192	.0345
840	705600	28.9828	.001190	.0345
841	707281	29.0000	.001189	.0345
842	708964	29.0172	.001188	.0345
843	710649	29.0345	.001186	.0344
844	712336	29.0517	.001185	.0344
845	714025	29.0689	.001183	.0344
846	715716	29.0861	.001182	.0344
847	717409	29.1033	.001181	.0344
848	719104	29.1204	.001179	.0343
849	720801	29.1376	.001178	.0343
850	722500	29.1548	.001176	.0343

n	n^2	$\sqrt{n}$	$\dfrac{1}{n}$	$\dfrac{1}{\sqrt{n}}$
851	724201	29.1719	.001175	.0343
852	725904	29.1890	.001174	.0343
853	727609	29.2062	.001172	.0342
854	729316	29.2233	.001171	.0342
855	731025	29.2404	.001170	.0342
856	732736	29.2575	.001168	.0342
857	734449	29.2746	.001167	.0342
858	736164	29.2916	.001166	.0341
859	737881	29.3087	.001164	.0341
860	739600	29.3258	.001163	.0341
861	741321	29.3428	.001161	.0341
862	743044	29.3598	.001160	.0341
863	744769	29.3769	.001159	.0340
864	746496	29.3939	.001157	.0340
865	748225	29.4109	.001156	.0340
866	749956	29.4279	.001155	.0340
867	751689	29.4449	.001153	.0340
868	753424	29.4618	.001152	.0339
869	755161	29.4788	.001151	.0339
870	756900	29.4958	.001149	.0339
871	758641	29.5127	.001148	.0339
872	760384	29.5296	.001147	.0339
873	762129	29.5466	.001145	.0338
874	763876	29.5635	.001144	.0338
875	765625	29.5804	.001143	.0338
876	767376	29.5973	.001142	.0338
877	769129	29.6142	.001140	.0338
878	770884	29.6311	.001139	.0337
879	772641	29.6479	.001138	.0337
880	774400	29.6648	.001136	.0337
881	776161	29.6816	.001135	.0337
882	777924	29.6985	.001134	.0337
883	779689	29.7153	.001133	.0337
884	781456	29.7321	.001131	.0336
885	783225	29.7489	.001130	.0336
886	784996	29.7658	.001129	.0336
887	786769	29.7825	.001127	.0336
888	788544	29.7993	.001126	.0336
889	790321	29.8161	.001125	.0335
890	792100	29.8329	.001124	.0335
891	793881	29.8496	.001122	.0335
892	795664	29.8664	.001121	.0335
893	797449	29.8831	.001120	.0335
894	799236	29.8998	.001119	.0334
895	801025	29.9166	.001117	.0334
896	802816	29.9333	.001116	.0334
897	804609	29.9500	.001115	.0334
898	806404	29.9666	.001114	.0334
899	808201	29.9833	.001112	.0334
900	810000	30.0000	.001111	.0333

n	n^2	$\sqrt{n}$	$\dfrac{1}{n}$	$\dfrac{1}{\sqrt{n}}$
901	811801	30.0167	.001110	.0333
902	813604	30.0333	.001109	.0333
903	815409	30.0500	.001107	.0333
904	817216	30.0666	.001106	.0333
905	819025	30.0832	.001105	.0332
906	820836	30.0998	.001104	.0332
907	822649	30.1164	.001103	.0332
908	824464	30.1330	.001101	.0332
909	826281	30.1496	.001100	.0332
910	828100	30.1662	.001099	.0331
911	829921	30.1828	.001098	.0331
912	831744	30.1993	.001096	.0331
913	833569	30.2159	.001095	.0331
914	835396	30.2324	.001094	.0331
915	837225	30.2490	.001093	.0331
916	839056	30.2655	.001092	.0330
917	840889	30.2820	.001091	.0330
918	842724	30.2985	.001089	.0330
919	844561	30.3150	.001088	.0330
920	846400	30.3315	.001087	.0330
921	848241	30.3480	.001086	.0330
922	850084	30.3645	.001085	.0329
923	851929	30.3809	.001083	.0329
924	853776	30.3974	.001082	.0329
925	855625	30.4138	.001081	.0329
926	857476	30.4302	.001080	.0329
927	859329	30.4467	.001079	.0238
928	861184	30.4631	.001078	.0328
929	863041	30.4795	.001076	.0328
930	864900	30.4959	.001075	.0328
931	866761	30.5123	.001074	.0328
932	868624	30.5287	.001073	.0328
933	870489	30.5450	.001072	.0327
934	872356	30.5614	.001071	.0327
935	874225	30.5778	.001070	.0327
936	876096	30.5941	.001068	.0327
937	877969	30.6105	.001067	.0327
938	879844	30.6268	.001066	.0327
939	881721	30.6431	.001065	.0326
940	883600	30.6594	.001064	.0326
941	885481	30.6757	.001063	.0326
942	887364	30.6920	.001062	.0326
943	889249	30.7083	.001060	.0326
944	891136	30.7246	.001059	.0325
945	893025	30.7409	.001058	.0325
946	894916	30.7571	.001057	.0325
947	896809	30.7734	.001056	.0325
948	898704	30.7896	.001055	.0325
949	900601	30.8058	.001054	.0325
950	902500	30.8221	.001053	.0324

n	n^2	$\sqrt{n}$	$\dfrac{1}{n}$	$\dfrac{1}{\sqrt{n}}$
951	904401	30.8383	.001052	.0324
952	906304	30.8545	.001050	.0324
953	908209	30.8707	.001049	.0324
954	910116	30.8869	.001048	.0324
955	912025	30.9031	.001047	.0324
956	913936	30.9192	.001046	.0323
957	915849	30.9354	.001045	.0323
958	917764	30.9516	.001044	.0323
959	919681	30.9677	.001043	.0323
960	921600	30.9839	.001042	.0323
961	923521	31.0000	.001041	.0323
962	925444	31.0161	.001040	.0322
963	927369	31.0322	.001038	.0322
964	929296	31.0483	.001037	.0322
965	931225	31.0644	.001036	.0322
966	933156	31.0805	.001035	.0322
967	935089	31.0966	.001034	.0322
968	937024	31.1127	.001033	.0321
969	938961	31.1288	.001032	.0321
970	940900	31.1448	.001031	.0321
971	942841	31.1609	.001030	.0321
972	944784	31.1769	.001029	.0321
973	946729	31.1929	.001028	.0321
974	948676	31.2090	.001027	.0320
975	950625	31.2250	.001026	.0320
976	952576	31.2410	.001025	.0320
977	954529	31.2570	.001024	.0320
978	956484	31.2730	.001022	.0320
979	958441	31.2890	.001021	.0320
980	960400	31.3050	.001020	.0319
981	962361	31.3209	.001019	.0319
982	964324	31.3369	.001018	.0319
983	966289	31.3528	.001017	.0319
984	968256	31.3688	.001016	.0319
985	970225	31.3847	.001015	.0319
986	972196	31.4006	.001014	.0318
987	974169	31.4166	.001013	.0318
988	976144	31.4325	.001012	.0318
989	978121	31.4484	.001011	.0318
990	980100	31.4643	.001010	.0318
991	982081	31.4802	.001009	.0318
992	984064	31.4960	.001008	.0318
993	986049	31.5119	.001007	.0317
994	988036	31.5278	.001006	.0317
995	990025	31.5436	.001005	.0317
996	992016	31.5595	.001004	.0317
997	994009	31.5753	.001003	.0317
998	996004	31.5911	.001002	.0317
999	998001	31.6070	.001001	.0316
1000	1000000	31.6228	.001000	.0316

SOURCE: "Descriptive and Sampling Statistics" by J. G. Peatman, Harper, New York, 1947.

INDEX

447